THE SCIENTIFIC PAPERS

OF

J. WILLARD GIBBS, Ph.D., LL.D.

Books by

J. WILLARD GIBBS

Elementary Principles in Statistical Mechanics

Vector Analysis

THE SCIENTIFIC PAPERS

OF

J. WILLARD GIBBS, PH.D., LL.D.

FORMERLY PROFESSOR OF MATHEMATICAL PHYSICS IN YALE UNIVERSITY

IN TWO VOLUMES

VOL. II.

DYNAMICS

VECTOR ANALYSIS AND MULTIPLE ALGEBRA

ELECTROMAGNETIC THEORY OF LIGHT

ETC.

DOVER PUBLICATIONS, INC.

NEW YORK NEW YORK

Published in the United Kingdom by Constable and Company Limited, 10 Orange Street, London W.C. 2.

This new Dover edition, first published in 1961, is an unabridged and unaltered republication of the first edition of the work originally published by Longmans, Green, and Company in 1906.

Manufactured in the United States of America

Dover Publications, Inc.
180 Varick Street
New York 14, N. Y.

PREFATORY NOTE.

THE present volume contains all the published papers of Professor J. Willard Gibbs except those upon Thermodynamics, which are placed in Volume I. of this collection.

In a few cases slight corrections had been made by the author in his own copies of the papers. These changes, together with the correction of obvious misprints in the originals, have been incorporated in the present edition without comment. Where for the sake of clearness it has seemed desirable to insert a word or two in a footnote or in the text itself, the addition has been indicated by enclosing it within square brackets [ ], a sign which is otherwise used only in the formulæ.

HENRY ANDREWS BUMSTEAD.
RALPH GIBBS VAN NAME.

YALE UNIVERSITY,
NEW HAVEN,
October, 1906.

CONTENTS OF VOLUME II.

DYNAMICS.

PAGE

I. ON THE FUNDAMENTAL FORMULAE OF DYNAMICS, - - 1

[*Amer. Jour. Math.*, vol. II, pp. 49-64, 1879.]

II. ON THE FUNDAMENTAL FORMULA OF STATISTICAL MECHANICS WITH APPLICATIONS TO ASTRONOMY AND THERMODYNAMICS. (ABSTRACT), - - - - - - - - 16

[*Proc. Amer. Assoc.*, vol. XXXIII, pp. 57, 58, 1884.]

VECTOR ANALYSIS AND MULTIPLE ALGEBRA.

III. ELEMENTS OF VECTOR ANALYSIS, ARRANGED FOR THE USE OF STUDENTS IN PHYSICS, - - - - - - 17

[Not published. Printed, New Haven, pp. 1-36, 1881; pp. 37-83, 1884.]

IV. ON MULTIPLE ALGEBRA. VICE-PRESIDENT'S ADDRESS BEFORE THE AMERICAN ASSOCIATION FOR THE ADVANCEMENT OF SCIENCE, - - - - - - - - - - - 91

[*Proc. Amer. Assoc.*, vol. XXXV, pp. 37-66, 1886.]

V. ON THE DETERMINATION OF ELLIPTIC ORBITS FROM THREE COMPLETE OBSERVATIONS, - - - - - - - - 118

[*Mem. Nat. Acad. Sci.*, vol. IV, part 2, pp. 79-104, 1889.]

VI. ON THE USE OF THE VECTOR METHOD IN THE DETERMINATION OF ORBITS. LETTER TO THE EDITOR OF KLINKERFUES' "THEORETISCHE ASTRONOMIE," - - - - - - - 149

[Hitherto unpublished.]

VII. ON THE RÔLE OF QUATERNIONS IN THE ALGEBRA OF VECTORS, 155

[*Nature*, vol. XLIII, pp. 511-513, 1891.]

VIII. QUATERNIONS AND THE "AUSDEHNUNGSLEHRE," - - - 161

[*Nature*, vol. XLIV, pp. 79-82, 1891.]

IX. QUATERNIONS AND THE ALGEBRA OF VECTORS, - - - 169

[*Nature*, vol. XLVII, pp. 463, 464, 1893.]

X. QUATERNIONS AND VECTOR ANALYSIS, - - - - - - 173

[*Nature*, vol. XLVIII, pp. 364-367, 1893.]

THE ELECTROMAGNETIC THEORY OF LIGHT.

PAGE

XI. ON DOUBLE REFRACTION AND THE DISPERSION OF COLORS IN PERFECTLY TRANSPARENT MEDIA, - - - - - 182
[*Amer. Jour. Sci.*, ser 3, vol. XXIII, pp. 262-275, 1882.]

XII. ON DOUBLE REFRACTION IN PERFECTLY TRANSPARENT MEDIA WHICH EXHIBIT THE PHENOMENA OF CIRCULAR POLARIZATION, - - - - - - - - - - - - - - - 195
[*Amer. Jour. Sci.*, ser. 3, vol. XXIII, pp. 460-476, 1882.]

XIII. ON THE GENERAL EQUATIONS OF MONOCHROMATIC LIGHT IN MEDIA OF EVERY DEGREE OF TRANSPARENCY, - - - 211
[*Amer. Jour. Sci.*, ser. 3, vol. XXV, pp. 107-118, 1883.]

XIV. A COMPARISON OF THE ELASTIC AND THE ELECTRICAL THEORIES OF LIGHT WITH RESPECT TO THE LAW OF DOUBLE REFRACTION AND THE DISPERSION OF COLORS, - 223
[*Amer. Jour. Sci.*, ser. 3, vol. XXXV, pp. 467-475, 1888.]

XV. A COMPARISON OF THE ELECTRIC THEORY OF LIGHT AND SIR WILLIAM THOMSON'S THEORY OF A QUASI-LABILE ETHER, - - - - - - - - - - - 232
[*Amer. Jour. Sci.*, ser. 3, vol. XXXVII, pp. 129-144, 1889.]

MISCELLANEOUS PAPERS.

XVI. REVIEWS OF NEWCOMB AND MICHELSON'S "VELOCITY OF LIGHT IN AIR AND REFRACTING MEDIA" AND OF KETTELER'S "THEORETISCHE OPTIK," - - - - - 247
[*Amer. Jour. Sci.*, ser. 3, vol. XXXI, pp. 62-67, 1886.]

XVII. ON THE VELOCITY OF LIGHT AS DETERMINED BY FOUCAULT'S REVOLVING MIRROR, - - - - - - - - - 253
[*Nature*, vol. XXXIII, p. 582, 1886.]

XVIII. VELOCITY OF PROPAGATION OF ELECTROSTATIC FORCE, - 255
[*Nature*, vol. LIII, p. 509, 1896.]

XIX. FOURIER'S SERIES, - - - - - - - - - - 258
[*Nature*, vol. LIX, pp. 200 and 606, 1898-99.]

XX. RUDOLF JULIUS EMANUEL CLAUSIUS, - - - - - - 261
[*Proc. Amer. Acad.*, new series, vol. XVI, pp. 458-465, 1889.]

XXI. HUBERT ANSON NEWTON, - - - - - - - - - 268
[*Amer. Jour. Sci.*, ser. 4, vol. III, pp. 359-376, 1897.]

THE SCIENTIFIC PAPERS

OF

J. WILLARD GIBBS, PH.D., LL.D.

I.

ON THE FUNDAMENTAL FORMULÆ OF DYNAMICS.

[*American Journal of Mathematics*, vol. II. pp. 49-64, 1879.]

Formation of a new Indeterminate Formula of Motion by the Substitution of the Variations of the Components of Acceleration for the Variations of the Coordinates in the usual Formula.

The laws of motion are frequently expressed by an equation of the form

$$\Sigma[(X-m\ddot{x})\delta x+(Y-m\ddot{y})\delta y+(Z-m\ddot{z})\delta z]=0, \qquad (1)$$

in which

m denotes the mass of a particle of the system considered,
x, y, z its rectangular coordinates,
$\ddot{x}, \ddot{y}, \ddot{z}$ the second differential coefficients of the coordinates with respect to the time,
X, Y, Z the components of the forces acting on the particle,
$\delta x, \delta y, \delta z$ any arbitrary variations of the coordinates which are simultaneously possible, and
Σ a summation with respect to all the particles of the system.

It is evident that we may substitute for $\delta x, \delta y, \delta z$ any other expressions which are capable of the same and only of the same sets of simultaneous values.

Now if the nature of the system is such that certain functions A, B, etc. of the coordinates must be constant, or given functions of the time, we have

$$\left.\begin{aligned}\Sigma\left(\frac{dA}{dx}\delta x+\frac{dA}{dy}\delta y+\frac{dA}{dz}\delta z\right)=0,\\ \Sigma\left(\frac{dB}{dx}\delta x+\frac{dB}{dy}\delta y+\frac{dB}{dz}\delta z\right)=0,\\ \text{etc.}\end{aligned}\right\} \qquad (2)$$

These are the *equations of condition*, to which the variations in the general equation of motion (1) are subject. But if A is constant or a determined function of the time, the same must be true of $\dot{A}$ and $\ddot{A}$. Now

$$\dot{A}=\Sigma\left(\frac{dA}{dx}\dot{x}+\frac{dA}{dy}\dot{y}+\frac{dA}{dz}\dot{z}\right)$$

and

$$\ddot{A}=\Sigma\left(\frac{dA}{dx}\ddot{x}+\frac{dA}{dy}\ddot{y}+\frac{dA}{dz}\ddot{z}\right)+H,$$

where H represents terms containing only the second differential coefficients of A with respect to the coordinates, and the first differential coefficients of the coordinates with respect to the time. Therefore, if we conceive of a variation affecting the accelerations of the particles at the time considered, but not their positions or velocities, we have

$$\left.\begin{array}{l} \delta \ddot{A} = \Sigma\left(\frac{dA}{dx}\,\delta\ddot{x} + \frac{dA}{dy}\,\delta\ddot{y} + \frac{dA}{dz}\,\delta\ddot{z}\right) = 0, \\ \text{and, in like manner,} \\ \delta \ddot{B} = \Sigma\left(\frac{dB}{dx}\,\delta\ddot{x} + \frac{dB}{dy}\,\delta\ddot{y} + \frac{dB}{dz}\,\delta\ddot{z}\right) = 0, \\ \text{etc.} \end{array}\right\} \quad (3)$$

Comparing these equations with (2), we see that when the *accelerations* of the particles are regarded as subject to the variation denoted by δ, but not their positions or velocities, the possible values of $\delta\ddot{x}$, $\delta\ddot{y}$, $\delta\ddot{z}$ are subject to precisely the same restrictions as the values of δx, δy, δz, when the *positions* of the particles are regarded as variable. We may, therefore, write for the general equation of motion

$$\Sigma\left[(X - m\ddot{x})\delta\ddot{x} + (Y - m\ddot{y})\delta\ddot{y} + (Z - m\ddot{z})\delta\ddot{z}\right] = 0, \quad (4)$$

regarding the positions and velocities of the particles as unaffected by the variation denoted by δ,—a condition which may be expressed by the equations

$$\left.\begin{array}{lll} \delta x = 0, & \delta y = 0, & \delta z = 0, \\ \delta\dot{x} = 0, & \delta\dot{y} = 0, & \delta\dot{z} = 0. \end{array}\right\} \quad (5)$$

We have so far supposed that the conditions which restrict the possible motions of the systems may be expressed by *equations* between the coordinates alone or the coordinates and the time. To extend the formula of motion to cases in which the conditions are expressed by the characters $\leqq$ or $\geqq$, we may write

$$\Sigma\left[(X - m\ddot{x})\delta\ddot{x} + (Y - m\ddot{y})\delta\ddot{y} + (Z - m\ddot{z})\delta\ddot{z}\right] \leqq 0. \quad (6)$$

The conditions which determine the possible values of $\delta\ddot{x}$, $\delta\ddot{y}$, $\delta\ddot{z}$ will not, in such cases, be entirely similar to those which determine the possible values of δx, δy, δz, when the coordinates are regarded as variable. Nevertheless, the laws of motion are correctly expressed by the formula (6), while the formula

$$\Sigma\left[(X - m\ddot{x})\delta x + (Y - m\ddot{y})\delta y + (Z - m\ddot{z})\delta z\right] \leqq 0, \quad (7)$$

does not, as naturally interpreted, give so complete and accurate an expression of the laws of motion.

This may be illustrated by a simple example.

Let it be required to find the acceleration of a material point, which, at a given instant, is moving with given velocity on the frictionless surface of a body (which it cannot penetrate, but which it may leave), and is acted on by given forces. For simplicity, we may suppose that the normal to the surface, drawn outward from the moving point at the moment considered, is parallel to the axis of X and in the positive direction. The only restriction on the values of δx, δy, δz is that

$$\delta x \geqq 0.$$

Formula (7) will therefore give

$$\ddot{x} \geqq \frac{X}{m}, \quad \ddot{y} = \frac{Y}{m}, \quad \ddot{z} = \frac{Z}{m}.$$

The condition that the point shall not penetrate the body gives another condition for the value of $\ddot{x}$. If the point remains upon the surface, $\ddot{x}$ must have a certain value N, determined by the form of the surface and the velocity of the point. If the value of $\ddot{x}$ is less than this, the point must penetrate the body. Therefore,

$$\ddot{x} \geqq N.$$

But this does not suffice to determine the acceleration of the point.

Let us now apply formula (6) to the same problem. Since $\ddot{x}$ cannot be less than N,

$$\text{if } \ddot{x} = N, \quad \delta\ddot{x} \geqq 0.$$

This is the only restriction on the value of $\delta\ddot{x}$, for if $\ddot{x} > N$, the value of $\delta\ddot{x}$ is entirely arbitrary. Formula (6), therefore, requires that

$$\text{if } \ddot{x} = N, \quad \ddot{x} \geqq \frac{X}{m};$$

$$\text{but if } \ddot{x} > N, \quad \ddot{x} = \frac{X}{m}:$$

—that is (since $\ddot{x}$ cannot be less than N), that $\ddot{x}$ shall be equal to the greater of the quantities N and $\frac{X}{m}$, or to both, if they are equal,—and that

$$\ddot{y} = \frac{Y}{m}, \quad \ddot{z} = \frac{Z}{m}.$$

The values of $\ddot{x}$, $\ddot{y}$, $\ddot{z}$ are therefore entirely determined by this formula in connection with the conditions afforded by the constraints of the system.*

The following considerations will show that what is true in this case is also true in general, when the conditions to which the system

---

* The failure of the formula (7) in this case is rather apparent than real; for, although the formula apparently allows to $\ddot{x}$, at the instant considered, a value exceeding both N and $\frac{X}{m}$, it does not allow this for any interval, however short. For if $\ddot{x} < N$, the point will immediately leave the surface, and then the formula requires that $\ddot{x} = \frac{X}{m}$.

is subject are such that certain functions of the coordinates cannot exceed certain limits, either constant or variable with the time. If certain values of $\delta\ddot{x}$, $\delta\ddot{y}$, $\delta\ddot{z}$ (with unvaried values of x, y, z, and $\dot{x}$, $\dot{y}$, $\dot{z}$) are simultaneously possible at a given instant, equal or proportional values with the same signs must be possible for δx, δy, δz immediately after the instant considered, and must satisfy formula (1), and therefore (6), in connection with the values of $\ddot{x}$, $\ddot{y}$, $\ddot{z}$, X, Y, Z immediately after that instant. The values of $\ddot{x}$, $\ddot{y}$, $\ddot{z}$, thus determined, are of course the very quantities which we wish to obtain, since the acceleration of a point at a given instant does not denote anything different from its acceleration immediately after that instant.

For an example of a somewhat different class of cases, we may suppose that in a system, otherwise free, $\dot{x}$ cannot have a negative value. Such a condition does not seem to affect the possible values of δx, as naturally interpreted in a dynamical problem. Yet, if we should regard the value of δx in (7) as arbitrary, we should obtain

$$\ddot{x}=\frac{X}{m},$$

which might be erroneous. But if we regard δx as expressing a velocity of which the system, if at rest, would be capable (which is not a natural signification of the expression), we should have $\delta x \geqq 0$, which, with (7), gives

$$\ddot{x} \geqq \frac{X}{m}.$$

This is not incorrect, but it leaves the acceleration undetermined. If we should regard δx as denoting such a variation of the velocity as is possible for the system when it has its given velocity (this also is not a natural signification of the expression), formula (7) would give the correct value of $\ddot{x}$ except when $\dot{x}=0$. In this case (which cannot be regarded as exceptional in a problem of this kind), we should have $\delta x \geqq 0$, which will leave $\ddot{x}$ undetermined, as before.

The application of formula (6), in problems of this kind, presents no difficulty. From the condition

$$\dot{x} \geqq 0,$$

we obtain, first, if $\dot{x}=0$, $\ddot{x} \geqq 0$,

then, if $\dot{x}=0$ and $\ddot{x}=0$, $\delta\ddot{x} \geqq 0$,

which is the only limitation on the value of $\delta\ddot{x}$. With this condition, we deduce from (6) that either

$$\dot{x}=0,\ \ddot{x}=0,\ \text{and}\ \ddot{x} \geqq \frac{X}{m};$$

or

$$\ddot{x}=\frac{X}{m}.$$

That is, if $\dot{x}=0$, $\ddot{x}$ has the greater of the values $\frac{X}{m}$ and 0; otherwise, $\ddot{x}=\frac{X}{m}$.

In cases of this kind also, in which the function which cannot exceed a certain value involves the velocities (with or without the coordinates), one may easily convince himself that formula (6) is always valid, and always sufficient to determine the accelerations with the aid of the conditions afforded by the constraints of the system.

But instead of examining such cases in detail, we shall proceed to consider the subject from a more general point of view.

Comparison of the New Formula with the Statical Principle of Virtual Velocities.—Case of Discontinuous Changes of Velocity.

Formula (1) has so far served as a point of departure. The general validity of this, the received form of the indeterminate equation of motion, being assumed, it has been shown that formula (6) will be valid and sufficient, even in cases in which both (1) and (7) fail. We now proceed to show that the statical principle of *virtual velocities*, when its real signification is carefully considered, leads directly to formula (6), or to an analogous formula for the determination of the discontinuous changes of velocity, when such occur. This will be the case even if we start with the usual analytical expression of the principle

$$\Sigma(X\delta x+Y\delta y+Z\delta z)\leqq 0, \tag{8}$$

to which, at first sight, formula (6) appears less closely related than (7). For the variations of the coordinates in this formula must be regarded as relating to differences between the configuration which the system has at a certain time, and which it will continue to have in case of equilibrium, and some other configuration which the system might be supposed to have at some subsequent time. These temporal relations are not indicated explicitly in the notation, and should not be, since the statical problem does not involve the time in any quantitative manner. But in a dynamical problem, in which we take account of the time, it is hardly natural to use δx, δy, δz in the same sense. In any problem in which x, y, z are regarded as functions of the time, δx, δy, δz are naturally understood to relate to differences between the configuration which the system has at a certain time, and some other configuration which it might (conceivably) have had at that time *instead of* that which it actually had.

Now when we suppose a point to have a certain position, specified by x, y, z, at a certain time, its position at that time is no longer a subject of hypothesis or of question. It is its future positions which form the subject of inquiry. Its position in the immediate future is naturally specified by

$$x+\dot{x}dt+\tfrac{1}{2}\ddot{x}dt^2+\text{etc.},\quad y+\dot{y}dt+\tfrac{1}{2}\ddot{y}dt^2+\text{etc.},\quad z+\dot{z}dt+\tfrac{1}{2}\ddot{z}dt^2+\text{etc.},$$

and we may regard the variations of these expressions as corresponding to the δx, δy, δz of the statical problem. It is evidently sufficient to take account of the first term of these expressions of which the variation is not zero. Now, x, y, z, as has already been said, are to be regarded as constant. With respect to the terms containing $\dot{x}$, $\dot{y}$, $\dot{z}$, two cases are to be distinguished, according as there is, or is not, a finite change of velocity at the instant considered.

Let us first consider the most important case, in which there is no discontinuous change of velocity. In this case, $\dot{x}$, $\dot{y}$, $\dot{z}$ are not to be regarded as variable (by δ), and the variations of the above expressions are represented by

$$\tfrac{1}{2}\delta\ddot{x}\,dt^2,\quad \tfrac{1}{2}\delta\ddot{y}\,dt^2,\quad \tfrac{1}{2}\delta\ddot{z}\,dt^2,$$

which are, therefore, to be substituted for δx, δy, δz in the general formula of equilibrium (8) to adapt it to the conditions of a dynamical problem. By this substitution (in which the common factor $\frac{1}{2}dt^2$ may of course be omitted), and the addition of the terms expressing the reaction against acceleration, we obtain formula (6).

But if the circumstances are such that there is (or may be) a discontinuity in the values of $\dot{x}$, $\dot{y}$, $\dot{z}$ at the instant considered, it is necessary to distinguish the values of these expressions before and after the abrupt change. For this purpose, we may apply $\dot{x}$, $\dot{y}$, $\dot{z}$ to the original values, and denote the changed values by $\dot{x}+\Delta\dot{x}$, $\dot{y}+\Delta\dot{y}$, $\dot{z}+\Delta\dot{z}$. The value of x at a time very shortly subsequent to the instant considered, will be expressed by $x+(\dot{x}+\Delta\dot{x})dt+\text{etc.}$, in which we may regard $\Delta\dot{x}$ as subject to the variation denoted by δ. The variation of the expression is therefore $\delta\,\Delta\dot{x}\,dt$. Instead of $-m\ddot{x}$, which expresses the reaction against acceleration, we need in the present case $-m\Delta\dot{x}$ to express the reaction against the abrupt change of velocity. A reaction against such a change of velocity is, of course, to be regarded as infinite in intensity in comparison with reactions due to acceleration, and ordinary forces (such as cause acceleration) may be neglected in comparison. If, however, we conceive of the system as acted on by impulsive forces (i.e., such as have no finite duration, but are capable of producing finite changes of velocity, and are measured numerically by the discontinuities of velocity which they produce in the unit of mass), these forces should be combined with the reactions due to the discontinuities of velocity in the general formula which determines these discontinuities. If the impulsive forces are specified by X, Y, Z, the formula will be

$$[(\mathrm{X}-m\Delta\dot{x})\,\delta\Delta\dot{x}+(\mathrm{Y}-m\Delta\dot{y})\,\delta\Delta\dot{y}+(\mathrm{Z}-m\Delta\dot{z})\,\delta\Delta\dot{z})]\leqq 0. \qquad (9)$$

The reader will remark the strict analogy between this formula and (6), which would perhaps be more clearly exhibited if we should write $\frac{d\dot{x}}{dt}, \frac{d\dot{y}}{dt}, \frac{d\dot{z}}{dt}$ for $\ddot{x}, \ddot{y}, \ddot{z}$ in that formula.

But these formulæ may be established in a much more direct manner. For the formula (8), although for many purposes the most convenient expression of the principle of virtual velocities, is by no means the most convenient for our present purpose. As the usual name of the principle implies, it holds true of velocities as well as of displacements, and is perhaps more simple and more evident when thus applied.*

If we wish to apply the principle, thus understood, to a moving system so as to determine whether certain changes of velocity specified by $\Delta\dot{x}, \Delta\dot{y}, \Delta\dot{z}$ are those which the system will really receive at a given instant, the velocities to be multiplied into the forces and reactions in the most simple application of the principle are manifestly such as may be imagined to be compounded with the assumed velocities, and are therefore properly specified by $\delta\Delta\dot{x}, \delta\Delta\dot{y}, \delta\Delta\dot{z}$. The formula (9) may therefore be regarded as the most direct application of the principle of virtual velocities to discontinuous changes of velocity in a moving system.

In the case of a system in which there are no discontinuous changes of velocity, but which is subject to forces tending to produce accelerations, when we wish to determine whether certain accelerations, specified by $\ddot{x}, \ddot{y}, \ddot{z}$, are such as the system will really receive, it is evidently necessary to consider whether any possible variation of these accelerations is favored more than it is opposed by the forces

* Even in Statics, the principle of virtual *velocities*, as distinguished from that of virtual *displacements*, has a certain advantage in respect of its evidence. The demonstration of the principle in the first section of the *Mécanique Analytique*, if velocities had been considered instead of displacements, would not have been exposed to an objection, which has been expressed by M. Bertrand in the following words: "On a objecté, avec raison, à cette assertion de Lagrange l'example d'un point pesant en équilibre au sommet le plus élevé d'une courbe; il est évident qu'un déplacement infiniment petit le ferait descendre, et, pourtant, ce déplacement ne se produit pas." (*Mécanique Analytique*, troisème édition, tome 1, page 22, note de M. Bertrand.) The value of z (the height of the point above a horizontal plane) can certainly be diminished by a displacement of the point, but the value of $\dot{z}$ is not affected by any velocity given to the point.

The real difficulty in the consideration of displacements is that they are only possible at a time subsequent to that in which the system has the configuration to which the question of equilibrium relates. We may make the interval of time infinitely short, but it will always be difficult, in the establishing of fundamental principles, to treat a conception of this kind (relating to what is possible after an infinitesimal interval of time) with the same rigor as the idea of velocities or accelerations, which, in the cases to which (9) and (6) respectively relate, we may regard as communicated immediately to the system.

and reactions of the system. The formula (6) expresses a criterion of this kind in the most simple and direct manner. If we regard a force as a tendency to increase a quantity expressed by $\ddot{x}$, the product of the force by $\delta\ddot{x}$ is the natural measure of the extent to which this tendency is satisfied by an arbitrary variation of the accelerations. The principle expressed by the formula may not be very accurately designated by the words *virtual velocities*, but it certainly does not differ from the principle of virtual velocities (in the stricter sense of the term), more than this differs from that of virtual displacements,—a difference so slight that the distinction of the names is rarely insisted upon, and that it is often very difficult to tell which form of the principle is especially intended, even when the principle is enunciated or discussed somewhat at length.

But, although the formulæ (6) and (9) differ so little from the ordinary formulæ, they not only have a marked advantage in respect of precision and accuracy, but also may be more satisfactory to the mind, in that the changes considered (to which δ relates), are not so violently opposed to all the possibilities of the case as are those which are represented by the variations of the coordinates.* Moreover, as we shall see, they naturally lead to various important laws of motion.

Transformation of the New Formula.

Let us now consider some of the transformations of which our general formula (6) is capable. If we separate the terms containing

* It may have seemed to some readers of the *Mécanique Analytique*—a work of which the unity of method is one of the most striking characteristics, and that to which its universally recognized artistic merit is in great measure due—that the treatment of dynamical problems in that work is not entirely analogous to the treatment of statical problems. The statical question, whether a system will remain in equilibrium in a given configuration, is determined by Lagrange by considering all possible motions of the system and inquiring whether there is any reason why the system should take any one of them. A similar method in dynamics would be based upon a comparison of a proposed motion with all other motions of which the system is capable without violating its kinematical conditions. Instead of this, Lagrange virtually reduces the dynamical problem to a statical one, and considers, not the possible variations of the proposed motion, but the motions which would be possible if the system were at rest. This reduction of a given problem to a simpler one, which has already been solved, is a method which has its advantages, but it is not the characteristic method of the *Mécanique Analytique*. That which most distinguishes the plan of this treatise from the usual type is the direct application of the general principle to each particular case.

The point is perhaps of small moment, and may be differently regarded by others, but it is mentioned here because it was a feeling of this kind (whether justified or not) and the desire to express the formula of motion by means of a maximum or minimum condition, in which the conditions under which the maximum or minimum subsists should be such as the problem naturally affords (Gauss's principle of *least constraint* being at the time unknown to the present writer, and the conditions under which the minimum subsists in the principle of *least action* being such that that is hardly satisfactory as a fundamental principle), which led to the formulæ proposed in this paper.

the masses of the particles from those which contain the forces, we have

$$\Sigma(X\delta\ddot{x}+Y\delta\ddot{y}+Z\delta\ddot{z})-\Sigma[\tfrac{1}{2}m\delta(\ddot{x}^2+\ddot{y}^2+\ddot{z}^2)]\leqq 0, \qquad (10)$$

or, if we write u for the acceleration of a particle,

$$\Sigma(X\delta\ddot{x}+Y\delta\ddot{y}+Z\delta\ddot{z})-\delta\Sigma(\tfrac{1}{2}mu^2)\leqq 0. \qquad (11)$$

If, instead of terms of the form $X\delta x$, or in addition to such terms, equation (1) had contained terms of the form $P\delta p$, in which p denotes any quantity determined by the configuration of the system, it is evident that these would give terms of the form $P\delta\ddot{p}$ in (6), (10) and (11). For the considerations which justified the substitution of $\delta\ddot{x}$, $\delta\ddot{y}$, $\delta\ddot{z}$ for δx, δy, δz in the usual formula were in no respect dependent upon the fact that x, y, z denote rectangular coordinates, but would apply equally to any other quantities which are determined by the configuration of the system.

Hence, if the moments of all the forces of the system are represented by the sum

$$\mathfrak{S}(Pdp),$$

the general formula of motion may be written

$$\mathfrak{S}(P\delta\ddot{p})-\delta\Sigma(\tfrac{1}{2}mu^2)\leqq 0 \qquad (12)$$

If the forces admit of a force-function V, we have

$$\delta\ddot{V}-\delta\Sigma(\tfrac{1}{2}mu^2)\leqq 0,$$

or

$$\delta[\ddot{V}-\Sigma(\tfrac{1}{2}mu^2)]\leqq 0. \qquad (13)$$

But if the forces are determined in any way whatever by the configuration and velocities of the system, with or without the time, X, Y, Z and P will be unaffected by the variation denoted by δ, and we may write the formula of motion in the form

$$\delta\Sigma(X\ddot{x}+Y\ddot{y}+Z\ddot{z}-\tfrac{1}{2}mu^2)\leqq 0, \qquad (14)$$

or

$$\delta[\mathfrak{S}(P\ddot{p})-\Sigma(\tfrac{1}{2}mu^2)]\leqq 0. \qquad (15)$$

If the forces are determined by the configuration alone, or the configuration and the time, $\delta\dot{X}=0$, $\delta\dot{Y}=0$, $\delta\dot{Z}=0$, $\delta\dot{P}=0$, and the general formula may be written

$$\delta\left[\frac{d}{dt}\Sigma(X\dot{x}+Y\dot{y}+Z\dot{z})-\Sigma(\tfrac{1}{2}mu^2)\right]\leqq 0, \qquad (16)$$

or

$$\delta\left[\frac{d}{dt}\mathfrak{S}(P\dot{p})-\Sigma(\tfrac{1}{2}mu^2)\right]\leqq 0. \qquad (17)$$

The quantity affected by δ in any one of the last five formulæ has not only a maximum value, but absolutely the greatest value consistent with the constraints of the system. This may be shown in reference to (15) by giving to $\ddot{p}$, $\ddot{x}$, $\ddot{y}$, $\ddot{z}$, contained explicitly or implicitly in the expression affected by δ, any possible finite increments $\ddot{p}'$, $\ddot{x}'$, $\ddot{y}'$. $\ddot{z}'$, and subtracting the original value of the expression from the value thus modified. Now,

$$\begin{aligned}\mathfrak{S}[P(\ddot{p}+\ddot{p}')]-\Sigma[\tfrac{1}{2}m\{(\ddot{x}+\ddot{x}')^2+(\ddot{y}+\ddot{y}')^2+(\ddot{z}+\ddot{z}')^2\}] \\ -\mathfrak{S}(P\ddot{p})+\Sigma[\tfrac{1}{2}m(\ddot{x}^2+\ddot{y}^2+\ddot{z}^2)] \\ =\mathfrak{S}(P\ddot{p}')-\Sigma[m(\ddot{x}\ddot{x}'+\ddot{y}\ddot{y}'+\ddot{z}\ddot{z}')]-\Sigma[\tfrac{1}{2}m(\ddot{x}'^2+\ddot{y}'^2+\ddot{z}'^2)].\end{aligned}$$

But since $\ddot{p}'$, $\ddot{x}'$, $\ddot{y}'$, $\ddot{z}'$ are proportional to and of the same sign with possible values of $\delta\ddot{p}$, $\delta\ddot{x}$, $\delta\ddot{y}$, $\delta\ddot{z}$, we have, by the general formula of motion,

$$\mathfrak{S}(P\ddot{p}')-\Sigma[m(\ddot{x}\ddot{x}'+\ddot{y}\ddot{y}'+\ddot{z}\ddot{z}')]\leqq 0.$$

The second member of the preceding equation is therefore negative. The first member is therefore negative, which proves the proposition with respect to (15). The demonstration is precisely the same with respect to (13) and (14), which may be regarded as particular cases of (15).

To show the same with regard to (16) and (17), we have only to observe that the quantities affected by δ in these formulæ differ from those affected by the same symbol in (14) and (15) only by the terms

$$\Sigma(\dot{X}\dot{x}+\dot{Y}\dot{y}+\dot{Z}\dot{z}) \quad \text{and} \quad \mathfrak{S}(\dot{P}\dot{p}),$$

which will not be affected by any change in the accelerations of the system.

When the forces are determined by the configuration (with or without the time), the principle may be enunciated as follows: The accelerations in the system are always such that the acceleration of the rate of work done by the forces diminished by one-half the sum of the products of the masses of the particles by the squares of their accelerations has the greatest possible value.

The formula (17), although in appearance less simple than (15), not only is more easily enunciated in words, but has the advantage that the quantity $\frac{d}{dt}\mathfrak{S}(P\dot{p})$ is entirely determined by the system with its forces and motions, which is not the case with $\mathfrak{S}(P\ddot{p})$. The value of the latter expression depends upon the manner in which we choose to represent the forces. For example, if a material point is revolving in a circle under the influence of a central force, we may write either $X\ddot{x}+Y\ddot{y}+Z\ddot{z}$ or $R\ddot{r}$ for $P\ddot{p}$, R and r denoting respectively the force and radius vector. Now $X\ddot{x}+Y\ddot{y}+Z\ddot{z}$ is manifestly unequal to $R\ddot{r}$. But $X\dot{x}+Y\dot{y}+Z\dot{z}$ is equal to $R\dot{r}$, and $\frac{d}{dt}(X\dot{x}+Y\dot{y}+Z\dot{z})$ is equal to $\frac{d}{dt}(R\dot{r})$.

It may not be without interest to see what shape our general formulæ will take in one of the most important cases of forces dependent upon the velocities. If a body which can be treated as a point is moving in a medium which presents a resistance expressed by any function of the velocity, the terms due to that resistance in the general formula of motion may be expressed in the form

$$\delta\left[\phi(v)\frac{\dot{x}}{v}\ddot{x}+\phi(v)\frac{\dot{y}}{v}\ddot{y}+\phi(v)\frac{\dot{z}}{v}\ddot{z}\right],$$

where v denotes the velocity and $\phi(v)$ the resistance. But

$$\frac{\dot{x}\ddot{x}}{v}+\frac{\dot{y}\ddot{y}}{v}+\frac{\dot{z}\ddot{z}}{v}=\frac{dv}{dt}=\dot{v}.$$

The terms due to the resistance reduce, therefore, to

$$\delta[\phi(v)\dot{v}],$$

or,

$$\delta\frac{d}{dt}f(v),$$

where f denotes the primitive of the function denoted by ϕ.

Discontinuous Changes of Velocity.—Formula (9), which relates to discontinuous changes of velocity, is capable of similar transformations. If we set

$$w^2=\Delta\dot{x}^2+\Delta\dot{y}^2+\Delta\dot{z}^2,$$

the formula reduces to

$$\delta\Sigma(\mathrm{X}\Delta\dot{x}+\mathrm{Y}\Delta\dot{y}+\mathrm{Z}\Delta\dot{z}-\tfrac{1}{2}mw^2)\leqq 0, \tag{18}$$

where X, Y, Z are to be regarded as constant. If $\mathbf{\$}(\mathrm{P}dp)$ represents the sum of the moments of the impulsive forces, and we regard P as constant, we have

$$\delta[\mathbf{\$}(\mathrm{P}\Delta\dot{p})-\Sigma(\tfrac{1}{2}mw^2)]\leqq 0. \tag{19}$$

The expressions affected by δ in these formulæ have a greater value than they would receive from any other changes of velocity consistent with the constraints of the system.

Deduction of other Properties of Motion.

The principles which have been established furnish a convenient point of departure for the demonstration of various properties of motion relating to *maxima* and *minima*. We may obtain several such properties by considering how the accelerations of a system, at a given instant, will be modified by changes of the forces or of the constraints to which the system is subject. Let us suppose that the forces X, Y, Z of a system receive the increments X', Y', Z', in consequence of which, and of certain additional constraints, which do not produce any discontinuity in the velocities, the components of acceleration $\ddot{x}, \ddot{y}, \ddot{z}$ receive the increments $\ddot{x}', \ddot{y}', \ddot{z}'$. The expression

$$\Sigma\big[(X+X')(\ddot{x}+\ddot{x}')+(Y+Y')(\ddot{y}+\ddot{y}')+(Z+Z')(\ddot{z}+\ddot{z}') \\ -\tfrac{1}{2}m\{(\ddot{x}+\ddot{x}')^2+(\ddot{y}+\ddot{y}')^2+(\ddot{z}+\ddot{z}')^2\}\big] \tag{20}$$

will be the greatest possible for any values of $\ddot{x}', \ddot{y}', \ddot{z}'$ consistent with the constraints. But this expression may be divided into three parts,

$$\Sigma[(X+X')\ddot{x}+(Y+Y')\ddot{y}+(Z+Z')\ddot{z}-\tfrac{1}{2}m(\ddot{x}^2+\ddot{y}^2+\ddot{z}^2)], \tag{21}$$

$$\Sigma[X\ddot{x}'+Y\ddot{y}'+Z\ddot{z}'-m(\ddot{x}\ddot{x}'+\ddot{y}\ddot{y}'+\ddot{z}\ddot{z}')], \tag{22}$$

and

$$\Sigma[X'\ddot{x}'+Y'\ddot{y}'+Z'\ddot{z}'-\tfrac{1}{2}m(\ddot{x}'^2+\ddot{y}'^2+\ddot{z}'^2)]. \tag{23}$$

The first part is evidently constant with reference to variations of $\ddot{x}'$, $\ddot{y}'$, $\ddot{z}'$, and may, therefore, be neglected. With respect to the second part we observe that by the general formula of the motion we have

$$\Sigma[X\delta\ddot{x}+Y\delta\ddot{y}+Z\delta\ddot{z}-m(\ddot{x}\delta\ddot{x}+\ddot{y}\delta\ddot{y}+\ddot{z}\delta\ddot{z})]=0$$

for all values of $\delta\ddot{x}$, $\delta\ddot{y}$, $\delta\ddot{z}$ which are possible and reversible before the addition of the new constraints. But values proportional to $\ddot{x}'$, $\ddot{y}'$, $\ddot{z}'$, and of the same sign, are evidently consistent with the original constraints, and when the components of acceleration are altered to $\ddot{x}+\ddot{x}'$, $\ddot{y}+\ddot{y}'$, $\ddot{z}+\ddot{z}'$, variations of these quantities proportional to and of the same sign as $-\ddot{x}'$, $-\ddot{y}'$, $-\ddot{z}'$ are evidently consistent with the original constraints. Now if these latter variations were not possible before the accelerations were modified by the addition of the new forces and constraints, it must be that some constraint was then operative which afterwards ceased to be so. The expression (22) will, therefore, be equal to zero, provided only that all the constraints which were operative before the addition of the new forces and constraints, remain operative afterwards.* With this limitation, therefore, the expression (23) must have the greatest value consistent with the constraints. This principle may be expressed without reference to rectangular coordinates. If we write u' for the relative acceleration due to the additional forces and constraints, we have

$$u'^2=\ddot{x}'^2+\ddot{y}'^2+\ddot{z}'^2,$$

and expression (23) reduces to

$$\Sigma(X'\ddot{x}'+Y'\ddot{y}'+Z'\ddot{z}'-\tfrac{1}{2}mu'^2). \tag{24}$$

If the sum of the moments of the additional forces which are considered is represented by $\mathfrak{S}(Qdq)$ (the q representing quantities determined by the configuration of the system), we have

$$\Sigma(X'\dot{x}+Y'\dot{y}+Z'\dot{z})=\mathfrak{S}(Q\dot{q}).$$

We may distinguish the values of $\dfrac{d^2q}{dt^2}$ immediately before and immediately after the application of the additional forces and constraints by the expressions $\ddot{q}$ and $\ddot{q}+\ddot{q}'$. With this understanding, we have, by differentiation of the preceding equation,

$$\Sigma[\dot{X}'\dot{x}+\dot{Y}'\dot{y}+\dot{Z}'\dot{z}+X'(\ddot{x}+\ddot{x}')+Y'(\ddot{y}+\ddot{y}')+Z'(\ddot{z}+\ddot{z}')]$$
$$=\mathfrak{S}[\dot{Q}\dot{q}+Q(\ddot{q}+\ddot{q}')];$$

* As an illustration of the significance of this limitation, we may consider the condition afforded by the impenetrability of two bodies in contact. Let us suppose that if subject only to the original forces and constraints they would continue in contact, but that, under the influence of the additional forces and constraints, the contact will cease. The impenetrability of the bodies then ceases to be operative as a constraint. Such cases form an exception to the principle which is to be established. But there are no exceptions when all the original constraints are expressed by *equations*.

whence it appears that $\Sigma(X'\ddot{x}'+Y'\ddot{y}'+Z'\ddot{z}')$ differs from $\mathfrak{S}(Q\ddot{q}')$ only by quantities which are independent of the relative acceleration due to the additional forces and constraints. It follows that these relative accelerations are such as to make

$$\mathfrak{S}(Q\ddot{q}')-\Sigma(\tfrac{1}{2}mu'^2) \qquad (25)$$

a maximum.

It will be observed that the condition which determines these relative accelerations is of precisely the same form as that which determines absolute accelerations.

An important case is that in which new constraints are added but no new forces. The relative accelerations are determined in this case by the condition that $\Sigma(\frac{1}{2}mu'^2)$ is a minimum. In any case of motion, in which finite forces do not act at points, lines or surfaces, we may first calculate the accelerations which would be produced if there were no constraints, and then determine the relative accelerations due to the constraints by the condition that $\Sigma(\frac{1}{2}mu'^2)$ is a minimum. This is Gauss's principle of *least constraint*.*

Again, in any case of motion, we may suppose u to denote the acceleration which would be produced by the constraints alone, and u' the relative acceleration produced by the forces; we then have

$$\Sigma[m(\ddot{x}\ddot{x}'+\ddot{y}\ddot{y}'+\ddot{z}\ddot{z}')]=0,$$

whence, if we write u'' for the resultant or actual acceleration,

$$\Sigma(\tfrac{1}{2}mu^2)+\Sigma(\tfrac{1}{2}mu'^2)=\Sigma(\tfrac{1}{2}mu''^2).$$

Moreover, differentiating (25), we obtain

$$\mathfrak{S}(Q\delta\ddot{q}')-\Sigma[m(\ddot{x}'\delta\ddot{x}'+\ddot{y}'\delta\ddot{y}'+\ddot{z}'\delta\ddot{z}')]=0,$$

whence, since $\delta\ddot{q}'$, $\delta\ddot{x}'$, $\delta\ddot{y}'$, $\delta\ddot{z}'$ may have values proportional to $\ddot{q}'$, $\ddot{x}'$, $\ddot{y}'$, $\ddot{z}'$,

$$\mathfrak{S}(Q\ddot{q}')=2\Sigma(\tfrac{1}{2}mu'^2).$$

These relations are similar to those which exist with respect to *vis viva* and impulsive forces.

Particular Equations of Motion.

From the general formula (12), we may easily obtain particular equations which will express the laws of motion in a very general form.

Let $d\omega_1$, $d\omega_2$, etc. be infinitesimals (not necessarily complete differentials) the values of which are independent, and by means

* This principle may be derived very directly from the general formula (6), or *vice versa*, for $\Sigma(\frac{1}{2}mu'^2)$ may be put in the form

$$\Sigma\left[\tfrac{1}{2}m\left\{\left(\ddot{x}-\frac{X}{m}\right)^2+\left(\ddot{y}-\frac{Y}{m}\right)^2+\left(\ddot{z}-\frac{Z}{m}\right)^2\right\}\right],$$

the variation of which, with the sign changed, is identical with the first member of (6).

of which we can perfectly define any infinitesimal change in the configuration of the system; and let

$$\dot{\omega}_1 = \frac{d\omega_1}{dt}, \quad \dot{\omega}_2 = \frac{d\omega_2}{dt}, \quad \text{etc.},$$

where $d\omega_1$, $d\omega_2$ are to be determined by the change in the configuration in the interval of time dt; and let

$$\ddot{\omega}_1 = \frac{d\dot{\omega}_1}{dt}, \quad \ddot{\omega}_2 = \frac{d\dot{\omega}_2}{dt}, \quad \text{etc.}$$

Also let $$U = \Sigma(\tfrac{1}{2}mu^2).$$

It is evident that U can be expressed in terms of $\dot{\omega}_1$, $\dot{\omega}_2$, etc., $\ddot{\omega}_1$, $\ddot{\omega}_2$, etc., and the quantities which express the configuration of the system, and that (since δ is used to denote a variation which does not affect the configuration or the velocities),

$$\delta U = \frac{dU}{d\ddot{\omega}_1}\delta\ddot{\omega}_1 + \frac{dU}{d\ddot{\omega}_2}\delta\ddot{\omega}_2 + \text{etc.}$$

Moreover, since the quantities p in the general formula are entirely determined by the configuration of the system

$$\dot{p} = \frac{dp}{d\omega_1}\dot{\omega}_1 + \frac{dp}{d\omega_2}\dot{\omega}_2 + \text{etc.},$$

where $\frac{dp}{d\omega_1}$ denotes the ratio of simultaneous values of dp and $d\omega_1$, when $d\omega_2$, etc. are equal to zero, and $\frac{dp}{d\omega_2}$, etc. are to be interpreted on the same principle. Multiplying by P, and taking the sum with respect to the several forces, we have

$$\mathfrak{S}(P\dot{p}) = \Omega_1\dot{\omega}_1 + \Omega_2\dot{\omega}_2 + \text{etc.},$$

where $$\Omega_1 = \mathfrak{S}\left(P\frac{dp}{d\omega_1}\right), \quad \Omega_2 = \mathfrak{S}\left(P\frac{dp}{d\omega_2}\right), \quad \text{etc.}$$

If we differentiate with respect to t, and take the variation denoted by δ, we obtain

$$\mathfrak{S}(P\delta\ddot{p}) = \Omega_1\delta\ddot{\omega}_1 + \Omega_2\delta\ddot{\omega}_2 + \text{etc.}$$

The general formula (12) is thus reduced to the form

$$\left(\Omega_1 - \frac{dU}{d\ddot{\omega}_1}\right)\delta\ddot{\omega}_1 + \left(\Omega_2 - \frac{dU}{d\ddot{\omega}_2}\right)\delta\ddot{\omega}_2 + \text{etc.} \geqq 0. \tag{26}$$

If the forces have a potential V, we may write

$$\left(\frac{dV}{d\omega_1} - \frac{dU}{d\ddot{\omega}_1}\right)\delta\ddot{\omega}_1 + \left(\frac{dV}{d\omega_2} - \frac{dU}{d\ddot{\omega}_2}\right)\delta\ddot{\omega}_2 + \text{etc.}, \tag{27}$$

where $\frac{dV}{d\omega_1}$ denotes the ratio of dV and $d\omega_1$ when $d\omega_2$, etc. have the value zero, and the analogous expressions are to be interpreted on the same principle.

If the variations $\delta\omega_1$, $\delta\omega_2$, etc. are capable both of positive and of negative values, we must have

$$\frac{dU}{d\ddot{\omega}_1}=\Omega_1, \quad \frac{dU}{d\ddot{\omega}_2}=\Omega_2, \text{ etc.,} \tag{28}$$

or,

$$\frac{dU}{d\ddot{\omega}_1}=\frac{dV}{d\omega_1}, \quad \frac{dU}{d\ddot{\omega}_2}=\frac{dV}{d\omega_2}, \text{ etc.} \tag{29}$$

To illustrate the use of these equations in a case in which $d\omega_1$, $d\omega_2$, etc. are not exact differentials, we may apply them to the problem of the rotation of a rigid body of which one point is fixed. If $d\omega_1$, $d\omega_2$, $d\omega_3$ denote infinitesimal rotations about the principal axes which pass through the fixed point, Ω_1, Ω_2, Ω_3 will denote the moments of the impressed forces about these axes, and the value of U will be given by the formula

$$\begin{aligned}2U=&(a+b+c)(\dot{\omega}_1^2+\dot{\omega}_2^2+\dot{\omega}_3^2)^2-(\dot{\omega}_1^2+\dot{\omega}_2^2+\dot{\omega}_3^2)(a\dot{\omega}_1^2+b\dot{\omega}_2^2+c\dot{\omega}_3^2)\\ &+2(b-c)\dot{\omega}_2\dot{\omega}_3\ddot{\omega}_1+2(c-a)\dot{\omega}_3\dot{\omega}_1\ddot{\omega}_2+2(a-b)\dot{\omega}_1\dot{\omega}_2\ddot{\omega}_3\\ &+(b+c)\ddot{\omega}_1^2+(c+a)\ddot{\omega}_2^2+(a+b)\ddot{\omega}_3^2,\end{aligned}$$

where a, b, and c are constants, $a+b$, $b+c$, $c+a$ being the *moments of inertia* about the three axes. Hence,

$$\frac{dU}{d\ddot{\omega}_1}=(b-c)\dot{\omega}_2\dot{\omega}_3+(b+c)\ddot{\omega}_1, \quad \frac{dU}{d\ddot{\omega}_2}=(c-a)\dot{\omega}_3\dot{\omega}_1+(c+a)\ddot{\omega}_2,$$

$$\frac{dU}{d\ddot{\omega}_3}=(a-b)\dot{\omega}_1\dot{\omega}_2+(a+b)\ddot{\omega}_3;$$

and the equations of motion are

$$\ddot{\omega}_1=\frac{(c-b)\dot{\omega}_2\dot{\omega}_3+\Omega_1}{c+b},$$

$$\ddot{\omega}_2=\frac{(a-c)\dot{\omega}_3\dot{\omega}_1+\Omega_2}{a+c},$$

$$\ddot{\omega}_3=\frac{(b-a)\dot{\omega}_1\dot{\omega}_2+\Omega_3}{b+a}.$$

II.

ON THE FUNDAMENTAL FORMULA OF STATISTICAL MECHANICS, WITH APPLICATIONS TO ASTRONOMY AND THERMODYNAMICS.

[*Proceedings of the American Association for the Advancement of Science*, vol. XXXIII. pp. 57, 58, 1884.]

(ABSTRACT.)

SUPPOSE that we have a great number of systems which consist of material points and are identical in character, but different in configuration and velocities, and in which the forces are determined by the configuration alone. Let the number of systems in which the coordinates and velocities lie severally between the following limits, viz., between

$$\begin{array}{l} x_1 \text{ and } x_1+dx_1, \\ y_1 \text{ and } y_1+dy_1, \\ z_1 \text{ and } z_1+dz_1, \\ x_2 \text{ and } x_2+dx_2, \\ \quad \text{etc.,} \\ \dot{x}_1 \text{ and } \dot{x}_1+d\dot{x}_1, \\ \dot{y}_1 \text{ and } \dot{y}_1+d\dot{y}_1, \\ \dot{z}_1 \text{ and } \dot{z}_1+d\dot{z}_1, \\ \dot{x}_2 \text{ and } \dot{x}_2+d\dot{x}_2, \\ \quad \text{etc.,} \end{array}$$

be denoted by

$$L\, dx_1\, dy_1\, dz_1\, dx_2 \text{ etc. } d\dot{x}_1\, d\dot{y}_1\, d\dot{z}_1\, d\dot{x}_2 \text{ etc.}$$

The manner in which the quantity L varies with the time is given by the equation

$$\frac{dL}{dt} = -\Sigma\left[\frac{dL}{dx}\dot{x} + \frac{dL}{d\dot{x}}\ddot{x}\right],$$

where t, x_1, y_1, z_1, x_2, etc., $\dot{x}_1$, $\dot{y}_1$, $\dot{z}_1$, $\dot{x}_2$, etc., are the independent variables, and the summation relates to all the coordinates.

The object of the paper is to establish this proposition (which is not claimed as new, but which has hardly received the recognition which it deserves) and to show its applications to astronomy and thermodynamics.

III.

ELEMENTS OF VECTOR ANALYSIS.

[Privately printed, New Haven, pp. 17–50, 1881; pp. 50–90, 1884.]

(The fundamental principles of the following analysis are such as are familiar under a slightly different form to students of quaternions. The manner in which the subject is developed is somewhat different from that followed in treatises on quaternions, since the object of the writer does not require any use of the conception of the quaternion, being simply to give a suitable notation for those relations between vectors, or between vectors and scalars, which seem most important, and which lend themselves most readily to analytical transformations, and to explain some of these transformations. As a precedent for such a departure from quaternionic usage, Clifford's *Kinematic* may be cited. In this connection, the name of Grassmann may also be mentioned, to whose system the following method attaches itself in some respects more closely than to that of Hamilton.)

CHAPTER I.

CONCERNING THE ALGEBRA OF VECTORS.

Fundamental Notions.

1. *Definition.*—If anything has magnitude and direction, its magnitude and direction taken together constitute what is called a vector. The numerical description of a vector requires three numbers, but nothing prevents us from using a single letter for its symbolical designation. An algebra or analytical method in which a single letter or other expression is used to specify a vector may be called a *vector algebra* or *vector analysis*.

Def.—As distinguished from vectors the real (positive or negative) quantities of ordinary algebra are called *scalars.**

As it is convenient that the form of the letter should indicate whether a vector or a scalar is denoted, we shall use the small Greek letters to denote vectors, and the small English letters to denote scalars. (The three letters, i, j, k, will make an exception, to be mentioned more particularly hereafter. Moreover, π will be used in its usual scalar sense, to denote the ratio of the circumference of a circle to its diameter.)

* The imaginaries of ordinary algebra may be called *biscalars*, and that which corresponds to them in the theory of vectors, *bivectors*. But we shall have no occasion to consider either of these. [See, however, footnote on p. 84.]

2. *Def.*—Vectors are said to be *equal* when they are the same both in direction and in magnitude. This equality is denoted by the ordinary sign, as $\alpha=\beta$. The reader will observe that this *vector equation* is the equivalent of three scalar equations.

A vector is said to be equal to zero, when its magnitude is zero. Such vectors may be set equal to one another, irrespectively of any considerations relating to direction.

3. Perhaps the most simple example of a vector is afforded by a directed straight line, as the line drawn from A to B. We may use the notation $\overline{\text{AB}}$ to denote this line as a vector, i.e., to denote its length and direction without regard to its position in other respects. The points A and B may be distinguished as the *origin* and the *terminus* of the vector. Since any magnitude may be represented by a length, any vector may be represented by a directed line; and it will often be convenient to use language relating to vectors, which refers to them as thus represented.

Reversal of Direction, Scalar Multiplication and Division.

4. The negative sign ($-$) reverses the direction of a vector. (Sometimes the sign $+$ may be used to call attention to the fact that the vector has not the negative sign.)

Def.—A vector is said to be *multiplied* or *divided by a scalar* when its magnitude is multiplied or divided by the numerical value of the scalar and its direction is either unchanged or reversed according as the scalar is positive or negative. These operations are represented by the same methods as multiplication and division in algebra, and are to be regarded as substantially identical with them. The terms *scalar multiplication* and *scalar division* are used to denote multiplication and division by scalars, whether the quantity multiplied or divided is a scalar or a vector.

5. *Def.*—A unit vector is a vector of which the magnitude is unity.

Any vector may be regarded as the product of a positive scalar (the magnitude of the vector) and a unit vector.

The notation α_0 may be used to denote the magnitude of the vector α.

Addition and Subtraction of Vectors.

6. *Def.*—The *sum* of the vectors α, β, etc. (written $\alpha+\beta+$etc.) is the vector found by the following process. Assuming any point A, we determine successively the points B, C, etc., so that $\overline{\text{AB}}=\alpha$, $\overline{\text{BC}}=\beta$, etc. The vector drawn from A to the last point thus determined is the sum required. This is sometimes called the *geometrical* sum, to distinguish it from an *algebraic* sum or an *arithmetical* sum. It is also called the resultant, and α, β, etc. are called the components.

When the vectors to be added are all parallel to the same straight line, geometrical addition reduces to algebraic; when they have all the same direction, geometrical addition like algebraic reduces to arithmetical.

It may easily be shown that the value of a sum is not affected by changing the order of two consecutive terms, and therefore that it is not affected by any change in the order of the terms. Again, it is evident from the definition that the value of a sum is not altered by uniting any of its terms in brackets, as $\alpha+[\beta+\gamma]+$etc., which is in effect to substitute the sum of the terms enclosed for the terms themselves among the vectors to be added. In other words, the commutative and associative principles of arithmetical and algebraic addition hold true of geometrical addition.

7. *Def.*—A vector is said to be subtracted when it is added after reversal of direction. This is indicated by the use of the sign $-$ instead of $+$.

8. It is easily shown that the distributive principle of arithmetical and algebraic multiplication applies to the multiplication of sums of vectors by scalars or sums of scalars, i.e.,

$$\begin{aligned}(m+n+\text{etc.})\,[\alpha+\beta+\text{etc.}]=m\alpha&+n\alpha+\text{etc.}\\ +m\beta&+n\beta+\text{etc.}\\ &+\text{etc.}\end{aligned}$$

9. *Vector Equations.*—If we have equations between sums and differences of vectors, we may transpose terms in them, multiply or divide by any scalar, and add or subtract the equations, precisely as in the case of the equations of ordinary algebra. Hence, if we have several such equations containing known and unknown vectors, the processes of elimination and reduction by which the unknown vectors may be expressed in terms of the known are precisely the same, and subject to the same limitations, as if the letters representing vectors represented scalars. This will be evident if we consider that in the multiplications incident to elimination in the supposed scalar equations the multipliers are the coefficients of the unknown quantities, or functions of these coefficients, and that such multiplications may be applied to the vector equations, since the coefficients are scalars.

10. *Linear relation of four vectors, Coordinates.*—If α, β, and γ are any given vectors not parallel to the same plane, any other vector ρ may be expressed in the form

$$\rho=a\alpha+b\beta+c\gamma.$$

If α, β, and γ are unit vectors, a, b, and c are the ordinary scalar components of ρ parallel to α, β, and γ. If $\rho=\overline{\text{OP}}$, ($\alpha$, β, γ being unit vectors), a, b, and c are the cartesian coordinates of the point P referred to axes through O parallel to α, β, and γ. When the values of these scalars are given, ρ is said to be given in terms of α, β, and γ.

It is generally in this way that the value of a vector is specified, viz., in terms of three known vectors. For such purposes of reference, a system of three mutually perpendicular vectors has certain evident advantages.

11. *Normal systems of unit vectors.*—The letters i, j, k are appropriated to the designation of a *normal system of unit vectors*, i.e., three unit vectors, each of which is at right angles to the other two and determined in direction by them in a perfectly definite manner. We shall always suppose that k is on the side of the i-j plane on which a rotation from i to j (through one right angle) appears counter-clockwise. In other words, the directions of i, j, and k are to be so determined that if they be turned (remaining rigidly connected with each other) so that i points to the east, and j to the north, k will point upward. When rectangular axes of X, Y, and Z are employed, their directions will be conformed to a similar condition, and i, j, k (when the contrary is not stated) will be supposed parallel to these axes respectively. We may have occasion to use more than one such system of unit vectors, just as we may use more than one system of coordinate axes. In such cases, the different systems may be distinguished by accents or otherwise.

12. *Numerical computation of a geometrical sum.*—If

$$\rho = a\alpha + b\beta + c\gamma,$$
$$\sigma = a'\alpha + b'\beta + c'\gamma,$$
$$\text{etc.,}$$

then

$$\rho + \sigma + \text{etc.} = (a + a' + \text{etc.})\,\alpha + (b + b' + \text{etc.})\,\beta + (c + c' + \text{etc.})\,\gamma,$$

i.e., the coefficients by which a geometrical sum is expressed in terms of three vectors are the sums of the coefficients by which the separate terms of the geometrical sum are expressed in terms of the same three vectors.

Direct and Skew Products of Vectors.

13. *Def.*—The *direct product* of α and β (written $\alpha.\beta$) is the scalar quantity obtained by multiplying the product of their magnitudes by the cosine of the angle made by their directions.

14. *Def.*—The *skew product* of α and β (written $\alpha\times\beta$) is a vector function of α and β. Its magnitude is obtained by multiplying the product of the magnitudes of α and β by the sine of the angle made by their directions. Its direction is at right angles to α and β, and on that side of the plane containing α and β (supposed drawn from a common origin) on which a rotation from α to β through an arc of less than 180° appears counter-clockwise.

The direction of $\alpha\times\beta$ may also be defined as that in which an ordinary screw advances as it turns so as to carry α toward β.

Again, if α be directed toward the east, and β lie in the same horizontal plane and on the north side of α, $\alpha\times\beta$ will be directed upward.

15. It is evident from the preceding definitions that

$$\alpha.\beta=\beta.\alpha, \quad \text{and} \quad \alpha\times\beta=-\beta\times\alpha.$$

16. Moreover, $\qquad [n\alpha].\beta=\alpha.[n\beta]=n[\alpha.\beta],$

and $\qquad [n\alpha]\times\beta=\alpha\times[n\beta]=n[\alpha\times\beta].$

The brackets may therefore be omitted in such expressions.

17. From the definitions of No. 11 it appears that

$$i.i=j.j=k.k=1,$$
$$i.j=j.i=i.k=k.i=j.k=k.j=0,$$
$$i\times i=0, \quad j\times j=0, \quad k\times k=0,$$
$$i\times j=k, \quad j\times k=i, \quad k\times i=j,$$
$$j\times i=-k, \quad k\times j=-i, \quad i\times k=-j.$$

18. If we resolve β into two components β' and β'', of which the first is parallel and the second perpendicular to α, we shall have

$$\alpha.\beta=\alpha.\beta' \qquad \text{and} \qquad \alpha\times\beta=\alpha\times\beta''.$$

19. $\qquad \alpha.[\beta+\gamma]=\alpha.\beta + \alpha.\gamma$ and $\alpha\times[\beta+\gamma]=\alpha\times\beta + \alpha\times\gamma.$

To prove this, let $\sigma=\beta+\gamma$, and resolve each of the vectors β, γ, σ into two components, one parallel and the other perpendicular to α. Let these be β', β'', γ', γ'', σ', σ''. Then the equations to be proved will reduce by the last section to

$$\alpha.\sigma'=\alpha.\beta'+\alpha.\gamma' \quad \text{and} \quad \alpha\times\sigma''=\alpha\times\beta''+\alpha\times\gamma''.$$

Now since $\sigma=\beta+\gamma$ we may form a triangle in space, the sides of which shall be β, γ, and σ. Projecting this on a plane perpendicular to α, we obtain a triangle having the sides β'', γ'', and σ'', which affords the relation $\sigma''=\beta''+\gamma''$. If we pass planes perpendicular to α through the vertices of the first triangle, they will give on a line parallel to α segments equal to β', γ', σ'. Thus we obtain the relation $\sigma'=\beta'+\gamma'$. Therefore $\alpha.\sigma'=\alpha.\beta'+\alpha.\gamma'$, since all the cosines involved in these products are equal to unity. Moreover, if α is a unit vector, we shall evidently have $\alpha\times\sigma''=\alpha\times\beta''+\alpha\times\gamma''$, since the effect of the skew multiplication by α upon vectors in a plane perpendicular to α is simply to rotate them all 90° in that plane. But any case may be reduced to this by dividing both sides of the equation to be proved by the magnitude of α. The propositions are therefore proved.

20. Hence,

$$[\alpha+\beta].\gamma=\alpha.\gamma+\beta.\gamma, \qquad [\alpha+\beta]\times\gamma=\alpha\times\gamma+\beta\times\gamma,$$
$$[\alpha+\beta].[\gamma+\delta]=\alpha.\gamma+\alpha.\delta+\beta.\gamma+\beta.\delta,$$
$$[\alpha+\beta]\times[\gamma+\delta]=\alpha\times\gamma+\alpha\times\delta+\beta\times\gamma+\beta\times\delta;$$

and, in general, direct and skew products of sums of vectors may be expanded precisely as the products of sums in algebra, except that in skew products the order of the factors must not be changed without compensation in the sign of the term. If any of the terms in the factors have negative signs, the signs of the expanded product (when there is no change in the order of the factors) will be determined by the same rules as in algebra. It is on account of this analogy with algebraic products that these functions of vectors are called *products* and that other terms relating to multiplication are applied to them.

21. *Numerical calculation of direct and skew products.*—The properties demonstrated in the last two paragraphs (which may be briefly expressed by saying that the operations of direct and skew multiplication are distributive) afford the rule for the numerical calculation of a direct product, or of the components of a skew product, when the rectangular components of the factors are given numerically. In fact, if

$$\alpha = xi + yj + zk, \quad \text{and} \quad \beta = x'i + y'j + z'k;$$

$$\alpha . \beta = xx' + yy' + zz',$$

and

$$\alpha \times \beta = (yz' - zy')i + (zx' - xz')j + (xy' - yx')k.$$

22. *Representation of the area of a parallelogram by a skew product.*—It will be easily seen that $\alpha \times \beta$ represents in magnitude the area of the parallelogram of which α and β (supposed drawn from a common origin) are the sides, and that it represents in direction the normal to the plane of the parallelogram on the side on which the rotation from α toward β appears counter-clockwise.

23. *Representation of the volume of a parallelopiped by a triple product.*—It will also be seen that $\alpha \times \beta . \gamma$* represents in numerical value the volume of the parallelopiped of which α, β, and γ (supposed drawn from a common origin) are the edges, and that the value of the expression is positive or negative according as γ lies on the side of the plane of α and β on which the rotation from α to β appears counter-clockwise, or on the opposite side.

24. Hence,

$$\begin{aligned} \alpha \times \beta . \gamma = \beta \times \gamma . \alpha = \gamma \times \alpha . \beta = \gamma . \alpha \times \beta = \alpha . \beta \times \gamma \\ = \beta . \gamma \times \alpha = -\beta \times \alpha . \gamma = -\gamma \times \beta . \alpha = -\alpha \times \gamma . \beta \\ = -\gamma . \beta \times \alpha = -\alpha . \gamma \times \beta = -\beta . \alpha \times \gamma . \end{aligned}$$

It will be observed that all the products of this type, which can be made with three given vectors, are the same in numerical value, and

---

* Since the sign $\times$ is only used between vectors, the skew multiplication in expressions of this kind is evidently to be performed first. In other words, the above expression must be interpreted as $[\alpha \times \beta] . \gamma$.

that any two such products are of the same or opposite character in respect to sign, according as the cyclic order of the letters is the same or different. The product vanishes when two of the vectors are parallel to the same line, or when the three are parallel to the same plane.

This kind of product may be called the scalar product of the three vectors. There are two other kinds of products of three vectors, both of which are vectors, viz., products of the type $(\alpha.\beta)\gamma$ or $\gamma(\alpha.\beta)$, and products of the type $\alpha\times[\beta\times\gamma]$ or $[\gamma\times\beta]\times\alpha$.

25. $i.j\times k=j.k\times i=k.i\times j=1. \qquad i.k\times j=k.j\times i=j.i\times k=-1.$

From these equations, which follow immediately from those of No. 17, the propositions of the last section might have been derived, viz., by substituting for α, β, and γ, respectively, expressions of the form $xi+yj+zk$, $x'i+y'j+z'k$, and $x''i+y''j+z''k$.* Such a method, which may be called *expansion in terms of* i, j, and k, will on many occasions afford very simple, although perhaps lengthy, demonstrations.

26. *Triple products containing only two different letters.*—The significance and the relations of $(\alpha.\alpha)\beta$, $(\alpha.\beta)\alpha$, and $\alpha\times[\alpha\times\beta]$ will be most evident, if we consider β as made up of two components, β' and β'', respectively parallel and perpendicular to α. Then

$$\beta=\beta'+\beta'',$$

$$(\alpha.\beta)\alpha=(\alpha.\beta')\alpha=(\alpha.\alpha)\beta',$$

$$\alpha\times[\alpha\times\beta]=\alpha\times[\alpha\times\beta'']=-(\alpha.\alpha)\beta''.$$

Hence,

$$\alpha\times[\alpha\times\beta]=(\alpha.\beta)\alpha-(\alpha.\alpha)\beta.$$

27. *General relation of the vector products of three factors.*—In the triple product $\alpha\times[\beta\times\gamma]$ we may set

$$\alpha=l\beta+m\gamma+n\beta\times\gamma,$$

unless β and γ have the same direction. Then

$$\begin{aligned}\alpha\times[\beta\times\gamma]&=l\beta\times[\beta\times\gamma]+m\gamma\times[\beta\times\gamma]\\&=l(\beta.\gamma)\beta-l(\beta.\beta)\gamma-m(\gamma.\beta)\gamma+m(\gamma.\gamma)\beta\\&=(l\beta.\gamma+m\gamma.\gamma)\beta-(l\beta.\beta+m\gamma.\beta)\gamma.\end{aligned}$$

But

$$l\beta.\gamma+m\gamma.\gamma=\alpha.\gamma, \text{ and } l\beta.\beta+m\gamma.\beta=\alpha.\beta.$$

Therefore

$$\alpha\times[\beta\times\gamma]=(\alpha.\gamma)\beta-(\alpha.\beta)\gamma,$$

which is evidently true, when β and γ have the same directions. It may also be written

$$[\gamma\times\beta]\times\alpha=\beta(\gamma.\alpha)-\gamma(\beta.\alpha).$$

---

* The student who is familiar with the nature of determinants will not fail to observe that the triple product $\alpha.\beta\times\gamma$ is the determinant formed by the nine rectangular components of α, β, and γ, nor that the rectangular components of $\alpha\times\beta$ are determinants of the second order formed from the components of α and β. (See the last equation of No. 21.)

28. This principle may be used in the transformation of more complex products. It will be observed that its application will always simultaneously eliminate, or introduce, two signs of skew multiplication.

The student will easily prove the following identical equations, which, although of considerable importance, are here given principally as exercises in the application of the preceding formulæ.

29. $\alpha\times[\beta\times\gamma]+\beta\times[\gamma\times\alpha]+\gamma\times[\alpha\times\beta]=0.$

30. $$[\alpha\times\beta].[\gamma\times\delta]=(\alpha.\gamma)(\beta.\delta)-(\alpha.\delta)(\beta.\gamma).$$

31. $$[\alpha\times\beta]\times[\gamma\times\delta]=(\alpha.\gamma\times\delta)\beta-(\beta.\gamma\times\delta)\,\alpha$$
$$=(\alpha.\beta\times\delta)\gamma-(\alpha.\beta\times\gamma)\delta.$$

32. $$\alpha\times[\beta\times[\gamma\times\delta]]=(\alpha.\gamma\times\delta)\beta-(\alpha.\beta)\,\gamma\times\delta$$
$$=(\beta.\delta)\,\alpha\times\gamma-(\beta.\gamma)\,\alpha\times\delta.$$

33. $$[\alpha\times\beta].[\gamma\times\delta]\times[\epsilon\times\zeta]=(\alpha.\beta\times\delta)(\gamma.\epsilon\times\zeta)-(\alpha.\beta\times\gamma)(\delta.\epsilon\times\zeta)$$
$$=(\alpha.\beta\times\epsilon)(\zeta.\gamma\times\delta)-(\alpha.\beta\times\zeta)(\epsilon.\gamma\times\delta)$$
$$=(\gamma.\delta\times\alpha)(\beta.\epsilon\times\zeta)-(\gamma.\delta\times\beta)(\alpha.\epsilon\times\zeta).$$

34. $[\alpha\times\beta].[\beta\times\gamma]\times[\gamma\times\alpha]=(\alpha.\beta\times\gamma)^2.$

35. The student will also easily convince himself that a product formed of any number of letters (representing vectors) combined in any possible way by scalar, direct, and skew multiplications may be reduced by the principles of Nos. 24 and 27 to a sum of products, each of which consists of scalar factors of the forms $\alpha.\beta$ and $\alpha.\beta\times\gamma$, with a single vector factor of the form α or $\alpha\times\beta$, when the original product is a vector.

36. *Elimination of scalars from vector equations.*—It has already been observed that the elimination of vectors from equations of the form

$$a\alpha+b\beta+c\gamma+d\delta+\text{etc.}=0$$

is performed by the same rule as the eliminations of ordinary algebra. (See No. 9.) But the elimination of scalars from such equations is at least formally different. Since a single vector equation is the equivalent of three scalar equations, we must be able to deduce from such an equation a scalar equation from which two of the scalars which appear in the original vector equation have been eliminated. We shall see how this may be done, if we consider the scalar equation

$$a\alpha.\lambda+b\beta.\lambda+c\gamma.\lambda+d\delta.\lambda+\text{etc.}=0,$$

which is derived from the above vector equation by direct multiplication by a vector λ. We may regard the original equation as the equivalent of the three scalar equations obtained by substituting for α, β, γ, δ, etc., their X-, Y-, and Z-components. The second equation would be derived from these by multiplying them respectively by the X-, Y-, and Z-components of λ and adding. Hence the second equation may be regarded as the most general form of a scalar equation of the first degree in a, b, c, d, etc., which can be derived from the original vector equation or its equivalent three scalar equations. If we wish to have two of the scalars, as b and c, disappear, we have only to choose for λ a vector perpendicular to β and γ. Such a vector is $\beta\times\gamma$. We thus obtain

$$a\alpha.\beta\times\gamma+d\delta.\beta\times\gamma+\text{etc.}=0.$$

37. *Relations of four vectors.*—By this method of elimination we may find the values of the coefficients a, b, and c in the equation

$$\rho=a\alpha+b\beta+c\gamma, \tag{1}$$

by which any vector ρ is expressed in terms of three others. (See No. 10.) If we multiply *directly* by $\beta\times\gamma$, $\gamma\times\alpha$, and $\alpha\times\beta$, we obtain

$$\rho.\beta\times\gamma=a\alpha.\beta\times\gamma, \quad \rho.\gamma\times\alpha=b\beta.\gamma\times\alpha, \quad \rho.\alpha\times\beta=c\gamma.\alpha\times\beta; \tag{2}$$

whence

$$a=\frac{\rho.\beta\times\gamma}{\alpha.\beta\times\gamma}, \quad b=\frac{\rho.\gamma\times\alpha}{\alpha.\beta\times\gamma}, \quad c=\frac{\rho.\alpha\times\beta}{\alpha.\beta\times\gamma}. \tag{3}$$

By substitution of these values, we obtain the identical equation,

$$(\alpha.\beta\times\gamma)\,\rho=(\rho.\beta\times\gamma)\,\alpha+(\rho.\gamma\times\alpha)\,\beta+(\rho.\alpha\times\beta)\,\gamma. \tag{4}$$

(Compare No. 31.) If we wish the four vectors to appear symmetrically in the equation we may write

$$(\alpha.\beta\times\gamma)\,\rho-(\beta.\gamma\times\rho)\,\alpha+(\gamma.\rho\times\alpha)\,\beta-(\rho.\alpha\times\beta)\,\gamma=0. \tag{5}$$

If we wish to express ρ as a sum of vectors having directions perpendicular to the planes of α and β, of β and γ, and of γ and α, we may write

$$\rho=e\beta\times\gamma+f\gamma\times\alpha+g\alpha\times\beta. \tag{6}$$

To obtain the values of e, f, g, we multiply *directly* by α, by β, and by γ. This gives

$$e=\frac{\rho.\alpha}{\beta.\gamma\times\alpha}, \quad f=\frac{\rho.\beta}{\gamma.\alpha\times\beta}, \quad g=\frac{\rho.\gamma}{\alpha.\beta\times\gamma}. \tag{7}$$

Substituting these values we obtain the identical equation

$$(\alpha.\beta\times\gamma)\,\rho=(\rho.\alpha)\,\beta\times\gamma+(\rho.\beta)\,\gamma\times\alpha+(\rho.\gamma)\,\alpha\times\beta. \tag{8}$$

(Compare No. 32.)

38. *Reciprocal systems of vectors.*—The results of the preceding section may be more compactly expressed if we use the abbreviations

$$\alpha'=\frac{\beta\times\gamma}{\alpha.\beta\times\gamma}, \quad \beta'=\frac{\gamma\times\alpha}{\beta.\gamma\times\alpha}, \quad \gamma'=\frac{\alpha\times\beta}{\gamma.\alpha\times\beta}. \tag{1}$$

The identical equations (4) and (8) of the preceding number thus become

$$\rho=(\rho.\alpha')\alpha+(\rho.\beta')\beta+(\rho.\gamma')\gamma, \tag{2}$$

$$\rho=(\rho.\alpha)\alpha'+(\rho.\beta)\beta'+(\rho.\gamma)\gamma'. \tag{3}$$

We may infer from the similarity of these equations that the relations of α, β, γ, and α', β', γ' are reciprocal, a proposition which is easily proved directly. For the equations

$$\alpha = \frac{\beta' \times \gamma'}{\alpha'.\beta' \times \gamma'}, \quad \beta = \frac{\gamma' \times \alpha'}{\beta'.\gamma' \times \alpha'}, \quad \gamma = \frac{\alpha' \times \beta'}{\gamma'.\alpha' \times \beta'} \tag{4}$$

are satisfied identically by the substitution of the values of α', β', and γ' given in equations (1). (See Nos. 31 and 34.)

Def.—It will be convenient to use the term *reciprocal* to designate these relations, i.e., we shall say that three vectors are *reciprocals* of three others, when they satisfy relations similar to those expressed in equations (1) or (4).

With this understanding we may say:—

The coefficients by which any vector is expressed in terms of three other vectors are the direct products of that vector with the reciprocals of the three.

Among other relations which are satisfied by reciprocal systems of vectors are the following:

$$\alpha.\alpha' = \beta.\beta' = \gamma.\gamma' = 1,$$

$$\alpha.\beta' = 0, \quad \alpha.\gamma' = 0, \quad \beta.\alpha' = 0, \quad \beta.\gamma' = 0, \quad \gamma.\alpha' = 0, \quad \gamma.\beta' = 0. \tag{5}$$

These nine equations may be regarded as defining the relations between α, β, γ and α', β', γ' as reciprocals.

$$(\alpha.\beta \times \gamma)(\alpha'.\beta' \times \gamma') = 1. \tag{6}$$

(See No. 34.)

$$\alpha \times \alpha' + \beta \times \beta' + \gamma \times \gamma' = 0. \tag{7}$$

(See No. 29.)

A system of three mutually perpendicular unit vectors is reciprocal to itself, and only such a system.

The identical equation

$$\rho = (\rho.i)i + (\rho.j)j + (\rho.k)k \tag{8}$$

may be regarded as a particular case of equation (2).

The system reciprocal to $\alpha \times \beta$, $\beta \times \gamma$, $\gamma \times \alpha$ is

$$\alpha' \times \beta', \quad \beta' \times \gamma', \quad \gamma' \times \alpha',$$

or

$$\frac{\alpha}{\alpha.\beta \times \gamma}, \quad \frac{\beta}{\alpha.\beta \times \gamma}, \quad \frac{\gamma}{\alpha.\beta \times \gamma}.$$

38*a*. If we multiply the identical equation (8) of No. 37 by $\sigma \times \tau$, we obtain the equation

$$(\alpha.\beta \times \gamma)(\rho.\sigma \times \tau) = \alpha.\rho(\beta.\sigma\,\gamma.\tau - \beta.\tau\,\gamma.\sigma)$$
$$+ \beta.\rho(\gamma.\sigma\,\alpha.\tau - \gamma.\tau\,\alpha.\sigma) + \gamma.\rho(\alpha.\sigma\,\beta.\tau - \alpha.\tau\,\beta.\sigma),$$

which is therefore identical. But this equation cannot subsist identically, unless

$$(\alpha.\beta \times \gamma)\sigma \times \tau = \alpha(\beta.\sigma\,\gamma.\tau - \beta.\tau\,\gamma.\sigma)$$
$$+ \beta(\gamma.\sigma\,\alpha.\tau - \gamma.\tau\,\alpha.\sigma) + \gamma(\alpha.\sigma\,\beta.\tau - \alpha.\tau\,\beta.\sigma)$$

is also an identical equation. (The reader will observe that in each of these equations the second member may be expressed as a determinant.)

From these transformations, with those already given, it follows that a product formed of any number of letters (representing vectors and scalars), combined in any possible way by scalar, direct, and skew multiplications, may be reduced to a sum of products, containing each the sign $\times$ once and only once, when the original product contains it an odd number of times, or entirely free from the sign, when the original product contains it an even number of times.

39. *Scalar equations of the first degree with respect to an unknown vector.*—It is easily shown that any scalar equation of the first degree with respect to an unknown vector ρ, in which all the other quantities are known, may be reduced to the form

$$\rho . \alpha = a,$$

in which α and a are known. (See No. 35.) Three such equations will afford the value of ρ (by equation (8) of No. 37, or equation (3) of No. 38), which may be used to eliminate ρ from any other equation either scalar or vector.

When we have four scalar equations of the first degree with respect to ρ, the elimination may be performed most symmetrically by substituting the values of $\rho . \alpha$, etc., in the equation

$$(\rho . \alpha)(\beta . \gamma \times \delta) - (\rho . \beta)(\gamma . \delta \times \alpha) + (\rho . \gamma)(\delta . \alpha \times \beta) - (\rho . \delta)(\alpha . \beta \times \gamma) = 0,$$

which is obtained from equation (8) of No. 37 by multiplying directly by δ. It may also be obtained from equation (5) of No. 37 by writing δ for ρ, and then multiplying directly by ρ.

40. *Solution of a vector equation of the first degree with respect to the unknown vector.*—It is now easy to solve an equation of the form

$$\delta = \alpha(\lambda . \rho) + \beta(\mu . \rho) + \gamma(\nu . \rho), \tag{1}$$

where α, β, γ, δ, λ, μ, and ν represent known vectors. Multiplying directly by $\beta \times \gamma$, by $\gamma \times \alpha$, and by $\alpha \times \beta$, we obtain

$$\beta . \gamma \times \delta = (\beta . \gamma \times \alpha)(\lambda . \rho), \quad \gamma . \alpha \times \delta = (\gamma . \alpha \times \beta)(\mu . \rho),$$
$$\alpha . \beta \times \delta = (\alpha . \beta \times \gamma)(\nu . \rho);$$

or

$$\alpha' . \delta = \lambda . \rho, \quad \beta' . \delta = \mu . \rho, \quad \gamma' . \delta = \nu . \rho,$$

where α', β', γ' are the reciprocals of α, β, γ. Substituting these values in the identical equation

$$\rho = \lambda'(\lambda . \rho) + \mu'(\mu . \rho) + \nu'(\nu . \rho),$$

in which λ', μ', ν' are the reciprocals of λ, μ, ν (see No. 38), we have

$$\rho = \lambda'(\alpha' . \delta) + \mu'(\beta' . \delta) + \nu'(\gamma' . \delta), \tag{2}$$

which is the solution required.

It results from the principle stated in No. 35, that any vector equation of the first degree with respect to ρ may be reduced to the form

$$\delta = \alpha(\lambda.\rho)+\beta(\mu.\rho)+\gamma(\nu.\rho)+a\rho+\epsilon\times\rho.$$

But

$$a\rho = a\lambda'(\lambda.\rho)+a\mu'(\mu.\rho)+a\nu'(\nu.\rho),$$

and

$$\epsilon\times\rho = \epsilon\times\lambda'(\lambda.\rho)+\epsilon\times\mu'(\mu.\rho)+\epsilon\times\nu'(\nu.\rho),$$

where λ', μ', ν' represent, as before, the reciprocals of λ, μ, ν. By substitution of these values the equation is reduced to the form of equation (1), which may therefore be regarded as the most general form of a vector equation of the first degree with respect to ρ.

41. *Relations between two normal systems of unit vectors.*—If i, j, k, and i', j', k' are two normal systems of unit vectors, we have

$$\left.\begin{aligned} i' &= (i.i')i+(j.i')j+(k.i')k, \\ j' &= (i.j')i+(j.j')j+(k.j')k, \\ k' &= (i.k')i+(j.k')j+(k.k')k, \end{aligned}\right\} \qquad (1)$$

and

$$\left.\begin{aligned} i &= (i.i')i'+(i.j')j'+(i.k')k', \\ j &= (j.i')i'+(j.j')j'+(j.k')k', \\ k &= (k.i')i'+(k.j')j'+(k.k')k'. \end{aligned}\right\} \qquad (2)$$

(See equation (8) of No. 38.)

The nine coefficients in these equations are evidently the cosines of the nine angles made by a vector of one system with a vector of the other system. The principal relations of these cosines are easily deduced. By direct multiplication of each of the preceding equations with itself, we obtain six equations of the type

$$(i.i')^2+(j.i')^2+(k.i')^2=1. \qquad (3)$$

By direct multiplication of equations (1) with each other, and of equations (2) with each other, we obtain six of the type

$$(i.i')(i.j')+(j.i')(j.j')+(k.i')(k.j')=0. \qquad (4)$$

By skew multiplication of equations (1) with each other, we obtain three of the type

$$k' = \{(j.i')(k.j')-(k.i')(j.j')\}i+\{(k.i')(i.j')-(i.i')(k.j')\}j \\ +\{(i.i')(j.j')-(j.i')(i.j')\}k.$$

Comparing these three equations with the original three, we obtain nine of the type

$$i.k' = (j.i')(k.j')-(k.i')(j.j'). \qquad (5)$$

Finally, if we equate the scalar product of the three right hand members of (1) with that of the three left hand members, we obtain

$$(i.i')(j.j')(k.k')+(i.j')(j.k')(k.i')+(i.k')(j.i')(k.j') \\ -(k.i')(j.j')(i.k')-(k.j')(j.k')(i.i')-(k.k')(j.i')(i.j')=1. \qquad (6)$$

Equations (1) and (2) (if the expressions in the parentheses are supposed replaced by numerical values) represent the linear relations which subsist between one vector of one system and the three vectors of the other system. If we desire to express the similar relations which subsist between two vectors of one system and two of the other, we may take the skew products of equations (1) with equations (2), after transposing all terms in the latter. This will afford nine equations of the type

$$(i.j')k' - (i.k')j' = (k.i')j - (j.i')k. \qquad (7)$$

We may divide an equation by an indeterminate direct factor. [MS. note by author.]

CHAPTER II.

CONCERNING THE DIFFERENTIAL AND INTEGRAL CALCULUS OF VECTORS.

42. *Differentials of vectors.*—The *differential* of a vector is the *geometrical* difference of two values of that vector which differ infinitely little. It is itself a vector, and may make any angle with the vector differentiated. It is expressed by the same sign (d) as the differentials of ordinary analysis.

With reference to any fixed axes, the components of the differential of a vector are manifestly equal to the differentials of the components of the vector, i.e., if α, β, and γ are fixed unit vectors, and

$$\rho = x\alpha + y\beta + z\gamma,$$
$$d\rho = dx\,\alpha + dy\,\beta + dz\,\gamma.$$

43. *Differential of a function of several variables.*—The differential of a vector or scalar function of any number of vector or scalar variables is evidently the sum (geometrical or algebraic, according as the function is vector or scalar) of the differentials of the function due to the separate variation of the several variables.

44. *Differential of a product.*—The differential of a product of any kind due to the variation of a single factor is obtained by prefixing the sign of differentiation to that factor in the product. This is evidently true of differentials, since it will hold true even of finite differences.

45. From these principles we obtain the following identical equations:

$$d(\alpha+\beta) = d\alpha + d\beta, \qquad (1)$$
$$d(n\alpha) = dn\,\alpha + n\,d\alpha, \qquad (2)$$
$$d(\alpha.\beta) = d\alpha.\beta + \alpha.d\beta, \qquad (3)$$
$$d[\alpha\times\beta] = d\alpha\times\beta + \alpha\times d\beta, \qquad (4)$$
$$d(\alpha.\beta\times\gamma) = d\alpha.\beta\times\gamma + \alpha.d\beta\times\gamma + \alpha.\beta\times d\gamma, \qquad (5)$$
$$d[(\alpha.\beta)\,\gamma] = (d\alpha.\beta)\,\gamma + (\alpha.d\beta)\,\gamma + (\alpha.\beta)\,d\gamma. \qquad (6)$$

46. *Differential coefficient with respect to a scalar.*—The quotient obtained by dividing the differential of a vector due to the variation of any scalar of which it is a function by the differential of that scalar is called the differential coefficient of the vector with respect to the scalar, and is indicated in the same manner as the differential coefficients of ordinary analysis.

If we suppose the quantities occurring in the six equations of the last section to be functions of a scalar t, we may substitute $\frac{d}{dt}$ for d in those equations since this is only to divide all terms by the scalar dt.

47. *Successive differentiations.*—The differential coefficient of a vector with respect to a scalar is of course a finite vector, of which we may take the differential, or the differential coefficient with respect to the same or any other scalar. We thus obtain differential coefficients of the higher orders, which are indicated as in the scalar calculus.

A few examples will serve for illustration.

If ρ is the vector drawn from a fixed origin to a moving point at any time t, $\frac{d\rho}{dt}$ will be the vector representing the velocity of the point, and $\frac{d^2\rho}{dt^2}$ the vector representing its acceleration.

If ρ is the vector drawn from a fixed origin to any point on a curve, and s the distance of that point measured on the curve from any fixed point, $\frac{d\rho}{ds}$ is a unit vector, tangent to the curve and having the direction in which s increases; $\frac{d^2\rho}{ds^2}$ is a vector directed from a point on the curve to the center of curvature, and equal to the curvature; $\frac{d\rho}{ds}\times\frac{d^2\rho}{ds^2}$ is the normal to the osculating plane, directed to the side on which the curve appears described counter-clockwise about the center of curvature, and equal to the curvature. The tortuosity (or rate of rotation of the osculating plane, considered as positive when the rotation appears counter-clockwise as seen from the direction in which s increases) is represented by

$$\frac{\frac{d\rho}{ds}\cdot\frac{d^2\rho}{ds^2}\times\frac{d^3\rho}{ds^3}}{\frac{d^2\rho}{ds^2}\cdot\frac{d^2\rho}{ds^2}}.$$

48. *Integration of an equation between differentials.*—If t and u are two single-valued continuous scalar functions of any number of scalar or vector variables, and

$$dt=du,$$

then

$$t=u+a,$$

where a is a scalar constant.

Or, if τ and ω are two single-valued continuous vector functions of any number of scalar or vector variables, and

$$d\tau = d\omega,$$

then
$$\tau = \omega + a,$$

where a is a vector constant.

When the above hypotheses are not satisfied in general, but will be satisfied if the variations of the independent variables are confined within certain limits, then the conclusions will hold within those limits, provided that we can pass by continuous variation of the independent variables from any values within the limits to any other values within them, without transgressing the limits.

49. So far, it will be observed, all operations have been entirely analogous to those of the ordinary calculus.

Functions of Position in Space.

50. *Def.*—If u is any scalar function of position in space (i.e., any scalar quantity having continuously varying values in space), ∇u is the vector function of position in space which has everywhere the direction of the most rapid increase of u, and a magnitude equal to the rate of that increase per unit of length. ∇u may be called the *derivative* of u, and u, the *primitive* of ∇u.

We may also take any one of the Nos. 51, 52, 53 for the definition of ∇u.

51. If ρ is the vector defining the position of a point in space,

$$du = \nabla u . d\rho.$$

52.
$$\nabla u = i\frac{du}{dx} + j\frac{du}{dy} + k\frac{du}{dz}.$$

53.
$$\frac{du}{dx} = i . \nabla u, \quad \frac{du}{dy} = j . \nabla u, \quad \frac{du}{dz} = k . \nabla u.$$

54. *Def.*—If ω is a vector having continuously varying values in space,

$$\nabla . \omega = i . \frac{d\omega}{dx} + j . \frac{d\omega}{dy} + k . \frac{d\omega}{dz}, \tag{1}$$

and
$$\nabla \times \omega = i \times \frac{d\omega}{dx} + j \times \frac{d\omega}{dy} + k \times \frac{d\omega}{dz}. \tag{2}$$

$\nabla . \omega$ is called the *divergence* of ω and $\nabla \times \omega$ its *curl.*

If we set

$$\omega = Xi + Yj + Zk,$$

we obtain by substitution the equations

$$\nabla . \omega = \frac{dX}{dx} + \frac{dY}{dy} + \frac{dZ}{dz}$$

and
$$\nabla \times \omega = i\left(\frac{dZ}{dy} - \frac{dY}{dz}\right) + j\left(\frac{dX}{dz} - \frac{dZ}{dx}\right) + k\left(\frac{dY}{dx} - \frac{dX}{dy}\right),$$

which may also be regarded as defining $\nabla . \omega$ and $\nabla \times \omega$.

55. *Surface-integrals.*—The integral $\iint \omega . d\sigma$, in which $d\sigma$ represents an element of some surface, is called the surface-integral of ω for that surface. It is understood here and elsewhere, when a vector is said to represent a plane surface (or an element of surface which may be regarded as plane), that the magnitude of the vector represents the area of the surface, and that the direction of the vector represents that of the normal drawn toward the positive side of the surface. When the surface is defined as the boundary of a certain space, the outside of the surface is regarded as positive.

The surface-integral of any given space (i.e., the surface-integral of the surface bounding that space) is evidently equal to the sum of the surface-integrals of all the parts into which the original space may be divided. For the integrals relating to the surfaces dividing the parts will evidently cancel in such a sum.

The surface-integral of ω for a closed surface bounding a space dv infinitely small in all its dimensions is

$$\nabla . \omega \, dv.$$

This follows immediately from the definition of $\nabla\omega$, when the space is a parallelopiped bounded by planes perpendicular to i, j, k. In other cases, we may imagine the space—or rather a space nearly coincident with the given space and of the same volume dv—to be divided up into such parallelopipeds. The surface-integral for the space made up of the parallelopipeds will be the sum of the surface-integrals of all the parallelopipeds, and will therefore be expressed by $\nabla . \omega \, dv$. The surface-integral of the original space will have sensibly the same value, and will therefore be represented by the same formula. It follows that the value of $\nabla . \omega$ does not depend upon the system of unit vectors employed in its definition.

It is possible to attribute such a physical signification to the quantities concerned in the above proposition, as shall make it evident almost without demonstration. Let us suppose ω to represent a flux of any substance. The rate of decrease of the density of that substance at any point will be obtained by dividing the surface-integral of the flux for any infinitely small closed surface about the point by the volume enclosed. This quotient must therefore be independent of the form of the surface. We may define $\nabla . \omega$ as representing that quotient, and then obtain equation (1) of No. 54 by applying the general principle to the case of the rectangular parallelopiped.

56. *Skew surface-integrals.*—The integral $\iint d\sigma \times \omega$ may be called the skew surface-integral of ω. It is evidently a vector. For a closed surface bounding a space dv infinitely small in all dimensions this integral reduces to $\nabla \times \omega \, dv$, as is easily shown by reasoning like that of No. 55.

57. *Integration.*—If dv represents an element of any space, and $d\sigma$ an element of the bounding surface,

$$\iiint \nabla . \omega \, dv = \iint \omega . d\sigma .$$

For the first member of this equation represents the sum of the surface-integrals of all the elements of the given space. We may regard this principle as affording a means of integration, since we may use it to reduce a triple integral (of a certain form) to a double integral.

The principle may also be expressed as follows:

The surface-integral of any vector function of position in space for a closed surface is equal to the volume-integral of the divergence of that function for the space enclosed.

58. *Line-integrals.*—The integral $\int \omega . d\rho$, in which $d\rho$ denotes the element of a line, is called the *line-integral* of ω for that line. It is implied that one of the directions of the line is distinguished as positive. When the line is regarded as bounding a surface, that side of the surface will always be regarded as positive, on which the surface appears to be circumscribed counter-clockwise.

59. *Integration.*—From No. 51 we obtain directly

$$\int \nabla u . d\rho = u'' - u' ,$$

where the single and double accents distinguish the values relating to the beginning and end of the line.

In other words,—The line-integral of the derivative of any (continuous and single-valued) scalar function of position in space is equal to the difference of the values of the function at the extremities of the line. For a closed line the integral vanishes.

60. *Integration.*—The following principle may be used to reduce double integrals of a certain form to simple integrals.

If $d\sigma$ represents an element of any surface, and $d\rho$ an element of the bounding line,

$$\iint \nabla \times \omega . d\sigma = \int \omega . d\rho .$$

In other words,—The line-integral of any vector function of position in space for a closed line is equal to the surface-integral of the curl of that function for any surface bounded by the line.

To prove this principle, we will consider the variation of the line-integral which is due to a variation in the closed line for which the integral is taken. We have, in the first place,

$$\delta \int \omega . d\rho = \int \delta \omega . d\rho + \int \omega . \delta \, d\rho .$$

But $$\omega . \delta \, d\rho = d(\omega . \delta\rho) - d\omega . \delta\rho .$$

Therefore, since $\int d(\omega . \delta\rho) = 0$ for a closed line,

$$\delta \int \omega . d\rho = \int \delta \omega . d\rho - \int d\omega . \delta\rho .$$

Now $$\delta\omega = \Sigma\left[\frac{d\omega}{dx}\delta x\right] = \Sigma\left[\frac{d\omega}{dx}(i.\delta\rho)\right],$$

and $$d\omega = \Sigma\left[\frac{d\omega}{dx}dx\right] = \Sigma\left[\frac{d\omega}{dx}(i.d\rho)\right],$$

where the summation relates to the coordinate axes and connected quantities. Substituting these values in the preceding equation, we get

$$\delta\int\omega.d\rho = \int\Sigma\left((i.\delta\rho)\left(\frac{d\omega}{dx}.d\rho\right) - (i.d\rho)\left(\frac{d\omega}{dx}.\delta\rho\right)\right),$$

or by No. 30,

$$\delta\int\omega.d\rho = \int\Sigma\left[i\times\frac{d\omega}{dx}\right].[\delta\rho\times d\rho] = \int\nabla\times\omega.[\delta\rho\times d\rho].$$

But $\delta\rho\times d\rho$ represents an element of the surface generated by the motion of the element $d\rho$, and the last member of the equation is the surface-integral of $\nabla\times\omega$ for the infinitesimal surface generated by the motion of the whole line. Hence, if we conceive of a closed curve passing gradually from an infinitesimal loop to any finite form, the differential of the line-integral of ω for that curve will be equal to the differential of the surface integral of $\nabla\times\omega$ for the surface generated: therefore, since both integrals commence with the value zero, they must always be equal to each other. Such a mode of generation will evidently apply to any surface closing any loop.

61. The line-integral of ω for a closed line bounding a plane surface $d\sigma$ infinitely small in all its dimensions is therefore

$$\nabla\times\omega.d\sigma.$$

This principle affords a definition of $\nabla\times\omega$ which is independent of any reference to coordinate axes. If we imagine a circle described about a fixed point to vary its orientation while keeping the same size, there will be a certain position of the circle for which the line-integral of ω will be a maximum, unless the line-integral vanishes for all positions of the circle. The axis of the circle in this position, drawn toward the side on which a positive motion in the circle appears counter-clockwise, gives the direction of $\nabla\times\omega$, and the quotient of the integral divided by the area of the circle gives the magnitude of $\nabla\times\omega$.

∇, $\nabla.$, *and* $\nabla\times$ *applied to Functions of Functions of Position.*

62. A constant scalar factor after ∇, $\nabla.$, or $\nabla\times$ may be placed before the symbol.

63. If $f(u)$ denotes any scalar function of u, and $f'(u)$ the derived function,

$$\nabla f(u) = f'(u)\nabla u.$$

64. If u or ω is a function of several scalar or vector variables which are themselves functions of the position of a single point, the value of ∇u or $\nabla . \omega$ or $\nabla \times \omega$ will be equal to the sum of the values obtained by making successively all but each one of these variables constant.

65. By the use of this principle we easily derive the following identical equations:

$$\nabla (t+u) = \nabla t + \nabla u. \tag{1}$$

$$\nabla . (\tau + \omega) = \nabla . \tau + \nabla . \omega. \qquad \nabla \times [\tau + \omega] = \nabla \times \tau + \nabla \times \omega. \tag{2}$$

$$\nabla (tu) = u \nabla t + t \nabla u. \tag{3}$$

$$\nabla . (u\omega) = \omega . \nabla u + u \nabla . \omega. \tag{4}$$

$$\nabla \times [u\omega] = u \nabla \times \omega - \omega \times \nabla u. \tag{5}$$

$$\nabla . [\tau \times \omega] = \omega . \nabla \times \tau - \tau . \nabla \times \omega. \tag{6}$$

The student will observe an analogy between these equations and the formulæ of multiplication. (In the last four equations the analogy appears most distinctly when we regard all the factors but one as constant.) Some of the more curious features of this analogy are due to the fact that the ∇ contains implicitly the vectors i, j and k, which are to be multiplied into the following quantities.

Combinations of the Operators ∇, $\nabla .$, and $\nabla \times$.

66. If u is any scalar function of position in space,

$$\nabla \times \nabla u = 0,$$

as may be derived directly from the definitions of these operators.

67. Conversely, if ω is such a vector function of position in space that

$$\nabla \times \omega = 0,$$

ω is the derivative of a scalar function of position in space. This will appear from the following considerations:

The line-integral $\int \omega . d\rho$ will vanish for any closed line, since it may be expressed as the surface-integral of $\nabla \times \omega$. (No. 60.) The line-integral taken from one given point P′ to another given point P″ is independent of the line between the points for which the integral is taken. (For, if two lines joining the same points gave different values, by reversing one we should obtain a closed line for which the integral would not vanish.) If we set u equal to this line-integral, supposing P″ to be variable and P′ to be constant in position, u will be a scalar function of the position of the point P″, satisfying the condition $du = \omega . d\rho$, or, by No. 51, $\nabla u = \omega$. There will evidently be an infinite number of functions satisfying this condition, which will differ from one another by constant quantities.

If the region for which $\nabla \times \omega = 0$ is unlimited, these functions will be single-valued. If the region is limited, but acyclic,* the functions will still be single-valued and satisfy the condition $\nabla u = \omega$ within the same region. If the region is cyclic, we may determine functions satisfying the condition $\nabla u = \omega$ within the region, but they will not necessarily be single-valued.

68. If ω is any vector function of position in space, $\nabla . \nabla \times \omega = 0$. This may be deduced directly from the definitions of No. 54.

The converse of this proposition will be proved hereafter.

69. If u is any scalar function of position in space, we have by Nos. 52 and 54

$$\nabla . \nabla u = \left(\frac{d^2}{dx^2} + \frac{d^2}{dy^2} + \frac{d^2}{dz^2} \right) u.$$

70. *Def.*—If ω is any vector function of position in space, we may define $\nabla . \nabla \omega$ by the equation

$$\nabla . \nabla \omega = \left(\frac{d^2}{dx^2} + \frac{d^2}{dy^2} + \frac{d^2}{dz^2} \right) \omega,$$

the expression $\nabla . \nabla$ being regarded, for the present at least, as a single operator when applied to a vector. (It will be remembered that no meaning has been attributed to ∇ before a vector.) It should be noticed that if

$$\omega = i\mathrm{X} + j\mathrm{Y} + k\mathrm{Z},$$

$$\nabla . \nabla \omega = i \nabla . \nabla \mathrm{X} + j \nabla . \nabla \mathrm{Y} + k \nabla . \nabla \mathrm{Z},$$

that is, the operator $\nabla . \nabla$ applied to a vector affects separately its scalar components.

71. From the above definition with those of Nos. 52 and 54 we may easily obtain

$$\nabla . \nabla \omega = \nabla \nabla . \omega - \nabla \times \nabla \times \omega.$$

The effect of the operator $\nabla . \nabla$ is therefore independent of the directions of the axes used in its definition.

72. The expression $-\frac{1}{6} a^2 \nabla . \nabla u$, where a is any infinitesimal scalar, evidently represents the excess of the value of the scalar function u

* If every closed line within a given region can contract to a single point without breaking its continuity, or passing out of the region, the region is called *acyclic*, otherwise *cyclic*.

A cyclic region may be made acyclic by diaphragms, which must then be regarded as forming part of the surface bounding the region, each diaphragm contributing its own area twice to that surface. This process may be used to reduce many-valued functions of position in space, having single-valued derivatives, to single-valued functions.

When functions are mentioned or implied in the notation, the reader will always understand single-valued functions, unless the contrary is distinctly intimated, or the case is one in which the distinction is obviously immaterial. Diaphragms may be applied to bring functions naturally many-valued under the application of some of the following theorems, as Nos. 74 ff.

at the point considered above the average of its values at six points at the following vector distances: ai, $-ai$, aj, $-aj$, ak, $-ak$. Since the directions of i, j, and k are immaterial (provided that they are at right angles to each other), the excess of the value of u at the central point above its average value in a spherical surface of radius a constructed about that point as the center will be represented by the same expression, $-\frac{1}{6}a^2\nabla.\nabla u$.

Precisely the same is true of a vector function, if it is understood that the additions and subtractions implied in the terms *average* and *excess* are geometrical additions and subtractions.

Maxwell has called $-\nabla.\nabla u$ the *concentration* of u, whether u is scalar or vector. We may call $\nabla.\nabla u$ (or $\nabla.\nabla\omega$), which is proportioned to the excess of the average value of the function in an infinitesimal spherical surface above the value at the center, the *dispersion* of u (or ω).

Transformation of Definite Integrals.

73. From the equations of No. 65, with the principles of integration of Nos. 57, 59, and 60, we may deduce various transformations of definite integrals, which are entirely analogous to those known in the scalar calculus under the name of *integration by parts.* The following formulæ (like those of Nos. 57, 59, and 60) are written for the case of continuous values of the quantities (scalar and vector) to which the signs ∇, $\nabla.$, and $\nabla\times$ are applied. It is left to the student to complete the formulæ for cases of discontinuity in these values. The manner in which this is to be done may in each case be inferred from the nature of the formula itself. The most important discontinuities of scalars are those which occur at surfaces: in the case of vectors discontinuities at surfaces, at lines, and at points, should be considered.

74. From equation (3) we obtain

$$\int\nabla(tu).d\rho = t''u'' - t'u' = \int u\nabla t.d\rho + \int t\nabla u.d\rho,$$

where the accents distinguish the quantities relating to the limits of the line-integrals. We are thus able to reduce a line-integral of the form $\int u\nabla t.d\rho$ to the form $-\int t\nabla u.d\rho$ with quantities free from the sign of integration.

75. From equation (5) we obtain

$$\iint\nabla\times(u\omega).d\sigma = \int u\omega.d\rho = \iint u\nabla\times\omega.d\sigma - \iint\omega\times\nabla u.d\sigma,$$

where, as elsewhere in these equations, the line-integral relates to the boundary of the surface-integral.

From this, by substitution of ∇t for ω, we may derive as a particular case

$$\iint\nabla u\times\nabla t.d\sigma = \int u\nabla t.d\rho = -\int t\nabla u.d\rho.$$

76. From equation (4) we obtain

$$\iiint \nabla.[u\omega]dv = \iint u\omega.d\sigma = \iiint \omega.\nabla u\, dv + \iiint u\nabla.\omega\, dv,$$

where, as elsewhere in these equations, the surface-integral relates to the boundary of the volume-integrals.

From this, by substitution of ∇t for ω, we derive as a particular case

$$\iiint \nabla t.\nabla u\, dv = \iint u\nabla t.d\sigma - \iiint u\nabla.\nabla t\, dv = \iint t\nabla u.d\sigma - \iiint t\nabla.\nabla u\, dv,$$

which is Green's Theorem. The substitution of $s\nabla t$ for ω gives the more general form of this theorem which is due to Thomson, viz.,

$$\iiint s\nabla t.\nabla u\, dv = \iint us\nabla t.d\sigma - \iiint u\nabla.[s\nabla t]dv$$
$$= \iint ts\nabla u.d\sigma - \iiint t\nabla.[s\nabla u]dv.$$

77. From equation (6) we obtain

$$\iiint \nabla.[\tau\times\omega]\, dv = \iint \tau\times\omega.d\sigma = \iiint \omega.\nabla\times\tau\, dv - \iiint \tau.\nabla\times\omega\, dv.$$

A particular case is

$$\iiint \nabla u.\nabla\times\omega\, dv = \iint \omega\times\nabla u.d\sigma.$$

Integration of Differential Equations.

78. If throughout any continuous space (or in all space)

$$\nabla u = 0,$$

then throughout the same space

$$u = \text{constant}.$$

79. If throughout any continuous space (or in all space)

$$\nabla.\nabla u = 0,$$

and in any finite part of that space, or in any finite surface in or bounding it,

$$\nabla u = 0,$$

then throughout the whole space

$$\nabla u = 0, \text{ and } u = \text{constant}.$$

This will appear from the following considerations:

If $\nabla u = 0$ in any finite part of the space, u is constant in that part. If u is not constant throughout, let us imagine a sphere situated principally in the part in which u is constant, but projecting slightly into a part in which u has a greater value, or else into a part in which u has a less. The surface-integral of ∇u for the part of the spherical surface in the region where u is constant will have the value zero: for the other part of the surface, the integral will be either greater than zero, or less than zero. Therefore the whole surface-integral for the spherical surface will not have the value zero, which is required by the general condition, $\nabla.\nabla u = 0$.

Again, if $\nabla u = 0$ only in a surface in or bounding the space in which $\nabla.\nabla u=0$, u will be constant in this surface, and the surface will be contiguous to a region in which $\nabla.\nabla u=0$ and u has a greater value than in the surface, or else a less value than in the surface. Let us imagine a sphere lying principally on the other side of the surface, but projecting slightly into this region, and let us particularly consider the surface-integral of ∇u for the small segment cut off by the surface $\nabla u=0$. The integral for that part of the surface of the segment which consists of part of the surface $\nabla u=0$ will have the value zero, the integral for the spherical part will have a value either greater than zero or else less than zero. Therefore the integral for the whole surface of the segment cannot have the value zero, which is demanded by the general condition, $\nabla.\nabla u=0$.

80. If throughout a certain space (which need not be continuous, and which may extend to infinity)

$$\nabla.\nabla u=0,$$

and in all the bounding surfaces

$$u=\text{constant}=a,$$

and (in case the space extends to infinity) if at infinite distances within the space $u=a$,—then throughout the space

$$\nabla u=0, \text{ and } u=a.$$

For, if anywhere in the interior of the space ∇u has a value different from zero, we may find a point P where such is the case, and where u has a value b different from a,—to fix our ideas we will say *less*. Imagine a surface enclosing all of the space in which $u<b$. (This must be possible, since that part of the space does not reach to infinity.) The surface-integral of ∇u for this surface has the value zero in virtue of the general condition $\nabla.\nabla u=0$. But, from the manner in which the surface is defined, no part of the integral can be negative. Therefore no part of the integral can be positive, and the supposition made with respect to the point P is untenable. That the supposition that $b>a$ is untenable may be shown in a similar manner. Therefore the value of u is constant.

This proposition may be generalized by substituting the condition $\nabla.[t\nabla u]=0$ for $\nabla.\nabla u=0$, t denoting any positive (or any negative) scalar function of position in space. The conclusion would be the same, and the demonstration similar.

81. If throughout a certain space (which need not be continuous, and which may extend to infinity)

$$\nabla.\nabla u=0,$$

and in all the bounding surfaces the normal component of ∇u vanishes, and at infinite distances within the space (if such there are) $r^2\dfrac{du}{dr}=0$, where r denotes the distance from a fixed origin, then throughout the space

$$\nabla u = 0,$$

and in each continuous portion of the same

$$u = \text{constant}.$$

For, if anywhere in the space in question ∇u has a value different from zero, let it have such a value at a point P, and let u be there equal to b. Imagine a spherical surface about the above-mentioned origin as center, enclosing the point P, and with a radius r. Consider that portion of the space to which the theorem relates which is within the sphere and in which $u < b$. The surface integral of ∇u for this space is equal to zero in virtue of the general condition $\nabla . \nabla u = 0$. That part of the integral (if any) which relates to a portion of the spherical surface has a value numerically not greater than $4\pi r^2 \left(\frac{du}{dr}\right)'$, where $\left(\frac{du}{dr}\right)'$ denotes the greatest numerical value of $\frac{du}{dr}$ in the portion of the spherical surface considered. Hence, the value of this part of the surface-integral may be made less (numerically) than any assignable quantity by giving to r a sufficiently great value. Hence, the other part of the surface-integral (viz., that relating to the surface in which $u = b$, and to the boundary of the space to which the theorem relates) may be given a value differing from zero by less than any assignable quantity. But no part of the integral relating to this surface can be negative. Therefore no part can be positive, and the supposition relative to the point P is untenable.

This proposition also may be generalized by substituting $\nabla . [t \nabla u] = 0$ for $\nabla . \nabla u = 0$, and $t r^2 \frac{du}{dr} = 0$ for $r^2 \frac{du}{dr} = 0$.

82. If throughout any continuous space (or in all space)

$$\nabla t = \nabla u,$$

then throughout the same space

$$t = u + \text{const.}$$

The truth of this and the three following theorems will be apparent if we consider the difference $t - u$.

83. If throughout any continuous space (or in all space)

$$\nabla . \nabla t = \nabla . \nabla u,$$

and in any finite part of that space, or in any finite surface in or bounding it,

$$\nabla t = \nabla u,$$

then throughout the whole space

$$\nabla t = \nabla u, \quad \text{and} \quad t = u + \text{const.}$$

84. If throughout a certain space (which need not be continuous, and which may extend to infinity)

$$\nabla . \nabla t = \nabla . \nabla u,$$

and in all the bounding surfaces

$$t = u,$$

and at infinite distances within the space (if such there are)

$$t = u,$$

then throughout the space

$$t = u.$$

85. If throughout a certain space (which need not be continuous, and which may extend to infinity)

$$\nabla . \nabla t = \nabla . \nabla u,$$

and in all the bounding surfaces the normal components of ∇t and ∇u are equal, and at infinite distances within the space (if such there are) $r^2 \left(\frac{dt}{dr} - \frac{du}{dr} \right) = 0$, where r denotes the distance from some fixed origin, —then throughout the space

$$\nabla t = \nabla u,$$

and in each continuous part of which the space consists

$$t - u = \text{constant}.$$

86. If throughout any continuous space (or in all space)

$$\nabla \times \tau = \nabla \times \omega \quad \text{and} \quad \nabla . \tau = \nabla . \omega,$$

and in any finite part of that space, or in any finite surface in or bounding it,

$$\tau = \omega,$$

then throughout the whole space

$$\tau = \omega.$$

For, since $\nabla \times (\tau - \omega) = 0$, we may set $\nabla u = \tau - \omega$, making the space acyclic (if necessary) by diaphragms. Then in the whole space u is single-valued and $\nabla . \nabla u = 0$, and in a part of the space, or in a surface in or bounding it, $\nabla u = 0$. Hence throughout the space $\nabla u = \tau - \omega = 0$.

87. If throughout an aperiphractic* space contained within finite boundaries but not necessarily continuous

$$\nabla \times \tau = \nabla \times \omega \quad \text{and} \quad \nabla . \tau = \nabla . \omega,$$

and in all the bounding surfaces the tangential components of τ and ω are equal, then throughout the space

$$\tau = \omega.$$

It is evidently sufficient to prove this proposition for a continuous space. Setting $\nabla u = \tau - \omega$, we have $\nabla . \nabla u = 0$ for the whole space,

* If a space encloses within itself another space, it is called *periphractic*, otherwise *aperiphractic*.

and u=constant for its boundary, which will be a single surface for a continuous aperiphractic space. Hence throughout the space

$$\nabla u = \tau - \omega = 0.$$

88. If throughout an acyclic space contained within finite boundaries but not necessarily continuous

$$\nabla \times \tau = \nabla \times \omega \quad \text{and} \quad \nabla . \tau = \nabla . \omega,$$

and in all the bounding surfaces the normal components of τ and ω are equal, then throughout the whole space

$$\tau = \omega.$$

Setting $\nabla u = \tau - \omega$, we have $\nabla . \nabla u = 0$ throughout the space, and the normal component of ∇u at the boundary equal to zero. Hence throughout the whole space $\nabla u = \tau - \omega = 0$.

89. If throughout a certain space (which need not be continuous, and which may extend to infinity)

$$\nabla . \nabla \tau = \nabla . \nabla \omega$$

and in all the bounding surfaces

$$\tau = \omega,$$

and at infinite distances within the space (if such there are)

$$\tau = \omega,$$

then throughout the whole space

$$\tau = \omega.$$

This will be apparent if we consider separately each of the scalar components of τ and ω.

Minimum Values of the Volume-integral $\iiint u\, \omega . \omega\, dv$. (*Thomson's Theorems.*)

90. Let it be required to determine for a certain space a vector function of position ω subject to certain conditions (to be specified hereafter), so that the volume-integral

$$\iiint u\, \omega . \omega\, dv$$

for that space shall have a minimum value, u denoting a given positive scalar function of position.

a. In the first place, let the vector ω be subject to the conditions that $\nabla . \omega$ is given within the space, and that the normal component of ω is given for the bounding surface. (This component must of course be such that the surface-integral of ω shall be equal to the volume-integral $\int \nabla . \omega\, dv$. If the space is not continuous, this must be true of each continuous portion of it. See No. 57.) The solution is that $\nabla \times (u\omega) = 0$, or more generally, that the line-integral of $u\omega$ for any closed curve in the space shall vanish.

The existence of the minimum requires that

$$\iiint u\,\omega.\delta\omega\,dv = 0,$$

while $\delta\omega$ is subject to the limitation that

$$\nabla.\delta\omega = 0,$$

and that the normal component of $\delta\omega$ at the bounding surface vanishes. To prove that the line-integral of $u\omega$ vanishes for any closed curve within the space, let us imagine the curve to be surrounded by an infinitely slender tube of normal section dz, which may be either constant or variable. We may satisfy the equation $\nabla.\delta\omega = 0$ by making $\delta\omega = 0$ outside of the tube, and $\delta\omega\,dz = \delta a \dfrac{d\rho}{ds}$ within it, δa denoting an arbitrary infinitesimal constant, ρ the position-vector, and ds an element of the length of the tube or closed curve. We have then

$$\iiint u\,\omega.\delta\omega\,dv = \int u\,\omega.\delta\omega\,dz\,ds = \int u\,\omega.d\rho\,\delta a = \delta a \int u\,\omega.d\rho = 0,$$

whence $$\int u\,\omega.d\rho = 0.$$ Q.E.D.

We may express this result by saying that $u\omega$ is the derivative of a single-valued scalar function of position in space. (See No. 67.)

If for certain parts of the surface the normal component of ω is not given for each point, but only the surface-integral of ω for each such part, then the above reasoning will apply not only to closed curves, but also to curves commencing and ending in such a part of the surface. The primitive of $u\omega$ will then have a constant value in each such part.

If the space extends to infinity and there is no special condition respecting the value of ω at infinite distances, the primitive of $u\omega$ will have a constant value at infinite distances within the space or within each separate continuous part of it.

If we except those cases in which the problem has no definite meaning because the data are such that the integral $\int u\,\omega.\omega\,dv$ must be infinite, it is evident that a minimum must always exist, and (on account of the quadratic form of the integral) that it is unique. That the conditions just found are sufficient to insure this minimum, is evident from the consideration that any allowable values of $\delta\omega$ may be made up of such values as we have supposed. Therefore, there will be one and only one vector function of position in space which satisfies these conditions together with those enumerated at the beginning of this number.

b. In the second place, let the vector ω be subject to the conditions that $\nabla\times\omega$ is given throughout the space, and that the tangential component of ω is given at the bounding surface. The solution is that

$$\nabla.[u\,\omega] = 0,$$

and, if the space is periphractic, that the surface-integral of $u\omega$ vanishes for each of the bounding surfaces.

The existence of the minimum requires that

$$\iiint u\,\omega\,.\,\delta\omega\,dv=0,$$

while $\delta\omega$ is subject to the conditions that

$$\nabla\times\delta\omega=0,$$

and that the tangential component of $\delta\omega$ in the bounding surface vanishes. In virtue of these conditions we may set

$$\delta\omega=\nabla\,\delta q,$$

where δq is an arbitrary infinitesimal scalar function of position, subject only to the condition that it is constant in each of the bounding surfaces. (See No. 67.) By substitution of this value we obtain

$$\iiint u\,\omega.\nabla\,\delta q\,dv=0,$$

or integrating by parts (No. 76)

$$\iint u\,\omega.d\sigma\,\delta q-\iiint\nabla.[u\,\omega]\delta q\,dv=0.$$

Since δq is arbitrary in the volume-integral, we have throughout the whole space

$$\nabla.[u\,\omega]=0\,;$$

and since δq has an arbitrary constant value in each of the bounding surfaces (if the boundary of the space consists of separate parts), we have for each such part

$$\iint u\,\omega.d\sigma=0.$$

Potentials, Newtonians, Laplacians.

91. *Def.*—If u' is the scalar quantity of something situated at a certain point ρ', the *potential* of u' for any point ρ is a scalar function of ρ, defined by the equation

$$\text{pot}\,u'=\frac{u'}{[\rho'-\rho]_0},$$

and the Newtonian of u' for any point ρ is a vector function of ρ defined by the equation

$$\text{new}\,u'=\frac{\rho'-\rho}{[\rho'-\rho]_0^3}\,u'.$$

Again, if ω' is the vector representing the quantity and direction of something situated at the point ρ', the potential and the Laplacian of ω' for any point ρ are vector functions of ρ defined by the equations

$$\text{pot}\,\omega'=\frac{\omega'}{[\rho'-\rho]_0},$$

$$\text{lap}\,\omega'=\frac{\rho'-\rho}{[\rho'-\rho]_0^3}\times\omega'.$$

92. If u or ω is a scalar or vector function of position in space, we may write Pot u, New u, Pot ω, Lap ω for the volume-integrals of pot u', etc., taken as functions of ρ'; i.e., we may set

$$\text{Pot}\, u = \iiint \text{pot}\, u' dv' = \iiint \frac{u'}{[\rho' - \rho]_0} dv',$$

$$\text{New}\, u = \iiint \text{new}\, u' dv' = \iiint \frac{\rho' - \rho}{[\rho' - \rho]_0^3} u' dv',$$

$$\text{Pot}\, \omega = \iiint \text{pot}\, \omega' dv' = \iiint \frac{\omega'}{[\rho' - \rho]_0} dv',$$

$$\text{Lap}\, \omega = \iiint \text{lap}\, \omega' dv' = \iiint \frac{\rho' - \rho}{[\rho' - \rho]_0^3} \times \omega' dv',$$

where the ρ is to be regarded as constant in the integration. This extends over all space, or wherever the u' or ω' have any values other than zero. These integrals may themselves be called (integral) potentials, Newtonians, and Laplacians.

93. $$\frac{d\, \text{Pot}\, u}{dx} = \text{Pot}\, \frac{du}{dx}, \qquad \frac{d\, \text{Pot}\, \omega}{dx} = \text{Pot}\, \frac{d\omega}{dx}.$$

This will be evident with respect both to scalar and to vector functions, if we suppose that when we differentiate the potential with respect to x (thus varying the position of the point for which the potential is taken) each element of volume dv' in the implied integral remains fixed, *not in absolute position*, but in position relative to the point for which the potential is taken. This supposition is evidently allowable whenever the integration indicated by the symbol Pot tends to a definite limit when the limits of integration are indefinitely extended.

Since we may substitute y and z for x in the preceding formula, and since a constant factor of any kind may be introduced under the sign of integration, we have

$$\nabla\, \text{Pot}\, u = \text{Pot}\, \nabla u,$$

$$\nabla . \text{Pot}\, \omega = \text{Pot}\, \nabla . \omega,$$

$$\nabla \times \text{Pot}\, \omega = \text{Pot}\, \nabla \times \omega,$$

$$\nabla . \nabla\, \text{Pot}\, u = \text{Pot}\, \nabla . \nabla u,$$

$$\nabla . \nabla\, \text{Pot}\, \omega = \text{Pot}\, \nabla . \nabla \omega,$$

i.e., the symbols ∇, $\nabla .$, $\nabla \times$, $\nabla . \nabla$ may be applied indifferently before or after the sign Pot.

Yet a certain restriction is to be observed. When the operation of taking the (integral) potential does not give a definite finite value, the first members of these equations are to be regarded as entirely indeterminate, but the second members may have perfectly definite values. This would be the case, for example, if u or ω had a constant value throughout all space. It might seem harmless to set an indefinite expression equal to a definite, but it would be dangerous, since we might with equal right set the indefinite expression equal to other definite expressions, and then be misled into supposing these definite expressions to be equal to one another. It will be safe to say that the above equations will hold, *provided that the potential of u or ω has a definite value.* It will be observed that whenever Pot u or Pot ω has a definite value *in general* (i.e., with the possible exception of certain points, lines, and surfaces),* the first members of all these equations will have definite values in general, and therefore the second members of the equation, being necessarily equal to the first members, when these have definite values, will also have definite values in general.

94. Again, whenever Pot u has a definite value we may write

$$\nabla \text{ Pot } u = \nabla \iiint \frac{u'}{r}\, dv' = \iiint \nabla \frac{1}{r}\, u'\, dv',$$

where r stands for $[\rho' - \rho]_0$. But

$$\nabla \frac{1}{r} = \frac{\rho' - \rho}{r^3},$$

whence
$$\nabla \text{ Pot } u = \text{New } u.$$

Moreover, New u will in general have a definite value, if Pot u has.

95. In like manner, whenever Pot ω has a definite value,

$$\nabla \times \text{Pot } \omega = \nabla \times \iiint \frac{\omega'}{r}\, dv' = \iiint \nabla \times \frac{\omega'}{r}\, dv' = \iiint \nabla \frac{1}{r} \times \omega'\, dv'.$$

Substituting the value of $\nabla \frac{1}{r}$ given above we have

$$\nabla \times \text{Pot } \omega = \text{Lap } \omega.$$

Lap ω will have a definite value in general whenever Pot ω has.

96. Hence, with the aid of No. 93, we obtain

$$\nabla \times \text{Lap } \omega = \text{Lap } \nabla \times \omega,$$
$$\nabla . \text{Lap } \omega = 0,$$

whenever Pot ω has a definite value.

97. By the method of No. 93 we obtain

$$\nabla . \text{New } u = \nabla . \iiint \frac{\rho' - \rho}{r^3}\, u'\, dv' = \iiint \nabla u' . \frac{\rho' - \rho}{r^3}\, dv'.$$

To find the value of this integral, we may regard the point ρ, which is constant in the integration, as the center of polar coordinates. Then r becomes the radius vector of the point ρ', and we may set

$$dv' = r^2\, dq\, dr,$$

* Whenever it is said that a function of position in space has a definite value *in general*, this phrase is to be understood as explained above. The term definite is intended to exclude both indeterminate and infinite values.

where $r^2 dq$ is the element of a spherical surface having center at ρ and radius r. We may also set

$$\nabla u'.\frac{\rho'-\rho}{r}=\frac{du'}{dr}.$$

We thus obtain

$$\nabla.\text{New}\, u=\iiint\frac{du'}{dr}\,dq\,dr=4\pi\int\frac{d\bar{u}'}{dr}\,dr=4\pi\bar{u}'_{r=\infty}-4\pi\bar{u}'_{r=0},$$

where $\bar{u}$ denotes the average value of u in a spherical surface of radius r about the point ρ as center.

Now if Pot u has in general a definite value, we must have $\bar{u}'=0$ for $r=\infty$. Also, ∇.New u will have in general a definite value. For $r=0$, the value of $\bar{u}'$ is evidently u. We have, therefore,

$$\nabla.\text{New}\, u=-4\pi u,$$

$$\nabla.\nabla\text{Pot}\, u=-4\pi u.^*$$

98. If Pot ω has in general a definite value,

$$\begin{aligned}\nabla.\nabla\,\text{Pot}\,\omega&=\nabla.\nabla\,\text{Pot}\,[ui+vj+wk]\\&=\nabla.\nabla\,\text{Pot}\,ui+\nabla.\nabla\,\text{Pot}\,vj+\nabla.\nabla\,\text{Pot}\,wk\\&=-4\pi ui-4\pi vj-4\pi wk\\&=-4\pi\omega.\end{aligned}$$

Hence, by No. 71,

$$\nabla\times\nabla\times\text{Pot}\,\omega-\nabla\nabla.\text{Pot}\,\omega=4\pi\omega.$$

That is,

$$\text{Lap}\,\nabla\times\omega-\text{New}\,\nabla.\omega=4\pi\omega.$$

If we set

$$\omega_1=\frac{1}{4\pi}\text{Lap}\,\nabla\times\omega,\quad\omega_2=\frac{-1}{4\pi}\text{New}\,\nabla.\omega,$$

we have

$$\omega=\omega_1+\omega_2,$$

where ω_1 and ω_2 are such functions of position that $\nabla.\omega_1=0$, and $\nabla\times\omega_2=0$. This is expressed by saying that ω_1 is *solenoidal*, and ω_2 *irrotational*. Pot ω_1 and Pot ω_2, like Pot ω, will have in general definite values.

It is worth while to notice that there is only one way in which a vector function of position in space having a definite potential can be thus divided into solenoidal and irrotational parts having definite potentials. For if $\omega_1+\epsilon$, $\omega_2-\epsilon$ are two other such parts,

$$\nabla.\epsilon=0\quad\text{and}\quad\nabla\times\epsilon=0.$$

Moreover, Pot ϵ has in general a definite value, and therefore

$$\epsilon=\frac{1}{4\pi}\text{Lap}\,\nabla\times\epsilon-\frac{1}{4\pi}\text{New}\,\nabla.\epsilon=0.$$ Q.E.D.

---

* Better thus: $\nabla.\nabla\,\text{Pot}\,u=\iiint\frac{1}{r}\nabla.\nabla u\,dv=\iiint\nabla.\left(\frac{1}{r}\nabla u\right)dv-\iiint\nabla.\left(u\nabla\frac{1}{r}\right)dv+\iiint u\nabla.\nabla\frac{1}{r}dv$ $=-\iint u\nabla\frac{1}{r}.d\sigma=-4\pi u.$ [MS. note by author.]

99. To assist the memory of the student, some of the principal results of Nos. 93–98 may be expressed as follows:

Let ω_1 be any solenoidal vector function of position in space, ω_2 any irrotational vector function, and u any scalar function, satisfying the conditions that their potentials have in general definite values.

With respect to the solenoidal function ω_1, $\frac{1}{4\pi}$ Lap and $\nabla\times$ are inverse operators; i.e.,

$$\frac{1}{4\pi}\,\text{Lap}\,\nabla\times\omega_1=\nabla\times\frac{1}{4\pi}\,\text{Lap}\,\omega_1=\omega_1.$$

Applied to the irrotational function ω_2, either of these operators gives zero; i.e.,

$$\text{Lap}\,\omega_2=0,\quad \nabla\times\omega_2=0.$$

With respect to the irrotational function ω_2, or the scalar function u, $\frac{1}{4\pi}$ New and $-\nabla.$ are inverse operators; i.e.,

$$-\frac{1}{4\pi}\,\text{New}\,\nabla.\omega_2=\omega_2,\quad -\nabla.\frac{1}{4\pi}\,\text{New}\,u=u.$$

Applied to the solenoidal function ω_1, the operator $\nabla.$ gives zero; i.e.

$$\nabla.\omega_1=0.$$

Since the most general form of a vector function having in general a definite potential may be written $\omega_1+\omega_2$, the effect of these operators on such a function needs no especial mention.

With respect to the solenoidal function ω_1, $\frac{1}{4\pi}$ Pot and $\nabla\times\nabla\times$ are inverse operators; i.e.,

$$\frac{1}{4\pi}\,\text{Pot}\,\nabla\times\nabla\times\omega_1=\nabla\times\frac{1}{4\pi}\,\text{Pot}\,\nabla\times\omega_1=\nabla\times\nabla\times\frac{1}{4\pi}\,\text{Pot}\,\omega_1=\omega_1.$$

With respect to the irrotational function ω_2, $\frac{1}{4\pi}$ Pot and $-\nabla\nabla.$ are inverse operators; i.e.,

$$-\frac{1}{4\pi}\,\text{Pot}\,\nabla\nabla.\omega_2=-\nabla\frac{1}{4\pi}\,\text{Pot}\,\nabla.\omega_2=-\nabla\nabla.\frac{1}{4\pi}\,\text{Pot}\,\omega_2=\omega_2.$$

With respect to any scalar or vector function having in general a definite potential $\frac{1}{4\pi}$ Pot and $-\nabla.\nabla$ are inverse operators; i.e.,

$$-\frac{1}{4\pi}\,\text{Pot}\,\nabla.\nabla u=-\nabla.\frac{1}{4\pi}\,\text{Pot}\,\nabla u=-\nabla.\nabla\frac{1}{4\pi}\,\text{Pot}\,u=u,$$

$$-\frac{1}{4\pi}\,\text{Pot}\,\nabla.\nabla[\omega_1+\omega_2]=-\nabla.\nabla\frac{1}{4\pi}\,\text{Pot}\,[\omega_1+\omega_2]=\omega_1+\omega_2.$$

With respect to the solenoidal function ω_1, $-\nabla.\nabla$ and $\nabla\times\nabla\times$ are equivalent; with respect to the irrotational function ω_2 $\nabla.\nabla$ and $\nabla\nabla.$ are equivalent; i.e.,

$$-\nabla.\nabla\omega_1=\nabla\times\nabla\times\omega_1,\quad \nabla.\nabla\omega_2=\nabla\nabla.\omega_2.$$

100. *On the interpretation of the preceding formulæ.*—Infinite values of the quantity which occurs in a volume-integral as the coefficient of the element of volume will not necessarily make the value of the integral infinite, when they are confined to certain surfaces, lines, or points. Yet these surfaces, lines, or points may contribute a certain finite amount to the value of the volume-integral, which must be separately calculated, and in the case of surfaces or lines is naturally expressed as a surface- or line-integral. Such cases are easily treated by substituting for the surface, line, or point, a very thin shell, or filament, or a solid very small in all dimensions, within which the function may be supposed to have a very large value.

The only cases which we shall here consider in detail are those of surfaces at which the functions of position (u or ω) are discontinuous, and the values of ∇u, $\nabla \times \omega$, $\nabla . \omega$ thus become infinite. Let the function u have the value u_1 on the side of the surface which we regard as the negative, and the value u_2 on the positive side. Let $\Delta u = u_2 - u_1$. If we substitute for the surface a shell of very small thickness a, within which the value of u varies uniformly as we pass through the shell, we shall have $\nabla u = \nu \frac{\nabla u}{a}$ within the shell, ν denoting a unit normal on the positive side of the surface. The elements of volume which compose the shell may be expressed by $a[d\sigma]_0$, where $[d\sigma]_0$ is the magnitude of an element of the surface, $d\sigma$ being the vector element. Hence,

$$\nabla u \, dv = \nu \, \Delta u [d\sigma]_0 = \Delta u \, d\sigma.$$

Hence, when there are surfaces at which the values of u are discontinuous, the full value of Pot ∇u should always be understood as including the surface-integral

$$\iint \frac{\Delta u'}{[\rho' - \rho]_0} d\sigma'$$

relating to such surfaces. ($\Delta u'$ and $d\sigma'$ are accented in the formula to indicate that they relate to the point ρ'.)

In the case of a vector function which is discontinuous at a surface, the expressions $\nabla . \omega \, dv$ and $\nabla \times \omega \, dv$, relating to the element of the shell which we substitute for the surface of discontinuity, are easily transformed by the principle that these expressions are the direct and skew surface-integrals of ω for the element of the shell. (See Nos. 55, 56.) The part of the surface-integrals relating to the edge of the element may evidently be neglected, and we shall have

$$\nabla . \omega \, dv = \omega_2 . d\sigma - \omega_1 . d\sigma = \Delta \omega . d\sigma,$$

$$\nabla \times \omega \, dv = d\sigma \times \omega_2 - d\sigma \times \omega_1 = d\sigma \times \Delta \omega.$$

Whenever, therefore, ω is discontinuous at surfaces, the expressions Pot $\nabla.\omega$ and New $\nabla.\omega$ must be regarded as implicitly including the surface-integrals

$$\iint \frac{1}{[\rho'-\rho]_0} \Delta\omega'.d\sigma' \quad \text{and} \quad \iint \frac{\rho'-\rho}{[\rho'-\rho]_0^3} \Delta\omega'.d\sigma'$$

respectively, relating to such surfaces, and the expressions Pot $\nabla\times\omega$ and Lap $\nabla\times\omega$ as including the surface-integrals

$$\iint \frac{1}{[\rho'-\rho]_0} d\sigma'\times\Delta\omega' \quad \text{and} \quad \iint \frac{\rho'-\rho}{[\rho'-\rho]_0^3}\times[d\sigma'\times\Delta\omega']$$

respectively, relating to such surfaces.

101. We have already seen that if ω is the curl of any vector function of position, $\nabla.\omega=0$. (No. 68.) The converse is evidently true, whenever the equation $\nabla.\omega=0$ holds throughout all space, and ω has in general a definite potential; for then

$$\omega=\nabla\times\frac{1}{4\pi}\text{Lap}\,\omega.$$

Again, if $\nabla.\omega=0$ within any aperiphractic space A, contained within finite boundaries, we may suppose that space to be enclosed by a shell B having its inner surface coincident with the surface of A. We may imagine a function of position ω', such that $\omega'=\omega$ in A, $\omega'=0$ outside of the shell B, and the integral $\iiint\omega'.\omega'\,dv$ for B has the least value consistent with the conditions that the normal component of ω' at the outer surface is zero, and at the inner surface is equal to that of ω, and that in the shell $\nabla.\omega'=0$ (compare No. 90). Then $\nabla.\omega'=0$ throughout all space, and the potential of ω' will have in general a definite value. Hence,

$$\omega'=\nabla\times\frac{1}{4\pi}\text{Lap}\,\omega',$$

and ω will have the same value within the space A.

†102. *Def.*—If ω is a vector function of position in space, the *Maxwellian* * of ω is a scalar function of position defined by the equation

$$\text{Max}\,\omega=\iiint\frac{\rho'-\rho}{[\rho'-\rho]_0^3}.\,\omega'dv'.$$

(Compare No. 92.) From this definition the following properties are easily derived. It is supposed that the functions ω and u are such that their potentials have in general definite values.

$$\text{Max}\,\omega=\nabla.\text{Pot}\,\omega=\text{Pot}\,\nabla.\omega,$$
$$\nabla\,\text{Max}\,\omega=\nabla\nabla.\text{Pot}\,\omega=\text{New}\,\nabla.\omega,$$
$$\text{Max}\,\nabla u=-4\pi u,$$
$$4\pi\omega=\nabla\times\text{Lap}\,\omega-\nabla\,\text{Max}\,\omega.$$

* The frequent occurrence of the integral in Maxwell's *Treatise on Electricity and Magnetism* has suggested this name.

† [The foregoing portion of this paper was printed in 1881, the rest in 1884.]

If the values of Lap Lap ω, New Max ω, and Max New u are in general definite, we may add

$$4\pi \operatorname{Pot} \omega = \operatorname{Lap} \operatorname{Lap} \omega - \operatorname{New} \operatorname{Max} \omega,$$

$$4\pi \operatorname{Pot} u = -\operatorname{Max} \operatorname{New} u.$$

In other words: The Maxwellian is the divergence of the potential, $-\frac{\text{Max}}{4\pi}$ and ∇ are inverse operators for scalars and irrotational vectors, for vectors in general $-\frac{1}{4\pi}\nabla$ Max is an operator which separates the irrotational from the solenoidal part. For scalars and irrotational vectors, $\frac{-1}{4\pi}$ Max New and $\frac{-1}{4\pi}$ New Max give the potential, for solenoidal vectors $\frac{1}{4\pi}$ Lap Lap gives the potential, for vectors in general $\frac{-1}{4\pi}$ New Max gives the potential of the irrotational part, and $\frac{1}{4\pi}$ Lap Lap the potential of the solenoidal part.

103. *Def.*—The following double volume-integrals are of frequent occurrence in physical problems. They are all scalar quantities, and none of them functions of position in space, as are the single volume-integrals which we have been considering. The integrations extend over all space, or as far as the expression to be integrated has values other than zero.

The *mutual potential*, or *potential product*, of two scalar functions of position in space is defined by the equation

$$\operatorname{Pot}(u, w) = \iiint\!\!\iiint \frac{uw'}{r}\, dv\, dv' = \iiint u \operatorname{Pot} w\, dv = \iiint w \operatorname{Pot} u\, dv.$$

In the double volume-integral, r is the distance between the two elements of volume, and u relates to dv as w' to dv'.

The *mutual potential*, or *potential product*, of two vector functions of position in space is defined by the equation

$$\operatorname{Pot}(\phi, \omega) = \iiint\!\!\iiint \frac{\phi . \omega'}{r}\, dv\, dv' = \iiint \phi . \operatorname{Pot} \omega\, dv = \iiint \omega . \operatorname{Pot} \phi\, dv.$$

The *mutual Laplacian*, or *Laplacian product*, of two vector functions of position in space is defined by the equation

$$\operatorname{Lap}(\phi, \omega) = \iiint\!\!\iiint \omega . \frac{\rho' - \rho}{r^3} \times \phi'\, dv\, dv'$$

$$= \iiint \omega . \operatorname{Lap} \phi\, dv = \iiint \phi . \operatorname{Lap} \omega\, dv.$$

The *Newtonian product* of a scalar and a vector function of position in space is defined by the equation

$$\operatorname{New}(u, \omega) = \iiint\!\!\iiint \omega . \frac{\rho' - \rho}{r^3} u'\, dv\, dv' = \iiint \omega . \operatorname{New} u\, dv.$$

The *Maxwellian product* of a vector and a scalar function of position in space is defined by the equation

$$\text{Max}(\omega, u) = \iiint\!\!\iiint u \frac{\rho' - \rho}{r^3} . \omega' \, dv \, dv' = \iiint u \, \text{Max} \, \omega \, dv = -\text{New}(u, \omega).$$

It is of course supposed that u, w, ϕ, ω are such functions of position that the above expressions have definite values.

104. By No. 97,

$$4\pi u \, \text{Pot} \, w = -\nabla . \text{New} \, u \, \text{Pot} \, w = -\nabla . [\text{New} \, u \, \text{Pot} \, w] + \text{New} \, u . \text{New} \, w.$$

The volume-integral of this equation gives

$$4\pi \, \text{Pot}(u, w) = \iiint \text{New} \, u . \text{New} \, w \, dv,$$

if the integral

$$\iint d\sigma . \text{New} \, u \, \text{Pot} \, w,$$

for a closed surface, vanishes when the space included by the surface is indefinitely extended in all directions. This will be the case when everywhere outside of certain assignable limits the values of u and w are zero.

Again, by No. 102,

$$\begin{aligned} 4\pi\omega . \text{Pot} \, \phi &= \nabla \times \text{Lap} \, \omega . \text{Pot} \, \phi - \nabla \, \text{Max} \, \omega . \text{Pot} \, \phi \\ &= \nabla . [\text{Lap} \, \omega \times \text{Pot} \, \phi] + \text{Lap} \, \omega . \text{Lap} \, \phi \\ &\quad - \nabla . [\text{Max} \, \omega \, \text{Pot} \, \phi] + \text{Max} \, \omega \, \text{Max} \, \phi. \end{aligned}$$

The volume-integral of this equation gives

$$4\pi \, \text{Pot}(\phi, \omega) = \iiint \text{Lap} \, \phi . \text{Lap} \, \omega \, dv + \iiint \text{Max} \, \phi \, \text{Max} \, \omega \, dv,$$

if the integrals

$$\iint d\sigma . \text{Lap} \, \omega \times \text{Pot} \, \phi, \qquad \iint d\sigma . \text{Pot} \, \phi \, \text{Max} \, \omega,$$

for a closed surface vanish when the space included by the surface is indefinitely extended in all directions. This will be the case if everywhere outside of certain assignable limits the values of ϕ and ω are zero.

CHAPTER III.

CONCERNING LINEAR VECTOR FUNCTIONS.

105. *Def.*—A vector function of a vector is said to be *linear*, when the function of the sum of any two vectors is equal to the sum of the functions of the vectors. That is, if

$$\text{func.}[\rho + \rho'] = \text{func.}[\rho] + \text{func.}[\rho']$$

for all values of ρ and ρ', the function is linear. In such cases it is easily shown that

$$\text{func.}[a\rho + b\rho' + c\rho'' + \text{etc.}] = a \, \text{func.}[\rho] + b \, \text{func.}[\rho'] + c \, \text{func.}[\rho''] + \text{etc.}$$

106. An expression of the form

$$\alpha\lambda.\rho+\beta\mu.\rho+\text{etc.}$$

evidently represents a linear function of ρ, and may be conveniently written in the form

$$\{\alpha\lambda+\beta\mu+\text{etc.}\}.\rho.$$

The expression $$\rho.\alpha\lambda+\rho.\beta\mu+\text{etc.},$$

or $$\rho.\{\alpha\lambda+\beta\mu+\text{etc.}\},$$

also represents a linear function of ρ, which is, in general, different from the preceding, and will be called its *conjugate*.

107. *Def.*—An expression of the form $\alpha\lambda$ or $\beta\mu$ will be called a *dyad*. An expression consisting of any number of dyads united by the signs + or − will be called a *dyadic binomial*, *trinomial*, etc., as the case may be, or more briefly, a *dyadic*. The latter term will be used so as to include the case of a single dyad. When we desire to express a dyadic by a single letter, the Greek capitals will be used, except such as are like the Roman, and also Δ and Σ. The letter I will also be used to represent a certain dyadic, to be mentioned hereafter.

Since any linear vector function may be expressed by means of a dyadic (as we shall see more particularly hereafter, see No. 110), the study of such functions, which is evidently of primary importance in the theory of vectors, may be reduced to that of dyadics.

108. *Def.*—Any two dyadics Φ and Ψ are equal,

when $\Phi.\rho=\Psi.\rho$ for all values of ρ,

or, when $\rho.\Phi=\rho.\Psi$ for all values of ρ,

or, when $\sigma.\Phi.\rho=\sigma.\Psi.\rho$ for all values of σ and of ρ.

The third condition is easily shown to be equivalent both to the first and to the second. The three conditions are therefore equivalent.

It follows that $\Phi=\Psi$, if $\Phi.\rho=\Psi.\rho$, or $\rho.\Phi=\rho.\Psi$, for three non-complanar values of ρ.

109. *Def.*—We shall call the vector $\Phi.\rho$ the (direct) product of Φ and ρ, the vector $\rho.\Phi$ the (direct) product of ρ and Φ, and the scalar $\sigma.\Phi.\rho$ the (direct) product of σ, Φ, and ρ.

In the combination $\Phi.\rho$, we shall say that Φ is used as a *prefactor*, in the combination $\rho.\Phi$, as a *postfactor*.

110. If τ is any linear function of ρ, and for $\rho=i$, $\rho=j$, $\rho=k$, the values of τ are respectively α, β, and γ, we may set

$$\tau=\{\alpha i+\beta j+\gamma k\}.\rho,$$

and also

$$\tau=\rho.\{i\alpha+j\beta+k\gamma\}.$$

Therefore, any linear function may be expressed by a dyadic as prefactor and also by a dyadic as postfactor.

111. *Def.*—We shall say that a dyadic is multiplied by a scalar, when one of the vectors of each of its component dyads is multiplied by that scalar. It is evidently immaterial to which vector of any dyad the scalar factor is applied. The product of the dyadic Φ and the scalar a may be written either $a\Phi$ or Φa. The minus sign before a dyadic reverses the signs of all its terms.

112. The sign $+$ in a dyadic, or connecting dyadics, may be regarded as expressing addition, since the combination of dyads and dyadics with this sign is subject to the laws of association and commutation.

113. The combination of vectors in a dyad is evidently distributive. That is,

$$[\alpha+\beta+\text{etc.}][\lambda+\mu+\text{etc.}]=\alpha\lambda+\alpha\mu+\beta\lambda+\beta\mu+\text{etc.}$$

We may therefore regard the dyad as a kind of product of the two vectors of which it is formed. Since this kind of product is not commutative, we shall have occasion to distinguish the factors as *antecedent* and *consequent*.

114. Since any vector may be expressed as a sum of i, j, and k with scalar coefficients, every dyadic may be reduced to a sum of the nine dyads

$$ii,\ ij,\ ik,\ ji,\ jj,\ jk,\ ki,\ kj,\ kk,$$

with scalar coefficients. Two such sums cannot be equal according to the definitions of No. 108, unless their coefficients are equal each to each. Hence dyadics are equal only when their equality can be deduced from the principle that the operation of forming a dyad is a distributive one.

On this account, we may regard the dyad as the most general form of product of two vectors. We shall call it the indeterminate product. The complete determination of a single dyad involves five independent scalars, of a dyadic, nine.

115. It follows from the principles of the last paragraph that if

$$\Sigma\,\alpha\beta=\Sigma\,\kappa\lambda,$$

then

$$\Sigma\,\alpha\times\beta=\Sigma\,\kappa\times\lambda,$$

and

$$\Sigma\,\alpha.\beta=\Sigma\,\kappa.\lambda.$$

In other words, the vector and the scalar obtained from a dyadic by insertion of the sign of skew or direct multiplication in each dyad are both independent of the particular form in which the dyadic is expressed.

We shall write $\Phi_\times$ and Φ_S to indicate the vector and the scalar thus obtained.

$$\Phi_\times=(j.\Phi.k-k.\Phi.j)i+(k.\Phi.i-i.\Phi.k)j+(i.\Phi.j-j.\Phi.i)k,$$

$$\Phi_S=i.\Phi.i+j.\Phi.j+k.\Phi.k,$$

as is at once evident, if we suppose Φ to be expanded in terms of ii, ij, etc.

116. *Def.*—The (*direct*) *product* of two dyads (indicated by a dot) is the dyad formed of the first and last of the four factors, multiplied by the direct product of the second and third. That is,

$$\{\alpha\beta\}.\{\gamma\delta\}=\alpha\,\beta.\gamma\,\delta=\beta.\gamma\,\alpha\delta.$$

The (direct) product of two dyadics is the sum of all the products formed by prefixing a term of the first dyadic to a term of the second. Since the direct product of one dyadic with another is a dyadic, it may be multiplied in the same way by a third, and so on indefinitely. This kind of multiplication is evidently associative, as well as distributive. The same is true of the direct product of a series of factors of which the first and the last are either dyadics or vectors, and the other factors are dyadics. Thus the values of the expressions

$$\alpha.\Phi.\Theta.\Psi.\beta, \qquad \alpha.\Phi.\Theta, \qquad \Phi.\Theta.\Psi.\beta, \qquad \Phi.\Theta.\Psi$$

will not be affected by any insertion of parentheses. But this kind of multiplication is not commutative, except in the case of the direct product of two vectors.

117. *Def.*—The expressions $\Phi\times\rho$ and $\rho\times\Phi$ represent dyadics which we shall call the *skew* products of Φ and ρ. If

$$\Phi=\alpha\lambda+\beta\mu+\text{etc.},$$

these skew products are defined by the equations

$$\Phi\times\rho=\alpha\,\lambda\times\rho+\beta\,\mu\times\rho+\text{etc.},$$
$$\rho\times\Phi=\rho\times\alpha\,\lambda+\rho\times\beta\,\mu+\text{etc.}$$

It is evident that

$$\{\rho\times\Phi\}.\Psi=\rho\times\{\Phi.\Psi\}, \qquad \Psi.\{\Phi\times\rho\}=\{\Psi.\Phi\}\times\rho,$$
$$\{\rho\times\Phi\}.\alpha=\rho\times[\Phi.\alpha], \qquad \alpha.\{\Phi\times\rho\}=[\alpha.\Phi]\times\rho,$$
$$\{\rho\times\Phi\}\times\alpha=\rho\times\{\Phi\times\alpha\}.$$

We may therefore write without ambiguity

$$\rho\times\Phi.\Psi, \quad \Psi.\Phi\times\rho, \quad \rho\times\Phi.\alpha, \quad \alpha.\Phi\times\rho, \quad \rho\times\Phi.\alpha.$$

This may be expressed a little more generally by saying that the associative principle enunciated in No. 116 may be extended to cases in which the initial or final vectors are connected with the other factors by the sign of skew multiplication.

Moreover,

$$\alpha.\rho\times\Phi=[\alpha\times\rho].\Phi \text{ and } \Phi\times\rho.\alpha=\Phi.[\rho\times\alpha].$$

These expressions evidently represent vectors. So

$$\Psi.\{\rho\times\Phi\}=\{\Psi\times\rho\}.\Phi.$$

These expressions represent dyadics. The braces cannot be omitted without ambiguity.

118. Since all the antecedents or all the consequents in any dyadic may be expressed in parts of any three non-complanar vectors, and since the sum of any number of dyads having the same antecedent or the same consequent may be expressed by a single dyad, it follows that any dyadic may be expressed as the sum of three dyads, and so, that either the antecedents or the consequents shall be any desired non-complanar vectors, but only in one way when either the antecedents or the consequents are thus given.

In particular, the dyadic

$$\begin{aligned} &aii+bij+cik \\ &+a'ji+b'jj+c'jk \\ &+a''ki+b''kj+c''kk, \end{aligned}$$

which may for brevity be written

$$\left\{\begin{matrix} a & b & c \\ a' & b' & c' \\ a'' & b'' & c'' \end{matrix}\right\},$$

is equal to

$$\alpha i+\beta j+\gamma k,$$

where

$$\begin{aligned} \alpha &= ai+a'j+a''k, \\ \beta &= bi+b'j+b''k, \\ \gamma &= ci+c'j+c''k, \end{aligned}$$

and to

$$i\lambda+j\mu+k\nu,$$

where

$$\begin{aligned} \lambda &= ai+bj+ck \\ \mu &= a'i+b'j+c'k \\ \nu &= a''i+b''j+c''k. \end{aligned}$$

119. By a similar process, the sum of three dyads may be reduced to the sum of two dyads, whenever either the antecedents or the consequents are complanar, and only in such cases. To prove the latter point, let us suppose that in the dyadic

$$\alpha\lambda+\beta\mu+\gamma\nu$$

neither the antecedents nor the consequents are complanar. The vector

$$\{\alpha\lambda+\beta\mu+\gamma\nu\}.\rho$$

is a linear function of ρ which will be parallel to α when ρ is perpendicular to μ and ν, which will be parallel to β when ρ is perpendicular to ν and λ, and which will be parallel to γ when ρ is perpendicular to λ and μ. Hence, the function may be given any value whatever by giving the proper value to ρ. This would evidently not be the case with the sum of two dyads. Hence, by No. 108, this dyadic cannot be equal to the sum of two dyads.

120. In like manner, the sum of two dyads may be reduced to a single dyad, if either the antecedents or the consequents are parallel, and only in such cases.

A sum of three dyads cannot be reduced to a single dyad, unless either their antecedents or consequents are parallel, or both antecedents and consequents are (separately) complanar. In the first case the reduction can always be made, in the second, occasionally.

121. *Def.*—A dyadic which cannot be reduced to the sum of less than three dyads will be called *complete.*

A dyadic which can be reduced to the sum of two dyads will be called *planar.* When the plane of the antecedents coincides with that of the consequents, the dyadic will be called *uniplanar.* These planes are invariable for a given dyadic, although the dyadic may be so expressed that either the two antecedents or the two consequents may have any desired values (which are not parallel) within their planes.

A dyadic which can be reduced to a single dyad will be called *linear.* When the antecedent and consequent are parallel, it will be called *unilinear.*

A dyadic is said to have the value zero when all its terms vanish.

122. If we set

$$\sigma = \Phi.\rho, \qquad \tau = \rho.\Phi,$$

and give ρ all possible values, σ and τ will receive all possible values, if Φ is complete. The values of σ and τ will be confined each to a plane if Φ is planar, which planes will coincide if Φ is uniplanar. The values of σ and τ will be confined each to a line if Φ is linear, which lines will coincide if Φ is unilinear.

123. The products of complete dyadics are complete, of complete and planar dyadics are planar, of complete and linear dyadics are linear.

The products of planar dyadics are planar, except that when the plane of the consequents of the first dyadic is perpendicular to the plane of the antecedents of the second dyadic, the product reduces to a linear dyadic.

The products of linear dyadics are linear, except that when the consequent of the first is perpendicular to the antecedent of the second, the product reduces to zero.

The products of planar and linear dyadics are linear, except when, the planar preceding, the plane of its consequents is perpendicular to the antecedent of the linear, or, the linear preceding, its consequent is perpendicular to the plane of the antecedents of the planar. In these cases the product is zero.

All these cases are readily proved, if we set

$$\sigma = \Phi.\Psi.\rho,$$

and consider the limits within which σ varies, when we give ρ all possible values.

The products $\Psi \times \rho$ and $\rho \times \Phi$ are evidently planar dyadics.

124. *Def.*—A dyadic Φ is said to be an *idemfactor*, when

$$\Phi . \rho = \rho \text{ for all values of } \rho,$$

or when $$\rho . \Phi = \rho \text{ for all values of } \rho.$$

If either of these conditions holds true, Φ must be reducible to the form

$$ii + jj + kk.$$

Therefore, both conditions will hold, if either does. All such dyadics are equal, by No. 108. They will be represented by the letter I.

The direct product of an idemfactor with another dyadic is equal to that dyadic. That is,

$$\mathrm{I} . \Phi = \Phi, \qquad \Phi . \mathrm{I} = \Phi,$$

where Φ is any dyadic.

A dyadic of the form

$$\alpha\alpha' + \beta\beta' + \gamma\gamma',$$

in which α', β', γ' are the reciprocals of α, β, γ, is an idemfactor. (See No. 38.) A dyadic trinomial cannot be an idemfactor, unless its antecedents and consequents are reciprocals.

125. If one of the direct products of two dyadics is an idemfactor, the other is also. For, if $\Phi . \Psi = \mathrm{I}$,

$$\sigma . \Phi . \Psi = \sigma$$

for all values of σ, and Φ is complete;

$$\sigma . \Phi . \Psi . \Phi = \sigma . \Phi$$

for all values of σ, therefore for all values of $\sigma . \Phi$, and therefore $\Psi . \Phi = \mathrm{I}$.

Def.—In this case, either dyadic is called the *reciprocal* of the other.

It is evident that an incomplete dyadic cannot have any (finite) reciprocal.

Reciprocals of the same dyadic are equal. For if Φ and Ψ are both reciprocals of Ω,

$$\Phi = \Phi . \Omega . \Psi = \Psi.$$

If two dyadics are reciprocals, the operators formed by using these dyadics as prefactors are inverse, also the operators formed by using them as postfactors.

126. The reciprocal of any complete dyadic

$$\alpha\lambda + \beta\mu + \gamma\nu$$

is $$\lambda'\alpha' + \mu'\beta' + \nu'\gamma',$$

where α', β', γ' are the reciprocals of α, β, γ, and λ', μ', ν' are the reciprocals of λ, μ, ν. (See No. 38.)

127. *Def.*—We shall write Φ^{-1} for the reciprocal of any (complete) dyadic Φ, also Φ^2 for $\Phi.\Phi$, etc., and Φ^{-2}, for $\Phi^{-1}.\Phi^{-1}$, etc. It is evident that Φ^{-n} is the reciprocal of Φ^n,

128. In the reduction of equations, if we have

$$\Phi.\Psi=\Phi.\Omega,$$

we may cancel the Φ (which is equivalent to multiplying by Φ^{-1}) if Φ is a complete dyadic, but not otherwise. The case is the same with such equations as

$$\Phi.\sigma=\Phi.\rho, \quad \Psi.\Phi=\Omega.\Phi, \quad \rho.\Phi=\sigma.\Phi.$$

To cancel an incomplete dyadic in such cases would be analogous to cancelling a zero factor in algebra.

129. *Def.*—If in any dyadic we transpose the factors in each term, the dyadic thus formed is said to be *conjugate* to the first. Thus

$$\alpha\lambda+\beta\mu+\gamma\nu \text{ and } \lambda\alpha+\mu\beta+\nu\gamma$$

are conjugate to each other. A dyadic of which the value is not altered by such transposition is said to be *self-conjugate.* The conjugate of any dyadic Φ may be written Φ_C. It is evident that

$$\rho.\Phi=\Phi_C.\rho \text{ and } \Phi.\rho=\rho.\Phi_C.$$

$\Phi_C.\rho$ and $\Phi.\rho$ are conjugate functions of ρ. (See No. 106.) Since $\{\Phi_C\}^2=\{\Phi^2\}_C$, we may write Φ_C^2, etc., without ambiguity.

130. The reciprocal of the product of any number of dyadics is equal to the product of their reciprocals taken in inverse order. Thus

$$\{\Phi.\Psi.\Omega\}^{-1}=\Omega^{-1}.\Psi^{-1}.\Phi^{-1}.$$

The conjugate of the product of any number of dyadics is equal to the product of their conjugates taken in inverse order. Thus

$$\{\Phi.\Psi.\Omega\}_C=\Omega_C.\Psi_C.\Phi_C.$$

Hence, since

$$\Phi_C.\{\Phi^{-1}\}_C=\{\Phi^{-1}.\Phi\}_C=I,$$

$$\{\Phi^{-1}\}_C=\{\Phi_C\}^{-1},$$

and we may write Φ_C^{-1} without ambiguity.

131. It is sometimes convenient to be able to express by a dyadic taken in direct multiplication the same operation which would be effected by a given vector (α) in skew multiplication. The dyadic $I\times\alpha$ will answer this purpose. For, by No. 117,

$$\{I\times\alpha\}.\rho=\alpha\times\rho, \qquad \rho.\{I\times\alpha\}=\rho\times\alpha,$$

$$\{I\times\alpha\}.\Phi=\alpha\times\Phi, \qquad \Phi.\{I\times\alpha\}=\Phi\times\alpha.$$

The same is true of the dyadic $\alpha\times I$, which is indeed identical with $I\times\alpha$, as appears from the equation $I.\{\alpha\times I\}=\{I\times\alpha\}.I$.

If α is a unit vector,

$$\{I\times\alpha\}^2 = -\{I-\alpha\alpha\},$$
$$\{I\times\alpha\}^3 = -I\times\alpha,$$
$$\{I\times\alpha\}^4 = I-\alpha\alpha,$$
$$\{I\times\alpha\}^5 = I\times\alpha,$$
etc.

If i, j, k are a normal system of unit vectors

$$I\times i = i\times I = kj - jk.$$
$$I\times j = j\times I = ik - ki,$$
$$I\times k = k\times I = ji - ij.$$

If α and β are any vectors,

$$[\alpha\times\beta]\times I = I\times[\alpha\times\beta] = \beta\alpha - \alpha\beta.$$

That is, the vector $\alpha\times\beta$ as a pre- or post-factor in skew multiplication is equivalent to the dyadic $\{\beta\alpha-\alpha\beta\}$ taken as pre- or post-factor in direct multiplication.

$$[\alpha\times\beta]\times\rho = \{\beta\alpha-\alpha\beta\}.\rho,$$
$$\rho\times[\alpha\times\beta] = \rho.\{\beta\alpha-\alpha\beta\}.$$

This is essentially the theorem of No. 27, expressed in a form more symmetrical, and more easily remembered.

132. The equation

$$\alpha\,\beta\times\gamma + \beta\,\gamma\times\alpha + \gamma\,\alpha\times\beta = \alpha.\beta\times\gamma\,I$$

gives, on multiplication by any vector ρ, the identical equation

$$\rho.\alpha\,\beta\times\gamma + \rho.\beta\,\gamma\times\alpha + \rho.\gamma\,\alpha\times\beta = \alpha.\beta\times\gamma\,\rho.$$

(See No. 37.) The former equation is therefore identically true. (See No. 108.) It is a little more general than the equation

$$\alpha\alpha' + \beta\beta' + \gamma\gamma' = I,$$

which we have already considered (No. 124), since, in the form here given, it is not necessary that α, β, and γ should be non-complanar. We may also write

$$\beta\times\gamma\,\alpha + \gamma\times\alpha\,\beta + \alpha\times\beta\,\gamma = \alpha.\beta\times\gamma\,I.$$

Multiplying this equation by ρ as prefactor (or the first equation by ρ as postfactor), we obtain

$$\rho.\beta\times\gamma\,\alpha + \rho.\gamma\times\alpha\,\beta + \rho.\alpha\times\beta\,\gamma = \alpha.\beta\times\gamma\,\rho.$$

(Compare No. 37.) For three complanar vectors we have

$$\alpha\,\beta\times\gamma + \beta\,\gamma\times\alpha + \gamma\,\alpha\times\beta = 0.$$

Multiplying this by ν, a unit normal to the plane of α, β, and γ we have

$$\alpha\,\beta\times\gamma.\nu + \beta\,\gamma\times\alpha.\nu + \gamma\,\alpha\times\beta.\nu = 0.$$

This equation expresses the well-known theorem that if the geometrical sum of three vectors is zero, the magnitude of each vector is proportional to the sine of the angle between the other two. It also indicates the numerical coefficients by which one of three complanar vectors may be expressed in parts of the other two.

133. *Def.*—If two dyadics Φ and Ψ are such that

$$\Phi.\Psi = \Psi.\Phi,$$

they are said to be *homologous.*

If any number of dyadics are homologous to one another, and any other dyadics are formed from them by the operations of taking multiples, sums, differences, powers, reciprocals, or products, such dyadics will be homologous to each other and to the original dyadics. This requires demonstration only in regard to reciprocals. Now if

$$\Phi.\Psi = \Psi.\Phi,$$

$$\Psi.\Phi^{-1} = \Phi^{-1}.\Phi.\Psi.\Phi^{-1} = \Phi^{-1}.\Psi.\Phi.\Phi^{-1} = \Phi^{-1}.\Psi.$$

That is, Φ^{-1} is homologous to Ψ, if Φ is.

134. If we call $\Psi.\Phi^{-1}$ or $\Phi^{-1}.\Psi$ the quotient of Ψ and Φ, we may say that the rules of addition, subtraction, multiplication and division of homologous dyadics are identical with those of arithmetic or ordinary algebra, except that limitations analogous to those respecting zero in algebra must be observed with respect to all incomplete dyadics.

It follows that the algebraic and higher analysis of homologous dyadics is substantially identical with that of scalars.

135. It is always possible to express a dyadic in three terms, so that both the antecedents and the consequents shall be perpendicular among themselves.

To show this for any dyadic Φ, let us set

$$\rho' = \Phi.\rho,$$

ρ being a unit-vector, and consider the different values of ρ' for all possible directions of ρ. Let the direction of the unit vector i be so determined that when ρ coincides with i, the value of ρ' shall be at least as great as for any other direction of ρ. And let the direction of the unit vector j be so determined that when ρ coincides with j, the value of ρ' shall be at least as great as for any other direction of ρ which is perpendicular to i. Let k have its usual position with respect to i and j. It is evidently possible to express Φ in the form

$$\alpha i + \beta j + \gamma k.$$

We have therefore

$$\rho' = \{\alpha i + \beta j + \gamma k\}.\rho,$$

and

$$d\rho' = \{\alpha i + \beta j + \gamma k\}.d\rho.$$

Now the supposed property of the direction of i requires that when ρ coincides with i and $d\rho$ is perpendicular to i, $d\rho'$ shall be perpendicular to ρ', which will then be parallel to α. But if $d\rho$ is parallel to j or k, it will be perpendicular to i, and $d\rho'$ will be parallel to β or γ, as the case may be. Therefore β and γ are perpendicular to α. In the same way it may be shown that the condition relative to j requires that γ shall be perpendicular to β. We may therefore set

$$\Phi = ai'i + bj'j + ck'k,$$

where i', j', k', like i, j, k, constitute a normal system of unit vectors (see No. 11), and a, b, c are scalars which may be either positive or negative.

It makes an important difference whether the number of these scalars which are negative is even or odd. If two are negative, say a and b, we may make them positive by reversing the directions of i' and j'. The vectors i', j', k' will still constitute a normal system. But if we should reverse the directions of an odd number of these vectors, they would cease to constitute a normal system, and to be superposable upon the system i, j, k. We may, however, always set either

$$\Phi = ai'i + bj'j + ck'k,$$

or

$$\Phi = -\{ai'i + bj'j + ck'k\},$$

with positive values of a, b, and c. At the limit between these cases are the planar dyadics, in which one of the three terms vanishes, and the dyadic reduces to the form

$$ai'i + bj'j,$$

in which a and b may always be made positive by giving the proper directions to i' and j'.

If the numerical values of a, b, c are all unequal, there will be only one way in which the value of Φ may be thus expressed. If they are not all unequal, there will be an infinite number of ways in which Φ may be thus expressed, in all of which the three scalar coefficients will have the same values with exception of the changes of signs mentioned above. If the three values are numerically identical, we may give to either system of normal vectors an arbitrary position.

136. It follows that any self-conjugate dyadic may be expressed in the form

$$aii + bjj + ckk,$$

where i, j, k are a normal system of unit vectors, and a, b, c are positive or negative scalars.

137. Any dyadic may be divided into two parts, of which one shall be self-conjugate, and the other of the form $I \times \alpha$. These parts are found by taking half the sum and half the difference of the dyadic and its conjugate. It is evident that

$$\Phi = \tfrac{1}{2}\{\Phi + \Phi_C\} + \tfrac{1}{2}\{\Phi - \Phi_C\}.$$

Now $\frac{1}{2}\{\Phi+\Phi_C\}$ is self-conjugate, and

$$\tfrac{1}{2}\{\Phi-\Phi_C\}=I\times[-\tfrac{1}{2}\Phi_\times].$$

(See No. 131.)

Rotations and Strains.

138. To illustrate the use of dyadics as operators, let us suppose that a body receives such a displacement that

$$\rho'=\Phi.\rho,$$

ρ and ρ' being the position-vectors of the same point of the body in its initial and subsequent positions. The same relation will hold of the vectors which unite any two points of the body in their initial and subsequent positions. For if ρ_1, ρ_2 are the original position-vectors of the points, and ρ_1', ρ_2' their final position-vectors, we have

$$\rho_1'=\Phi.\rho_1, \qquad \rho_2'=\Phi.\rho_2,$$

whence

$$\rho_2'-\rho_1'=\Phi.[\rho_2-\rho_1].$$

In the most general case, the body is said to receive a *homogeneous strain*. In special cases, the displacement reduces to a rotation. Lines in the body initially straight and parallel will be straight and parallel after the displacement, and surfaces initially plane and parallel will be plane and parallel after the displacement.

139. The vectors (σ, σ') which represent any plane surface in the body in its initial and final positions will be linear functions of each other. (This will appear, if we consider the four sides of a tetrahedron in the body.) To find the relation of the dyadics which express σ' as a function of σ, and ρ' as a function of ρ, let

$$\rho'=\{\alpha\lambda+\beta\mu+\gamma\nu\}.\rho.$$

Then, if we write λ', μ', ν' for the reciprocals of λ, μ, ν, the vectors λ', μ', ν' become by the strain α, β, γ. Therefore the surfaces $\mu'\times\nu'$, $\nu'\times\lambda'$, $\lambda'\times\mu'$ become $\beta\times\gamma$, $\gamma\times\alpha$, $\alpha\times\beta$. But $\mu'\times\nu'$, $\nu'\times\lambda'$, $\lambda'\times\mu'$ are the reciprocals of $\mu\times\nu$, $\nu\times\lambda$, $\lambda\times\mu$. The relation sought is therefore

$$\sigma'=\{\beta\times\gamma\,\mu\times\nu+\gamma\times\alpha\,\nu\times\lambda+\alpha\times\beta\,\lambda\times\mu\}.\sigma.$$

140. The volume $\lambda'.\mu'\times\nu'$ becomes by the strain $\alpha.\beta\times\gamma$. The unit of volume becomes therefore $(\alpha.\beta\times\gamma)(\lambda.\mu\times\nu)$.

Def.—It follows that the scalar product of the three antecedents multiplied by the scalar product of the three consequents of a dyadic expressed as a trinomial is independent of the particular form in which the dyadic is thus expressed. This quantity is the determinant of the coefficients of the nine terms of the form

$$aii+bij+\text{etc.},$$

into which the dyadic may be expanded. We shall call it the *determinant* of the dyadic, and shall denote it by the notation

$$|\Phi|$$

when the dyadic is expressed by a single letter.

If a dyadic is incomplete, its determinant is zero, and conversely.

The determinant of the product of any number of dyadics is equal to the product of their determinants. The determinant of the reciprocal of a dyadic is the reciprocal of the determinant of that dyadic. The determinants of a dyadic and its conjugate are equal.

The relation of the surfaces σ' and σ may be expressed by the equation

$$\sigma' = |\Phi| \Phi_C{}^{-1}.\sigma.^*$$

141. Let us now consider the different cases of rotation and strain as determined by the nature of the dyadic Φ.

If Φ is reducible to the form

$$i'i + j'j + k'k,$$

i, j, k, i', j', k' being normal systems of unit vectors (see No. 11), the body will suffer no change of form. For if

$$\rho = xi + yj + zk,$$

we shall have

$$\rho' = xi' + yj' + zk'.$$

Conversely, if the body suffers no change of form, the operating dyadic is reducible to the above form. In such cases, it appears from simple geometrical considerations that the displacement of the body may be produced by a rotation about a certain axis. A dyadic reducible to the form

$$i'i + j'j + k'k$$

may therefore be called a *versor*.

142. The conjugate operator evidently produces the reverse rotation. A versor, therefore, is the reciprocal of its conjugate.

Conversely, if a dyadic is the reciprocal of its conjugate, it is either a versor, or a versor multiplied by -1. For the dyadic may be expressed in the form

$$\alpha i + \beta j + \gamma k.$$

Its conjugate will be $\qquad i\alpha + j\beta + k\gamma.$

If these are reciprocals, we have

$$\{\alpha i + \beta j + \gamma k\}.\{i\alpha + j\beta + k\gamma\} = \alpha\alpha + \beta\beta + \gamma\gamma = I.$$

But this relation cannot subsist unless α, β, γ are reciprocals to themselves, i.e., unless they are mutually perpendicular unit-vectors. Therefore, they either are a normal system of unit-vectors, or will become such if their directions are reversed. Therefore, one of the dyadics

$$\alpha i + \beta j + \gamma k \quad \text{and} \quad -\alpha i - \beta j - \gamma k$$

is a versor.

* [See note on p. 90.]

The criterion of a versor may therefore be written

$$\Phi.\Phi_C = I, \quad \text{and} \quad |\Phi| = 1.$$

For the last equation we may substitute

$$|\Phi| > 0, \quad \text{or} \quad |\Phi| \gtrless -1.$$

It is evident that the resultant of successive finite rotations is obtained by multiplication of the versors.

143. If we take the axis of the rotation for the direction of i, i' will have the same direction, and the versor reduces to the form

$$ii + j'j + k'k,$$

in which i, j, k and i, j', k' are normal systems of unit vectors.

We may set

$$j' = \cos q\, j + \sin q\, k,$$

$$k' = \cos q\, k - \sin q\, j,$$

and the versor reduces to

$$ii + \cos q\, \{jj + kk\} + \sin q\, \{kj - jk\},$$

or

$$ii + \cos q\, \{I - ii\} + \sin q\, I \times i,$$

where q is the angle of rotation, measured from j toward k, if the versor is used as a prefactor.

144. When any versor Φ is used as a prefactor, the vector $-\Phi_\times$ will be parallel to the axis of rotation, and equal in magnitude to twice the sine of the angle of rotation measured counter-clockwise as seen from the direction in which the vector points. (This will appear if we suppose Φ to be represented in the form given in the last paragraph.) The scalar Φ_S will be equal to unity increased by twice the cosine of the same angle. Together, $-\Phi_\times$ and Φ_S determine the versor without ambiguity. If we set

$$\theta = \frac{-\Phi_\times}{1 + \Phi_S},$$

the magnitude of θ will be

$$\frac{2 \sin q}{2 + 2 \cos q} \quad \text{or} \quad \tan \tfrac{1}{2} q,$$

where q is measured counter-clockwise as seen from the direction in which θ points. This vector θ, which we may call the *vector semi-tangent of version*, determines the versor without ambiguity.

145. The versor Φ may be expressed in terms of θ in various ways. Since Φ (as prefactor) changes $a - \theta \times a$ into $a + \theta \times a$ (a being any vector), we have

$$\Phi = \{I + I \times \theta\}.\{I - I \times \theta\}^{-1}.$$

Again

$$\Phi = \frac{\theta\theta + \{I + I \times \theta\}^2}{1 + \theta.\theta} = \frac{(1 - \theta.\theta) I + 2\theta\theta + 2 I \times \theta}{1 + \theta.\theta},$$

as will be evident on considering separately in the expression $\Phi.\rho$ the components perpendicular and parallel to θ, or on substituting in

$$ii + \cos q\,(jj+kk) + \sin q\,(kj-jk)$$

for $\cos q$ and $\sin q$ their values in terms of $\tan \frac{1}{2}q$.

If we set, in either of these equations,

$$\theta = ai+bj+ck,$$

we obtain, on reduction, the formula

$$\Phi = \frac{\left\{\begin{array}{l}(1+a^2-b^2-c^2)ii+(2ab-2c)ij+(2ac+2b)ik \\ +(2ab+2c)ji+(1-a^2+b^2-c^2)jj+(2bc-2a)jk \\ +(2ac-2b)ki+(2bc+2a)kj+(1-a^2-b^2+c^2)kk\end{array}\right\}}{1+a^2+b^2+c^2},$$

in which the versor is expressed in terms of the rectangular components of the vector semitangent of version.

146. If α, β, γ are unit vectors, expressions of the form

$$2\alpha\alpha-\mathrm{I}, \qquad 2\beta\beta-\mathrm{I}, \qquad 2\gamma\gamma-\mathrm{I},$$

are biquadrantal versors. A product like

$$\{2\beta\beta-\mathrm{I}\}.\{2\alpha\alpha-\mathrm{I}\}$$

is a versor of which the axis is perpendicular to α and β, and the amount of rotation twice that which would carry α to β. It is evident that any versor may be thus expressed, and that either α or β may be given any direction perpendicular to the axis of rotation. If

$$\Phi = \{2\beta\beta-\mathrm{I}\}.\{2\alpha\alpha-\mathrm{I}\}, \quad \text{and} \quad \Psi = \{2\gamma\gamma-\mathrm{I}\}.\{2\beta\beta-\mathrm{I}\},$$

we have for the resultant of the successive rotations

$$\Psi.\Phi = \{2\gamma\gamma-\mathrm{I}\}.\{2\alpha\alpha-\mathrm{I}\}.$$

This may be applied to the composition of any two successive rotations, β being taken perpendicular to the two axes of rotation, and affords the means of determining the resultant rotation by construction on the surface of a sphere. It also furnishes a simple method of finding the relations of the vector semitangents of version for the versors Φ, Ψ, and $\Psi.\Phi$. Let

$$\theta_1 = \frac{-\Phi_\times}{1+\Phi_S}, \qquad \theta_2 = \frac{-\Psi_\times}{1+\Psi_S}, \qquad \theta_3 = \frac{-\{\Psi.\Phi\}_\times}{1+\{\Psi.\Phi\}_S}.$$

Then, since

$$\Phi = 4\,\alpha.\beta\,\beta\alpha - 2\alpha\alpha - 2\beta\beta + \mathrm{I},$$

$$\theta_1 = \frac{\alpha\times\beta}{\alpha.\beta},$$

which is moreover geometrically evident. In like manner,

$$\theta_2 = \frac{\beta\times\gamma}{\beta.\gamma}, \qquad \theta_3 = \frac{\alpha\times\gamma}{\alpha.\gamma}.$$

Therefore,

$$\theta_1 \times \theta_2 = \frac{[\alpha\times\beta]\times[\beta\times\gamma]}{\alpha.\beta\,\beta.\gamma} = \frac{\alpha\times\beta.\gamma\,\beta}{\alpha.\beta\,\beta.\gamma}$$

$$= \frac{\beta.\alpha\,\beta\times\gamma + \beta.\beta\,\gamma\times\alpha + \beta.\gamma\,\alpha\times\beta}{\alpha.\beta\,\beta.\gamma}.$$

(See No. 38.) That is,

$$\theta_1\times\theta_2 = \theta_2 - \frac{\alpha.\gamma}{\alpha.\beta\,\beta.\gamma}\theta_3 + \theta_1.$$

Also,

$$\theta_1.\theta_2 = \frac{\alpha\times\beta.\beta\times\gamma}{\alpha.\beta\,\beta.\gamma} = 1 - \frac{\alpha.\gamma}{\alpha.\beta\,\beta.\gamma}.$$

Hence,

$$\theta_1\times\theta_2 = \theta_2 - (1-\theta_1.\theta_2)\theta_3 + \theta_1,$$

$$\theta_3 = \frac{\theta_1 + \theta_2 + \theta_2\times\theta_1}{1-\theta_1.\theta_2},$$

which is the formula for the composition of successive finite rotations by means of their vector semitangents of version.

147. The versors just described constitute a particular class under the more general form

$$\alpha\alpha' + \cos q\,\{\beta\beta' + \gamma\gamma'\} + \sin q\,\{\gamma\beta' - \beta\gamma'\},$$

in which α, β, γ are any non-complanar vectors, and α', β', γ' their reciprocals. A dyadic of this form as a prefactor does not affect any vector parallel to α. Its effect on a vector in the β-γ plane will be best understood if we imagine an ellipse to be described of which β and γ are conjugate semi-diameters. If the vector to be operated on be a radius of this ellipse, we may evidently regard the ellipse with β, γ, and the other vector, as the projections of a circle with two perpendicular radii and one other radius. A little consideration will show that if the third radius of the circle is advanced an angle q, its projection in the ellipse will be advanced as required by the dyadic prefactor. The effect, therefore, of such a prefactor on a vector in the β-γ plane may be obtained as follows: Describe an ellipse of which β and γ are conjugate semi-diameters. Then describe a similar and similarly placed ellipse of which the vector to be operated on is a radius. The effect of the operator is to advance the radius in this ellipse, in the angular direction from β toward γ, over a segment which is to the total area of the ellipse as q is to 2π. When used as a postfactor, the properties of the dyadic are similar, but the axis of no motion and the planes of rotation are in general different.

Def.—Such dyadics we shall call *cyclic.*

The Nth power (N being any whole number) of such a dyadic is obtained by multiplying q by N. If q is of the form $2\pi N/M$ (N and M being any whole numbers) the Mth power of the dyadic will be an idemfactor. A cyclic dyadic, therefore, may be regarded as a root of

I, or at least capable of expression with any required degree of accuracy as a root of I.

It should be observed that the value of the above dyadic will not be altered by the substitution for α of any other parallel vector, or for β and γ of any other conjugate semi-diameters (which succeed one another in the same angular direction) of the same or any similar and similarly situated ellipse, with the changes which these substitutions require in the values of α', β', γ'. Or, to consider the same changes from another point of view, the value of the dyadic will not be altered by the substitution for α' of any other parallel vector or for β' and γ' of any other conjugate semi-diameters (which succeed one another in the same angular direction) of the same or any similar and similarly situated ellipse, with the changes which these substitutions require in the values of α, β, and γ, defined as reciprocals of α', β', γ'.

148. The strain represented by the equation

$$\rho' = \{aii + bjj + ckk\} . \rho$$

where a, b, c are positive scalars, may be described as consisting of three elongations (or contractions) parallel to the axes i, j, k, which are called the *principal axes of the strain*, and which have the property that their directions are not affected by the strain. The scalars a, b, c are called the *principal ratios of elongation*. (When one of these is less than unity, it represents a contraction.) The order of the three elongations is immaterial, since the original dyadic is equal to the product of the three dyadics

$$aii + jj + kk, \qquad ii + bjj + kk, \qquad ii + jj + ckk$$

taken in any order.

Def.—A dyadic which is reducible to this form we shall call a *right tensor*. The displacement represented by a right tensor is called a *pure strain*. A right tensor is evidently self-conjugate.

149. We have seen (No. 135) that every dyadic may be expressed in the form

$$\pm \{ai'i + bj'j + ck'k\},$$

where a, b, c are positive scalars. This is equivalent to

$$\pm \{ai'i' + bj'j' + ck'k'\} . \{i'i + j'j + k'k\}$$

and to

$$\pm \{i'i + j'j + k'k\} . \{aii + bjj + ckk\}.$$

Hence every dyadic may be expressed as the product of a versor and a right tensor with the scalar factor ± 1. The versor may precede or follow. It will be the same versor in either case, and the ratios of elongation will be the same; but the position of the principal axes of the tensor will differ in the two cases, either system being derived from the other by multiplication by the versor.

Def.—The displacement represented by the equation

$$\rho' = -\rho$$

is called *inversion.* The most general case of a homogeneous strain may therefore be produced by a pure strain and a rotation with or without inversion.

150. If

$$\Phi = a i' i + b j' j + c k' k,$$

$$\Phi . \Phi_C = a^2 i' i' + b^2 j' j' + c^2 k' k',$$

and

$$\Phi_C . \Phi = a^2 ii + b^2 jj + c^2 kk.$$

The general problem of the determination of the principal ratios and axes of strain for a given dyadic may thus be reduced to the case of a right tensor.

151. *Def.*—The effect of a prefactor of the form

$$a\alpha\alpha' + b\beta\beta' + c\gamma\gamma',$$

where a, b, c are positive or negative scalars, α, β, γ non-complanar vectors, and α', β', γ' their reciprocals, is to change α into $a\alpha$, β into $b\beta$, and γ into $c\gamma$. As a postfactor, the same dyadic will change α' into $a\alpha'$, β' into $b\beta'$, and γ' into $c\gamma'$. Dyadics which can be reduced to this form we shall call *tonic* (Gr. τείνω). The right tensor already described constitutes a particular case, distinguished by perpendicular axes and positive values of the coefficients a, b, c.

The value of the dyadic is evidently not affected by substituting vectors of different lengths but the same or opposite directions for α, β, γ, with the necessary changes in the values of α', β', γ', defined as reciprocals of α, β, γ. But, except this change, if a, b, c are unequal, the dyadic can be expressed only in one way in the above form. If, however, two of these coefficients are equal, say a and b, any two non-collinear vectors in the α-β plane may be substituted for α and β, or, if the three coefficients are equal, any three non-complanar vectors may be substituted for α, β, γ.

152. Tonics having the same axes (determined by the directions of α, β, γ) are homologous, and their multiplication is effected by multiplying their coefficients. Thus,

$$\{a_1\alpha\alpha' + b_1\beta\beta' + c_1\gamma\gamma'\}.\{a_2\alpha\alpha' + b_2\beta\beta' + c_2\gamma\gamma'\}$$
$$= \{a_1a_2\alpha\alpha' + b_1b_2\beta\beta' + c_1c_2\gamma\gamma'\}.$$

Hence, division of such dyadics is effected by division of their coefficients. A tonic of which the three coefficients a, b, c are unequal, is homologous only with such dyadics as can be obtained by varying the coefficients.

153. The effect of a prefactor of the form

$$a\alpha\alpha' + b\{\beta\beta' + \gamma\gamma'\} + c\{\gamma\beta' - \beta\gamma'\},$$

or

$$a\alpha\alpha' + p\cos q\{\beta\beta' + \gamma\gamma'\} + p\sin q\{\gamma\beta' - \beta\gamma'\},$$

where α', β', γ' are the reciprocals of α, β, γ, and a, b, c, p, and q are scalars, of which p is positive, will be most evident if we resolve it into the factors

$$a\alpha\alpha'+\beta\beta'+\gamma\gamma',$$

$$\alpha\alpha'+p\beta\beta'+p\gamma\gamma',$$

$$\alpha\alpha'+\cos q\{\beta\beta'+\gamma\gamma'\}+\sin q\{\gamma\beta'-\beta\gamma'\},$$

of which the order is immaterial, and if we suppose the vector on which we operate to be resolved into two factors, one parallel to α, and the other in the β-γ plane. The effect of the first factor is to multiply by a the component parallel to α, without affecting the other. The effect of the second is to multiply by p the component in the β-γ plane without affecting the other. The effect of the third is to give the component in the β-γ plane the kind of elliptic rotation described in No. 147.

The effect of the same dyadic as a postfactor is of the same nature.

The value of the dyadic is not affected by the substitution for α of another vector having the same direction, nor by the substitution for β and γ of two other conjugate semi-diameters of the same or a similar and similarly situated ellipse, and which follow one another in the same angular direction.

Def.—Such dyadics we shall call *cyclotonic*.

154. Cyclotonics which are reducible to the same form except with respect to the values of a, p, and q are homologous. They are multiplied by multiplying the values of a, and also those of p, and adding those of q. Thus, the product of

$$a_1\alpha\alpha'+p_1\cos q_1\{\beta\beta'+\gamma\gamma'\}+p_1\sin q_1\{\gamma\beta'-\beta\gamma'\}$$

and

$$a_2\alpha\alpha'+p_2\cos q_2\{\beta\beta'+\gamma\gamma'\}+p_2\sin q_2\{\gamma\beta'-\beta\gamma'\}$$

is

$$a_1a_2\alpha\alpha'+p_1p_2\cos(q_1+q_2)\{\beta\beta'+\gamma\gamma'\}$$
$$+p_1p_2\sin(q_1+q_2)\{\gamma\beta'-\beta\gamma'\}.$$

A dyadic of this form, in which the value of q is not zero, or the product of π and a positive or negative integer, is homologous only with such dyadics as are obtained by varying the values of a, p, and q.

155. In general, any dyadic may be reduced to the form either of a tonic or of a cyclotonic. (The exceptions are such as are made by the limiting cases.) We may show this, and also indicate how the reduction may be made, as follows. Let Φ be any dyadic. We have first to show that there is at least one direction of ρ for which

$$\Phi.\rho=a\rho.$$

This equation is equivalent to

$$\Phi.\rho-a\rho=0,$$

or,

$$\{\Phi-a\mathrm{I}\}.\rho=0.$$

That is, $\Phi - a\mathrm{I}$ is a planar dyadic, which may be expressed by the equation

$$|\Phi - a\mathrm{I}| = 0.$$

(See No. 140.) Let

$$\Phi = \lambda i + \mu j + \nu k;$$

the equation becomes

$$|[\lambda - ai]i + [\mu - aj]j + [\nu - ak]k| = 0,$$

or,

$$[\lambda - ai] \times [\mu - aj] . [\nu - ak] = 0,$$

or, $a^3 - (i.\lambda + j.\mu + k.\nu)a^2 + (i.\mu\times\nu + j.\nu\times\lambda + k.\lambda\times\mu)a - \lambda\times\mu.\nu = 0.$

This may be written

$$a^3 - \Phi_S a^2 + \{\Phi^{-1}\}_S |\Phi| a - |\Phi| = 0.*$$

Now if the dyadic Φ is given in any form, the scalars

$$\Phi_S, \quad \{\Phi^{-1}\}_S, \quad |\Phi|$$

are easily determined. We have therefore a cubic equation in a, for which we can find at least one and perhaps three roots. That is, we can find at least one value of a, and perhaps three, which will satisfy the equation

$$|\Phi - a\mathrm{I}| = 0.$$

By substitution of such a value, $\Phi - a\mathrm{I}$ becomes a planar dyadic, the planes of which may be easily determined.† Let α be a vector normal to the plane of the consequents. Then

$$\{\Phi - a\mathrm{I}\}.\alpha = 0,$$

$$\Phi.\alpha = a\alpha.$$

If Φ is a tonic, we may obtain three equations of this kind, say

$$\Phi.\alpha = a\alpha, \qquad \Phi.\beta = b\beta, \qquad \Phi.\gamma = c\gamma,$$

in which α, β, γ are not complanar. Hence (by No. 108),

$$\Phi = a\alpha\alpha' + b\beta\beta' + c\gamma\gamma',$$

where α', β', γ' are the reciprocals of α, β, γ.

In any case, we may suppose a to have the same sign as $|\Phi|$, since the cubic equation must have such a root. Let α (as before) be normal to the plane of the consequents of the planar $\Phi - a\mathrm{I}$, and α' normal to the plane of the antecedents, the lengths of α and α' being such that $\alpha.\alpha' = 1$.‡ Let β be any vector normal to α', and such that $\Phi.\beta$ is not parallel to β. (The case in which $\Phi.\beta$ is always parallel to β, if β is perpendicular to α', is evidently that of a tonic, and needs no farther discussion.) $\{\Phi - a\mathrm{I}\}.\beta$ and therefore $\Phi.\beta$ will be perpendicular to α'. The same will be true of $\Phi^2.\beta$. Now (by No. 140)

$$[\Phi.\alpha].[\Phi^2.\beta]\times[\Phi.\beta] = |\Phi|\,\alpha.[\Phi.\beta]\times\beta,$$

that is,

$$a\alpha.[\Phi^2.\beta]\times[\Phi.\beta] = |\Phi|\,\alpha.[\Phi.\beta]\times\beta.$$

---

* [See note on p. 90.]

† In particular cases, $\Phi - a\mathrm{I}$ may reduce to a linear dyadic, or to zero. These, however, will present no difficulties to the student.

‡ For the case in which the two planes are perpendicular to each other, see No. 157.

Hence, since $[\Phi^2.\beta]\times[\Phi.\beta]$ and $[\Phi.\beta]\times\beta$ are parallel,

$$a[\Phi^2.\beta]\times[\Phi.\beta]=|\Phi|\,[\Phi.\beta]\times\beta.$$

Since $a^{-1}|\Phi|$ is positive, we may set

$$p^2=a^{-1}|\Phi|.$$

If we also set

$$\beta_1=p^{-1}\Phi.\beta, \qquad \beta_2=p^{-2}\Phi^2.\beta, \quad \text{etc.},$$
$$\beta_{-1}=p\Phi^{-1}.\beta, \qquad \beta_{-2}=p^2\Phi^{-2}.\beta, \quad \text{etc.},$$

the vectors β, β_1, β_2, etc., β_{-1}, β_{-2}, etc., will all lie in the plane perpendicular to a', and we shall have

$$\beta_2\times\beta_1=\beta_1\times\beta,$$
$$[\beta_2+\beta]\times\beta_1=0.$$

We may therefore set $\qquad \beta_2+\beta=2n\beta_1.$

Multiplying by $p^{-1}\Phi$, and by $p\Phi^{-1}$,

$$\beta_3+\beta_1=2n\beta_2, \qquad \beta_4+\beta_2=2n\beta_3, \quad \text{etc.},$$
$$\beta_1+\beta_{-1}=2n\beta, \qquad \beta+\beta_{-2}=2n\beta_{-1}, \quad \text{etc.}$$

Now, if $n>1$, and we lay off from a common origin the vectors

$$\beta,\ \beta_1,\ \beta_2,\ \text{etc.};\ \ \beta_{-1},\ \beta_{-2},\ \text{etc.},$$

the broken line joining the termini of these vectors will be convex toward the origin. All these vectors must therefore lie between two limiting lines, which may be drawn from the origin, and which may be described as having the directions of β_∞ and $\beta_{-\infty}$.* A vector having either of these directions is unaffected in direction by multiplication by Φ. In this case, therefore, Φ is a tonic. If $n<-1$ we may obtain the same result by considering the vectors

$$\beta,\ -\beta_1,\ \beta_2,\ -\beta_3,\ \beta_4,\ \text{etc.},\ \ -\beta_{-1},\ \beta_{-2},\ -\beta_{-3},\ \text{etc.},$$

except that a vector in the limiting directions will be reversed in direction by multiplication by Φ, which implies that the two corresponding coefficients of the tonic are negative.

If $1>n>-1$,† we may set

$$n=\cos q.$$

Then $\qquad \beta_{-1}+\beta_1=2\cos q\,\beta.$

Let us now determine γ by the equation

$$\beta_1=\cos q\,\beta+\sin q\,\gamma.$$

This gives $\qquad \beta_{-1}=\cos q\,\beta-\sin q\,\gamma.$

Now a' is one of the reciprocals of a, β, and γ. Let β' and γ' be the others. If we set

$$\Psi=\cos q\,\{\beta\beta'+\gamma\gamma'\}+\sin q\,\{\gamma\beta'-\beta\gamma'\},$$

we have $\qquad \Psi.a=0, \qquad \Psi.\beta=\beta_1, \qquad \Psi.\beta_{-1}=\beta.$

---

* The termini of the vectors will in fact lie on a hyperbola.

† For the limiting cases, in which $n=1$, or $n=-1$, see No. 156.

Therefore, since
$$\{a\alpha\alpha'+p\Psi\}.\alpha = a\alpha = \Phi.\alpha,$$
$$\{a\alpha\alpha'+p\Psi\}.\beta = p\beta_1 = \Phi.\beta,$$
$$\{a\alpha\alpha'+p\Psi\}.\beta_{-1} = p\beta = \Phi.\beta_{-1},$$

it follows (by No. 108) that

$$\Phi = a\alpha\alpha'+p\Psi = a\alpha\alpha' + p\cos q\{\beta\beta'+\gamma\gamma'\} + p\sin q\{\gamma\beta'-\beta\gamma'\}.$$

156. It will be sufficient to indicate (without demonstration) the forms of dyadics which belong to the particular cases which have been passed over in the preceding paragraph, so far as they present any notable peculiarities.

If $n = \pm 1$ (page 72), the dyadic may be reduced to the form

$$a\alpha\alpha'+b\{\beta\beta'+\gamma\gamma'\}+bc\beta\gamma',$$

where α, β, γ are three non-complanar vectors, α', β', γ' their reciprocals, and a, b, c positive or negative scalars. The effect of this as an operator, will be evident if we resolve it into the three homologous factors

$$a\alpha\alpha'+\beta\beta'+\gamma\gamma',$$
$$\alpha\alpha'+b\{\beta\beta'+\gamma\gamma'\},$$
$$\alpha\alpha'+\beta\beta'+\gamma\gamma'+c\beta\gamma'.$$

The displacement due to the last factor may be called a *simple shear.* It consists (when the dyadic is used as prefactor) of a motion parallel to β, and proportioned to the distance from the α-β plane. This factor may be called a *shearer.*

This dyadic is homologous with such as are obtained by varying the values of a, b, c, and only with such, when the values of a and b are different, and that of c other than zero.

157. If the planar $\Phi - a\mathrm{I}$ (page 71) has perpendicular planes, there may be another value of a, of the same sign as $|\Phi|$, which will give a planar which has not perpendicular planes. When this is not the case, the dyadic may always be reduced to the form

$$a\{\alpha\alpha'+\beta\beta'+\gamma\gamma'\}+ab\{\alpha\beta'+\beta\gamma'\}+ac\alpha\gamma',$$

where α, β, γ are three non-complanar vectors, α', β', γ', their reciprocals, and a, b, c, positive or negative scalars. This may be resolved into the homologous factors

$$a\mathrm{I} \quad\text{and}\quad \mathrm{I}+b\{\alpha\beta'+\beta\gamma'\}+c\alpha\gamma'.$$

The displacement due to the last factor may be called a *complex shear.* It consists (when the dyadic is used as prefactor) of a motion parallel to α which is proportional to the distance from the α-γ plane, together with a motion parallel to $b\beta+c\alpha$ which is proportional to the distance from the α-β plane. This factor may be called a *complex shearer.*

This dyadic is homologous with such as are obtained by varying the values of a, b, c, and only such, unless $b=0$.

It is always possible to take three mutually perpendicular vectors for α, β, and γ; or, if it be preferred, to take such values for these vectors as shall make the term containing c vanish.

158. The dyadics described in the two last paragraphs may be called *shearing dyadics.*

The criterion of a shearer is

$$\{\Phi-I\}^3=0, \qquad \Phi-I\neq 0.$$

The criterion of a simple shearer is

$$\{\Phi-I\}^2=0, \qquad \Phi-I\neq 0.$$

The criterion of a complex shearer is

$$\{\Phi-I\}^3=0, \qquad \{\Phi-I\}^2\neq 0.$$

NOTE.—If a dyadic Φ is a linear function of a vector ρ (the term *linear* being used in the same sense as in No. 105), we may represent the relation by an equation of the form

$$\Phi=\alpha\beta\,\gamma.\rho+\epsilon\zeta\,\eta.\rho+\text{etc.},$$

or

$$\Phi=\{\alpha\beta\gamma+\epsilon\zeta\eta+\text{etc.}\}.\rho,$$

where the expression in the braces may be called a *triadic polynomial*, and a single term $\alpha\beta\gamma$ a *triad*, or the indeterminate product of the three vectors α, β, γ. We are thus led successively to the consideration of higher orders of indeterminate products of vectors, *triads*, *tetrads*, etc., in general *polyads*, and of polynomials consisting of such terms, *triadics*, *tetradics*, etc., in general *polyadics*. But the development of the subject in this direction lies beyond our present purpose.

It may sometimes be convenient to use notations like

$$\frac{\lambda,\ \mu,\ \nu}{|\alpha,\ \beta,\ \gamma} \text{ and } \frac{\lambda,\ \mu,\ \nu}{\alpha,\ \beta,\ \gamma|}$$

to represent the conjugate dyadics which, the first as prefactor, and the second as postfactor, change α, β, γ into λ, μ, ν, respectively. In the notations of the preceding chapter these would be written

$$\lambda\alpha'+\mu\beta'+\nu\gamma' \text{ and } \alpha'\lambda+\beta'\mu+\gamma'\nu$$

respectively, α', β', γ' denoting the reciprocals of α, β, γ. If τ is a linear function of ρ, the dyadics which as prefactor and postfactor change ρ into τ may be written respectively

$$\frac{\tau}{|\rho} \text{ and } \frac{\tau}{\rho|}.$$

If τ is any function of ρ, the dyadics which as prefactor and postfactor change $d\rho$ into $d\tau$ may be written respectively

$$\frac{d\tau}{|d\rho} \text{ and } \frac{d\tau}{d\rho|}.$$

In the notation of the following chapter the second of these (when ρ denotes a position-vector) would be written $\nabla\tau$. The triadic which as prefactor changes $d\rho$ into $\frac{d\tau}{|d\rho}$ may be written $\frac{d^2\tau}{|d\rho^2}$, and that which as postfactor changes $d\rho$ into $\frac{d\tau}{d\rho|}$ may be written $\frac{d^2\tau}{d\rho^2|}$. The latter would be written $\nabla\nabla\tau$ in the notations of the following chapter.

CHAPTER IV.

(SUPPLEMENTARY TO CHAPTER II.)

CONCERNING THE DIFFERENTIAL AND INTEGRAL CALCULUS OF VECTORS.

159. If ω is a vector having continuously varying values in space, and ρ the vector determining the position of a point, we may set

$$\rho = xi + yj + zk,$$

$$d\rho = dx\, i + dy\, j + dz\, k,$$

and regard ω as a function of ρ, or of x, y, and z. Then,

$$d\omega = dx \frac{d\omega}{dx} + dy \frac{d\omega}{dy} + dz \frac{d\omega}{dz},$$

that is,

$$d\omega = d\rho . \left\{ i \frac{d\omega}{dx} + j \frac{d\omega}{dy} + k \frac{d\omega}{dz} \right\}.$$

If we set

$$\nabla \omega = i \frac{d\omega}{dx} + j \frac{d\omega}{dy} + k \frac{d\omega}{dz},$$

$$d\omega = d\rho . \nabla \omega.$$

Here ∇ stands for

$$i \frac{d}{dx} + j \frac{d}{dy} + k \frac{d}{dz},$$

exactly as in No. 52, except that it is here applied to a vector and produces a dyadic, while in the former case it was applied to a scalar and produced a vector. The dyadic $\nabla\omega$ represents the nine differential coefficients of the three components of ω with respect to x, y, and z, just as the vector ∇u (where u is a scalar function of ρ) represents the three differential coefficients of the scalar u with respect to x, y, and z.

It is evident that the expressions $\nabla . \omega$ and $\nabla \times \omega$ already defined (No. 54) are equivalent to $\{\nabla\omega\}_S$ and $\{\nabla\omega\}_\times$.

160. An important case is that in which the vector operated on is of the form ∇u. We have then

$$d\nabla u = d\rho . \nabla\nabla u,$$

where

$$\nabla\nabla u = \left\{ \begin{array}{lll} \dfrac{d^2u}{dx^2} ii & + \dfrac{d^2u}{dx\,dy} ij & + \dfrac{d^2u}{dx\,dz} ik \\ + \dfrac{d^2u}{dy\,dx} ji & + \dfrac{d^2u}{dy^2} jj & + \dfrac{d^2u}{dy\,dz} jk \\ + \dfrac{d^2u}{dz\,dx} ki & + \dfrac{d^2u}{dz\,dy} kj & + \dfrac{d^2u}{dz^2} kk. \end{array} \right\}$$

This dyadic, which is evidently self-conjugate, represents the six differential coefficients of the second order of u with respect to x, y, and z.*

161. The operators $\nabla\times$ and $\nabla.$ may be applied to dyadics in a manner entirely analogous to their use with scalars. Thus we may define $\nabla\times\Phi$ and $\nabla.\Phi$ by the equations

$$\nabla\times\Phi = i\times\frac{d\Phi}{dx} + j\times\frac{d\Phi}{dy} + k\times\frac{d\Phi}{dz}$$

$$\nabla.\Phi = i.\frac{d\Phi}{dx} + j.\frac{d\Phi}{dy} + k.\frac{d\Phi}{dz}.$$

Then, if $$\Phi = \alpha i + \beta j + \gamma k,$$

$$\nabla\times\Phi = \nabla\times\alpha i + \nabla\times\beta j + \nabla\times\gamma k.$$

$$\nabla.\Phi = \nabla.\alpha i + \nabla.\beta j + \nabla.\gamma k.$$

Or, if $$\Phi = i\alpha + j\beta + k\gamma,$$

$$\nabla\times\Phi = i\left[\frac{d\gamma}{dy} - \frac{d\beta}{dz}\right] + j\left[\frac{d\alpha}{dz} - \frac{d\gamma}{dx}\right] + k\left[\frac{d\beta}{dx} - \frac{d\alpha}{dy}\right],$$

$$\nabla.\Phi = \frac{d\alpha}{dx} + \frac{d\beta}{dy} + \frac{d\gamma}{dz}.$$

162. We may now regard $\nabla.\nabla$ in expressions like $\nabla.\nabla\omega$ as representing two successive operations, the result of which will be

$$\frac{d^2\omega}{dx^2} + \frac{d^2\omega}{dy^2} + \frac{d^2\omega}{dz^2}$$

in accordance with the definition of No. 70. We may also write $\nabla.\nabla\Phi$ for

$$\frac{d^2\Phi}{dx^2} + \frac{d^2\Phi}{dy^2} + \frac{d^2\Phi}{dz^2},$$

although in this case we cannot regard $\nabla.\nabla$ as representing two successive operations until we have defined $\nabla\Phi$.†

That $\nabla.\nabla\Phi = \nabla\nabla.\Phi - \nabla\times\nabla\times\Phi$ will be evident if we suppose Φ to be expressed in the form $\alpha i + \beta j + \gamma k$. (See No. 71.)

163. We have already seen that

$$u'' - u' = \int d\rho.\nabla u,$$

where u' and u'' denote the values of u at the beginning and the end of the line to which the integral relates. The same relation will hold for a vector; i.e.,

$$\omega'' - \omega' = \int d\rho.\nabla\omega.$$

* We might proceed to higher steps in differentiation by means of the triadics $\nabla\nabla\omega$, $\nabla\nabla\nabla u$, the tetradics $\nabla\nabla\nabla\omega$, $\nabla\nabla\nabla\nabla u$, etc. See note on page 74. In like manner a dyadic function of position in space (Φ) might be differentiated by means of the triadic $\nabla\Phi$, the tetradic $\nabla\nabla\Phi$, etc.

† See footnote to No. 160.

164. The following equations between surface-integrals for a closed surface and volume-integrals for the space enclosed seem worthy of mention. One or two have already been given, and are here repeated for the sake of comparison.

$$\iint d\sigma\, u = \iiint dv\, \nabla u, \tag{1}$$
$$\iint d\sigma\, \omega = \iiint dv\, \nabla \omega, \tag{2}$$
$$\iint d\sigma . \omega = \iiint dv\, \nabla . \omega, \tag{3}$$
$$\iint d\sigma . \Phi = \iiint dv\, \nabla . \Phi, \tag{4}$$
$$\iint d\sigma \times \omega = \iiint dv\, \nabla \times \omega, \tag{5}$$
$$\iint d\sigma \times \Phi = \iiint dv\, \nabla \times \Phi. \tag{6}$$

It may aid the memory of the student to observe that the transformation may be effected in each case by substituting $\iiint dv\, \nabla$ for $\iint d\sigma$.

165. The following equations between line-integrals for a closed line and surface-integrals for any surface bounded by the line, may also be mentioned. (One of these has already been given. See No. 60.)

$$\int d\rho\, u = \iint d\sigma \times \nabla u, \tag{1}$$
$$\int d\rho\, \omega = \iint d\sigma \times \nabla \omega, \tag{2}$$
$$\int d\rho . \omega = \iint d\sigma . \nabla \times \omega, \tag{3}$$
$$\int d\rho . \Phi = \iint d\sigma . \nabla \times \Phi, \tag{4}$$
$$\int d\rho \times \omega = \iint \nabla \omega . d\sigma - \iint d\sigma \nabla . \omega. \tag{5}$$

These transformations may be effected by substituting $\iint [d\sigma \times \nabla]$ for $\int d\rho$. The brackets are here introduced to indicate that the multiplication of $d\sigma$ with the i, j, k implied in ∇ is to be performed before any other multiplication which may be required by a subsequent sign. (This notation is not recommended for ordinary use, but only suggested as a mnemonic artifice.)

166. To the equations in No. 65 may be added many others, as,

$$\nabla [u\omega] = \nabla u\, \omega + u \nabla \omega, \tag{1}$$
$$\nabla [\tau \times \omega] = \nabla \tau \times \omega - \nabla \omega \times \tau, \tag{2}$$
$$\nabla \times [\tau \times \omega] = \omega . \nabla \tau - \nabla . \tau \omega - \tau . \nabla \omega + \nabla . \omega \tau, \tag{3}$$
$$\nabla (\tau . \omega) = \nabla \tau . \omega + \nabla \omega . \tau, \tag{4}$$
$$\nabla . \{\tau \omega\} = \nabla . \tau \omega + \tau . \nabla \omega, \tag{5}$$
$$\nabla \times \{\tau \omega\} = \nabla \times \tau \omega - \tau \times \nabla \omega, \tag{6}$$
$$\nabla . \{u \Phi\} = \nabla u . \Phi + u \nabla . \Phi, \tag{7}$$

etc.

The principle in all these cases is that if we have one of the operators ∇, $\nabla .$, $\nabla \times$ prefixed to a product of any kind, and we make any transformation of the expression which would be allowable if the ∇ were a vector (viz., by changes in the order of the factors, in the signs of multiplication, in the parentheses written or implied, etc.), by which changes the ∇ is brought into connection with one particular factor, the expression thus transformed will represent the part of the value of the original expression which results from the variation of that factor.

167. From the relations indicated in the last four paragraphs, may be obtained directly a great number of transformations of definite integrals similar to those given in Nos. 74-77, and corresponding to those known in the scalar calculus by the name of *integration by parts.*

168. The student will now find no difficulty in generalizing the integrations of differential equations given in Nos. 78-89 by applying to vectors those which relate to scalars, and to dyadics those which relate to vectors.

169. The propositions in No. 90 relating to minimum values of the volume-integral $\iiint u\omega.\omega\, dv$ may be generalized by substituting $\omega.\Phi.\omega$ for $u\omega.\omega$, Φ being a given dyadic function of position in space.

170. The theory of the integrals which have been called potentials, Newtonians, etc. (see Nos. 91-102) may be extended to cases in which the operand is a vector instead of a scalar or a dyadic instead of a vector. So far as the demonstrations are concerned, the case of a vector may be reduced to that of a scalar by considering separately its three components, and the case of a dyadic may be reduced to that of a vector, by supposing the dyadic expressed in the form $\phi i + \chi j + \omega k$ and considering each of these terms separately.

CHAPTER V.

CONCERNING TRANSCENDENTAL FUNCTIONS OF DYADICS.

171. *Def.*—The *exponential function*, the *sine* and the *cosine* of a dyadic may be defined by infinite series, exactly as the corresponding functions in scalar analysis, viz.,

$$e^{\Phi} = \mathrm{I} + \Phi + \tfrac{1}{2}\Phi^2 + \tfrac{1}{2.3}\Phi^3 + \text{etc.},$$

$$\sin\Phi = \Phi - \tfrac{1}{2.3}\Phi^3 + \tfrac{1}{2.3.4.5}\Phi^5 - \text{etc.},$$

$$\cos\Phi = \mathrm{I} - \tfrac{1}{2}\Phi^2 + \tfrac{1}{2.3.4}\Phi^4 - \text{etc.}$$

These series are always convergent. For every value of Φ there is one and only one value of each of these functions. The exponential function may also be defined as the limit of the expression

$$\left(\mathrm{I} + \frac{\Phi}{\mathrm{N}}\right)^{\mathrm{N}},$$

when N, which is a whole number, is increased indefinitely. That this definition is equivalent to the preceding, will appear if the expression is expanded by the binomial theorem, which is evidently applicable in a case of this kind.

These functions of Φ are homologous with Φ.

172. We may define the logarithm as the function which is the inverse of the exponential, so that the equations

$$e^{\Psi} = \Phi,$$
$$\Psi = \log \Phi,$$

are equivalent, leaving it undetermined for the present whether every dyadic has a logarithm, and whether a dyadic can have more than one.

173. It follows at once from the second definition of the exponential function that, if Φ and Ψ are homologous,

$$e^{\Phi} . e^{\Psi} = e^{\Phi + \Psi},$$

and that, if T is a positive or negative whole number,

$$\{e^{\Phi}\}^{\mathrm{T}} = e^{\mathrm{T}\Phi}.$$

174. If Ξ and Φ are homologous dyadics, and such that

$$\Xi^2 . \Phi = -\Phi,$$

the definitions of No. 171 give immediately

$$e^{\Xi . \Phi} = \cos \Phi + \Xi \sin \Phi,$$
$$e^{-\Xi . \Phi} = \cos \Phi - \Xi \sin \Phi,$$

whence

$$\cos \Phi = \tfrac{1}{2}\{e^{\Xi\Phi} + e^{-\Xi\Phi}\},$$
$$\sin \Phi = -\tfrac{1}{2}\Xi\{e^{\Xi\Phi} - e^{-\Xi\Phi}\}.$$

175. If $\Phi.\Psi = \Psi.\Phi = 0$,

$$\{\Phi + \Psi\}^2 = \Phi^2 + \Psi^2, \qquad \{\Phi + \Psi\}^3 = \Phi^3 + \Psi^3, \text{ etc.}$$

Therefore

$$e^{\Phi + \Psi} = e^{\Phi} + e^{\Psi} - \mathrm{I},$$
$$\cos\{\Phi + \Psi\} = \cos \Phi + \cos \Psi - \mathrm{I},$$
$$\sin\{\Phi + \Psi\} = \sin \Phi + \sin \Psi.$$

176.

$$|e^{\Phi}| = e^{\Phi_S}.$$

For the first member of this equation is the limit of

$$|\{\mathrm{I} + \mathrm{N}^{-1}\Phi\}^{\mathrm{N}}|, \quad \text{that is, of} \quad |\mathrm{I} + \mathrm{N}^{-1}\Phi|^{\mathrm{N}}.$$

If we set $\Phi = \alpha i + \beta j + \gamma k$, the limit becomes that of

$$(1 + \mathrm{N}^{-1}\alpha . i + \mathrm{N}^{-1}\beta . j + \mathrm{N}^{-1}\gamma . k)^{\mathrm{N}}, \quad \text{or} \quad (1 + \mathrm{N}^{-1}\Phi_S)^{\mathrm{N}},$$

the limit of which is the second member of the equation to be proved.

177. By the definition of exponentials, the expression

$$e^{q\{kj - jk\}}$$

represents the limit of

$$\{\mathrm{I} + q\mathrm{N}^{-1}\{kj - jk\}\}^{\mathrm{N}}.$$

Now $I + qN^{-1}\{kj - jk\}$ evidently represents a versor having the axis i and the infinitesimal angle of version qN^{-1}. Hence the above exponential represents a versor having the same axis and the angle of version q. If we set $qi = \omega$, the exponential may be written

$$e^{I \times \omega}.$$

Such an expression therefore represents a versor. The axis and direction of rotation are determined by the direction of ω, and the angle of rotation is equal to the magnitude of ω. The value of the versor will not be affected by increasing or diminishing the magnitude of ω by 2π.

178. If, as in No. 151,

$$\Phi = a\alpha\alpha' + b\beta\beta' + c\gamma\gamma',$$

the definitions of No. 171 give

$$e^{\Phi} = e^{a}\alpha\alpha' + e^{b}\beta\beta' + e^{c}\gamma\gamma',$$

$$\cos\Phi = \cos a\,\alpha\alpha' + \cos b\,\beta\beta' + \cos c\,\gamma\gamma',$$

$$\sin\Phi = \sin a\,\alpha\alpha' + \sin b\,\beta\beta' + \sin c\,\gamma\gamma'.$$

If a, b, c are positive and unequal, we may add, by No. 172,

$$\log\Phi = \log a\,\alpha\alpha' + \log b\,\beta\beta' + \log c\,\gamma\gamma'.$$

179. If, as in No. 153,

$$\Phi = a\alpha\alpha' + b\{\beta\beta' + \gamma\gamma'\} + c\{\gamma\beta' - \beta\gamma'\}$$
$$= a\alpha\alpha' + p\cos q\,\{\beta\beta' + \gamma\gamma'\} + p\sin q\,\{\gamma\beta' - \beta\gamma'\},$$

we have by No. 173 $\quad e^{\Phi} = e^{a\alpha\alpha'} . e^{b\{\beta\beta' + \gamma\gamma'\}} . e^{c\{\gamma\beta' - \beta\gamma'\}}.$

But

$$e^{a\alpha\alpha'} = e^{a}\alpha\alpha' + \beta\beta' + \gamma\gamma',$$

$$e^{b\{\beta\beta' + \gamma\gamma'\}} = \alpha\alpha' + e^{b}\{\beta\beta' + \gamma\gamma'\},$$

$$e^{c\{\gamma\beta' - \beta\gamma'\}} = \alpha\alpha' + \cos c\,\{\beta\beta' + \gamma\gamma'\} + \sin c\,\{\gamma\beta' - \beta\gamma'\}.$$

Therefore, $\quad e^{\Phi} = e^{a}\alpha\alpha' + e^{b}\cos c\,\{\beta\beta' + \gamma\gamma'\} + e^{b}\sin c\,\{\gamma\beta' - \beta\gamma'\}.$

Hence, if a is positive,

$$\log\Phi = \log a\,\alpha\alpha' + \log p\,\{\beta\beta' + \gamma\gamma'\} + q\,\{\gamma\beta' - \beta\gamma'\}.$$

Since the value of Φ is not affected by increasing or diminishing q by 2π, the function $\log\Phi$ is many-valued.

To find the value of $\cos\Phi$ and $\sin\Phi$, let us set

$$\Theta = b\,\{\beta\beta' + \gamma\gamma'\} + c\,\{\gamma\beta' - \beta\gamma'\},$$

$$\Xi = \gamma\beta' - \beta\gamma'.$$

Then, by No, 175,

$$\cos\Phi = \cos\{a\alpha\alpha'\} + \cos\Theta - I.$$

But $\quad \cos\{a\alpha\alpha'\} - I = \cos a\alpha\alpha' - \alpha\alpha'.$

Therefore, $\quad \cos\Phi = \cos a\alpha\alpha' - \alpha\alpha' + \cos\Theta.$

Now, by No. 174,

$$\cos\Theta = \tfrac{1}{2}\{e^{\Xi.\Theta} + e^{-\Xi.\Theta}\}.$$

Since

$$\Xi.\Theta = -c\{\beta\beta' + \gamma\gamma'\} + b\{\gamma\beta' - \beta\gamma'\},$$

$$e^{\Xi.\Theta} = \alpha\alpha' + e^{-c}\cos b\,\{\beta\beta' + \gamma\gamma'\} + e^{-c}\sin b\,\{\gamma\beta' - \beta\gamma'\},$$

$$e^{-\Xi.\Theta} = \alpha\alpha' + e^{c}\cos b\,\{\beta\beta' + \gamma\gamma'\} - e^{c}\sin b\,\{\gamma\beta' - \beta\gamma'\}.$$

Therefore

$$\cos\Theta = \alpha\alpha' + \tfrac{1}{2}(e^{c} + e^{-c})\cos b\,\{\beta\beta' + \gamma\gamma'\} - \tfrac{1}{2}(e^{c} - e^{-c})\sin b\,\{\gamma\beta' - \beta\gamma'\},$$

and

$$\cos\Phi = \cos a\,\alpha\alpha' + \tfrac{1}{2}(e^{c} + e^{-c})\cos b\,\{\beta\beta' + \gamma\gamma'\} - \tfrac{1}{2}(e^{c} - e^{-c})\sin b\,\{\gamma\beta' - \beta\gamma'\}.$$

In like manner we find

$$\sin\Phi = \sin a\,\alpha\alpha' + \tfrac{1}{2}(e^{c} + e^{-c})\sin b\,\{\beta\beta' + \gamma\gamma'\} + \tfrac{1}{2}(e^{c} - e^{-c})\cos b\,\{\gamma\beta' - \beta\gamma'\}.$$

180. If α, β, γ and α', β', γ' are reciprocals, and

$$\Phi = a\,\alpha\alpha' + b\{\beta\beta' + \gamma\gamma'\} + c\,\beta\gamma',$$

and N is any whole number,

$$\Phi^{\mathrm{N}} = a^{\mathrm{N}}\alpha\alpha' + b^{\mathrm{N}}\{\beta\beta' + \gamma\gamma'\} + \mathrm{N}b^{\mathrm{N}-1}c\,\beta\gamma'.$$

Therefore,

$$e^{\Phi} = e^{a}\alpha\alpha' + e^{b}\{\beta\beta' + \gamma\gamma'\} + e^{b}c\,\beta\gamma',$$

$$\cos\Phi = \cos a\,\alpha\alpha' + \cos b\,\{\beta\beta' + \gamma\gamma'\} - c\sin b\,\beta\gamma',$$

$$\sin\Phi = \sin a\,\alpha\alpha' + \sin b\,\{\beta\beta' + \gamma\gamma'\} + c\cos b\,\beta\gamma'.$$

If a and b are unequal, and c other than zero, we may add

$$\log\Phi = \log a\,\alpha\alpha' + \log b\{\beta\beta' + \gamma\gamma'\} + cb^{-1}\beta\gamma.$$

181. If α, β, γ, and α', β', γ' are reciprocals, and

$$\Phi = a\mathrm{I} + b\{\alpha\beta' + \beta\gamma'\} + c\,\alpha\gamma',$$

and N is a whole number,

$$\Phi^{\mathrm{N}} = a^{\mathrm{N}}\mathrm{I} + \mathrm{N}a^{\mathrm{N}-1}b\{\alpha\beta' + \beta\gamma'\} + (\mathrm{N}a^{\mathrm{N}-1}c + \tfrac{1}{2}\mathrm{N}(\mathrm{N}-1)a^{\mathrm{N}-2}b^{2})\alpha\gamma'.$$

Therefore

$$e^{\Phi} = e^{a}\,\mathrm{I} + e^{a}\,b\{\alpha\beta' + \beta\gamma'\} + e^{a}\,(\tfrac{1}{2}b^{2} + c)\alpha\gamma',$$

$$\cos\Phi = \cos a\,\mathrm{I} - b\sin a\,\{\alpha\beta' + \beta\alpha'\} - (\tfrac{1}{2}b^{2}\cos a + c\sin a)\alpha\gamma',$$

$$\sin\Phi = \sin a\,\mathrm{I} + b\cos a\,\{\alpha\beta' + \beta\alpha'\} - (\tfrac{1}{2}b^{2}\sin a - c\cos a)\alpha\gamma'.$$

Unless $b = 0$, we may add

$$\log\Phi = \log a\,\mathrm{I} + ba^{-1}\{\alpha\beta' + \beta\alpha'\} + (ca^{-1} - \tfrac{1}{2}b^{2}a^{-2})\alpha\gamma'.$$

182. If we suppose any dyadic Φ to vary, but with the limitation that all its values are homologous, we may obtain from the definitions of No. 171

$$d\{e^{\Phi}\} = e^{\Phi}.d\Phi, \tag{1}$$

$$d\sin\Phi = \cos\Phi.d\Phi, \tag{2}$$

$$d\cos\Phi = -\sin\Phi.d\Phi, \tag{3}$$

$$d\log\Phi = \Phi^{-1}.d\Phi, \tag{4}$$

as in the ordinary calculus, but we must not apply these equations to cases in which the values of Φ are not homologous.

183. If, however, Γ is any constant dyadic, the variations of $t\Gamma$ will necessarily be homologous with $t\Gamma$, and we may write without other limitation than that Γ is constant,

$$\frac{d\{e^{t\Gamma}\}}{dt}=\Gamma.e^{t\Gamma} \tag{1}$$

$$\frac{d\sin\{t\Gamma\}}{dt}=\Gamma.\cos\{t\Gamma\}, \tag{2}$$

$$\frac{d\cos\{t\Gamma\}}{dt}=-\Gamma.\sin\{t\Gamma\}, \tag{3}$$

$$\frac{d\log\{t\Gamma\}}{dt}=\frac{\mathrm{I}}{t}. \tag{4}$$

A second differentiation gives

$$\frac{d^2\{e^{t\Gamma}\}}{dt^2}=\Gamma^2.e^{t\Gamma}, \tag{5}$$

$$\frac{d^2\sin\{t\Gamma\}}{dt^2}=-\Gamma^2.\sin\{t\Gamma\}, \tag{6}$$

$$\frac{d^2\cos\{t\Gamma\}}{dt^2}=-\Gamma^2.\cos\{t\Gamma\}. \tag{7}$$

184. It follows that if we have a differential equation of the form

$$\frac{d\rho}{dt}=\Gamma.\rho,$$

the integral equation will be of the form

$$\rho=e^{t\Gamma}.\rho',$$

ρ' representing the value of ρ for $t=0$. For this gives

$$\frac{d\rho}{dt}=\Gamma.e^{t\Gamma}.\rho'=\Gamma.\rho,$$

and the proper value of ρ for $t=0$.

185. *Def.*—A flux which is a linear function of the position-vector is called a *homogeneous-strain-flux* from the nature of the strain which it produces. Such a flux may evidently be represented by a dyadic.

In the equations of the last paragraph, we may suppose ρ to represent a position-vector, t the time, and Γ a homogeneous-strain-flux. Then $e^{t\Gamma}$ will represent the strain produced by the flux Γ in the time t.

In like manner, if Λ represents a homogeneous strain, $\{\log\Lambda\}/t$ will represent a homogeneous-strain-flux which would produce the strain Λ in the time t.

186. If we have

$$\frac{d^2\rho}{dt^2}=\Gamma^2.\rho,$$

where Γ is complete, the integral equation will be of the form

$$\rho=e^{t\Gamma}.\alpha+e^{-t\Gamma}.\beta.$$

For this gives

$$\frac{d\rho}{dt}=\Gamma.e^{t\Gamma}.\alpha-\Gamma.e^{-t\Gamma}.\beta,$$

$$\frac{d^2\rho}{dt^2}=\Gamma^2.e^{t\Gamma}.\alpha+\Gamma^2.e^{-t\Gamma}.\beta=\Gamma^2.\rho,$$

and α and β may be determined so as to satisfy the equations

$$\rho_{t=0}=\alpha+\beta,$$

$$\left[\frac{d\rho}{dt}\right]_{t=0}=\Gamma.\{\alpha-\beta\}.$$

187. The differential equation

$$\frac{d^2\rho}{dt^2}=-\Gamma^2.\rho$$

will be satisfied by

$$\rho=\cos\{t\Gamma\}.\alpha+\sin\{t\Gamma\}.\beta,$$

whence

$$\frac{d\rho}{dt}=-\Gamma.\sin\{t\Gamma\}.\alpha+\Gamma.\cos\{t\Gamma\}.\beta,$$

$$\frac{d^2\rho}{dt^2}=-\Gamma^2.\cos\{t\Gamma\}.\alpha-\Gamma^2.\sin\{t\Gamma\}.\beta=-\Gamma^2.\rho.$$

If Γ is complete, the constants α and β may be determined to satisfy the equations

$$\rho_{t=0}=\alpha,$$

$$\left[\frac{d\rho}{dt}\right]_{t=0}=\Gamma.\beta.$$

188. If

$$\frac{d^2\rho}{dt^2}=\{\Gamma^2-\Lambda^2\}.\rho,$$

where $\Gamma^2-\Lambda^2$ is a complete dyadic, and

$$\Gamma.\Lambda=\Lambda.\Gamma=0,$$

we may set

$$\rho=\{\tfrac{1}{2}e^{t\Gamma}+\tfrac{1}{2}e^{-t\Gamma}+\cos\{t\Lambda\}-\mathrm{I}\}.\alpha+\{\tfrac{1}{2}e^{t\Gamma}-\tfrac{1}{2}e^{-t\Gamma}+\sin\{t\Lambda\}\}.\beta,$$

which gives

$$\frac{d\rho}{dt}=\{\tfrac{1}{2}\Gamma.e^{t\Gamma}-\tfrac{1}{2}\Gamma.e^{-t\Gamma}-\Lambda.\sin\{t\Lambda\}\}.\alpha$$
$$+\{\tfrac{1}{2}\Gamma.e^{t\Gamma}+\tfrac{1}{2}\Gamma.e^{-t\Gamma}+\Lambda.\cos\{t\Lambda\}\}.\beta,$$

$$\frac{d^2\rho}{dt^2}=\{\tfrac{1}{2}\Gamma^2.e^{t\Gamma}+\tfrac{1}{2}\Gamma^2.e^{-t\Gamma}-\Lambda^2.\cos\{t\Lambda\}\}.\alpha$$
$$+\{\tfrac{1}{2}\Gamma^2.e^{t\Gamma}-\tfrac{1}{2}\Gamma^2.e^{-t\Gamma}-\Lambda^2.\sin\{t\Lambda\}\}.\beta$$
$$=\{\Gamma^2-\Lambda^2\}.\rho.$$

The constants α and β are to be determined by

$$\rho_{t=0}=\alpha,$$

$$\left[\frac{d\rho}{dt}\right]_{t=0}=\{\Gamma+\Lambda\}.\beta.$$

189. It will appear, on reference to Nos. 155–157, that every complete dyadic may be expressed in one of three forms, viz., as a square, as a square with the negative sign, or as a difference of squares of two dyadics of which both the direct products are equal to zero. It follows that every equation of the form

$$\frac{d^2\rho}{dt^2}=\Theta.\rho,$$

where Θ is any constant and complete dyadic, may be integrated by the preceding formulæ.

NOTE ON BIVECTOR ANALYSIS.*

1. A vector is determined by three algebraic quantities. It often occurs that the solution of the equations by which these are to be determined gives imaginary values, i.e., instead of scalars we obtain biscalars, or expressions of the form $a+\iota b$, where a and b are scalars, and $\iota=\sqrt{-1}$. It is most simple, and always allowable, to consider the vector as determined by its components parallel to a normal system of axes. In other words, a vector may be represented in the form

$$xi+yj+zk.$$

Now if the vector is required to satisfy certain conditions, the solution of the equations which determine the values of x, y, and z, in the most general case, will give results of the form

$$x=x_1+\iota x_2,$$

$$y=y_1+\iota y_2,$$

$$z=z_1+\iota z_2,$$

* Thus far, in accordance with the purpose expressed in the footnote on page 17, we have considered only real values of scalars and vectors. The object of this limitation has been to present the subject in the most elementary manner. The limitation is however often inconvenient, and does not allow the most symmetrical and complete development of the subject in many important directions. Thus in Chapter V, and the latter part of Chapter III, the exclusion of imaginary values has involved a considerable sacrifice of simplicity both in the enunciation of theorems and in their demonstration. The student will find an interesting and profitable exercise in working over this part of the subject with the aid of imaginary values, especially in the discussion of the imaginary roots of the cubic equation on page 71, and in the use of the formula

$$e^{\iota\Phi}=\cos\Phi+\iota\sin\Phi$$

in developing the properties of the *sines*, *cosines*, and *exponentials* of dyadics.

where $x_1, x_2, y_1, y_2, z_1, z_2$ are scalars. Substituting these values in

$$xi+yj+zk,$$

we obtain $$(x_1+\iota x_2)i+(y_1+\iota y_2)j+(z_1+\iota z_2)k;$$

or, if we set $$\rho_1=x_1 i+y_1 j+z_1 k,$$

$$\rho_2=x_2 i+y_2 j+z_2 k,$$

we obtain $$\rho_1+\iota\rho_2.$$

We shall call this a *bivector*, a term which will include a vector as a particular case. When we wish to express a bivector by a single letter, we shall use the small German letters. Thus we may write

$$\mathfrak{r}=\rho_1+\iota\rho_2.$$

An important case is that in which ρ_1 and ρ_2 have the same direction. The bivector may then be expressed in the form $(a+\iota b)\rho$, in which the vector factor, if we choose, may be a unit vector. In this case, we may say that the bivector has a *real direction*. In fact, if we express the bivector in the form

$$(x_1+\iota x_2)i+(y_1+\iota y_2)j+(z_1+\iota z_2)k$$

the ratios of the coefficients of i, j, and k, which determine the direction cosines of the vector, will in this case be real.

2. The consideration that operations upon bivectors may be regarded as operations upon their biscalar x-, y- and z-components is sufficient to show the possibility of a bivector analysis and to indicate what its rules must be. But this point of view does not afford the most simple conception of the operations which we have to perform upon bivectors. It is desirable that the definitions of the fundamental operations should be independent of such extraneous considerations as any system of axes.

The various signs of our analysis, when applied to bivectors, may therefore be defined as follows, viz.,

The bivector equation

$$\mu'+\iota\nu'=\mu''+\iota\nu''$$

implies the two vector equations

$$\mu'=\mu'', \quad \text{and} \quad \nu'=\nu''.$$

$$-[\mu+\iota\nu]=-\mu+\iota[-\nu].$$

$$[\mu'+\iota\nu']+[\mu''+\iota\nu'']=[\mu'+\mu'']+\iota[\nu'+\nu''].^*$$

$$[\mu'+\iota\nu'].[\mu''+\iota\nu'']=[\mu'.\mu''-\nu'.\nu'']+\iota[\mu'.\nu''+\nu'.\mu''].$$

$$[\mu'+\iota\nu']\times[\mu''+\iota\nu'']=[\mu'\times\mu''-\nu'\times\nu'']+\iota[\mu'\times\nu''+\nu'\times\mu''].$$

---

* $(a+\iota b)[\mu+\iota\nu]=a\mu-b\nu+\iota[a\nu+b\mu].$
$[\mu+\iota\nu](a+\iota b)=\mu a-\nu b+\iota[\mu b+\nu a].$
Therefore the position of the scalar factor is indifferent. [MS. note by author.]

With these definitions, a great part of the laws of vector analysis may be applied at once to bivector expressions. But an equation which is impossible in vector analysis may be possible in bivector analysis, and in general the number of roots of an equation, or of the values of a function, will be different according as we recognize, or do not recognize, imaginary values.

3. *Def.*—Two bivectors, or two biscalars, are said to be *conjugate*, when their real parts are the same, and their imaginary parts differ in sign, and in sign only.

Hence, the product of the conjugates of any number of bivectors and biscalars is the conjugate of the product of the bivectors and biscalars. This is true of any kind of product.

The products of a vector and its conjugate are as follows:

$$[\mu+\iota\nu].[\mu-\iota\nu]=\mu.\mu+\nu.\nu$$

$$[\mu+\iota\nu]\times[\mu-\iota\nu]=2\iota\nu\times\mu$$

$$[\mu+\iota\nu]\,[\mu-\iota\nu]=\{\mu\mu+\nu\nu\}+\iota\{\nu\mu-\mu\nu\}.$$

Hence, if μ and $\iota\nu$ represent the real and imaginary parts of a bivector, the values of

$$\mu.\mu+\nu.\nu, \qquad \mu\times\nu, \qquad \mu\mu+\nu\nu, \qquad \nu\mu-\mu\nu,$$

are not affected by multiplying the bivector by a biscalar of the form $a+\iota b$, in which $a^2+b^2=1$, say a *cyclic scalar*. Thus, if we set

$$\mu'+\iota\nu'=(a+\iota b)\,[\mu+\iota\nu],$$

we shall have

$$\mu'-\iota\nu'=(a-\iota b)\,[\mu-\iota\nu],$$

and

$$[\mu'+\iota\nu'].[\mu'-\iota\nu']=[\mu+\iota\nu].[\mu-\iota\nu].$$

That is,

$$\mu'.\mu'+\nu'.\nu'=\mu.\mu+\nu.\nu;$$

and so in the other cases.

4. *Def.*—In biscalar analysis, the product of a biscalar and its conjugate is a positive scalar. The positive square root of this scalar is called the modulus of the biscalar. In bivector analysis, the direct product of a bivector and its conjugate is, as seen above, a positive scalar. The positive square root of this scalar may be called the *modulus* of the *bivector*. When this modulus vanishes, the bivector vanishes, and only in this case. If the bivector is multiplied by a biscalar, its modulus is multiplied by the modulus of the biscalar. The conjugate of a (real) vector is the vector itself, and the modulus of the vector is the same as its magnitude.

5. *Def.*—If between two vectors, α and β, there subsists a relation of the form

$$\alpha=n\beta,$$

where n is a scalar, we say that the vectors are parallel. Analogy leads us to call two bivectors *parallel*, when there subsists between them a relation of the form

$$\mathfrak{a} = m\mathfrak{b},$$

where m (in the most general case) is a biscalar.

To aid us in comprehending the geometrical signification of this relation, we may regard the biscalar as consisting of two factors, one of which is a positive scalar (the modulus of the biscalar), and the other may be put in the form $\cos q + \iota \sin q$. The effect of multiplying a bivector by a positive scalar is obvious. To understand the effect of a multiplier of the form $\cos q + \iota \sin q$ upon a bivector $\mu + \iota\nu$, let us set

$$\mu' + \iota\nu' = (\cos q + \iota \sin q)[\mu + \iota\nu].$$

We have then

$$\mu' = \cos q\, \mu - \sin q\, \nu,$$

$$\nu' = \cos q\, \nu + \sin q\, \mu.$$

Now if μ and ν are of the same magnitude and at right angles, the effect of the multiplication is evidently to rotate these vectors in their plane an angular distance q, which is to be measured in the direction from ν to μ. In any case we may regard μ and ν as the projections (by parallel lines) of two perpendicular vectors of the same length. The two last equations show that μ' and ν' will be the projections of the vectors obtained by the rotation of these perpendicular vectors in their plane through the angle q. Hence, if we construct an ellipse of which μ and ν are conjugate semi-diameters, μ' and ν' will be another pair of conjugate semi-diameters, and the sectors between μ and μ' and between ν and ν', will each be to the whole area of the ellipse as q to 2π, the sector between ν and ν' lying on the same side of ν and μ, and that between μ and μ' lying on the same side of μ as $-\nu$.

It follows that any bivector $\mu + \iota\nu$ may be put in the form

$$(\cos q + \iota \sin q)[\alpha + \iota\beta],$$

in which α and β are at right angles, being the semi-axes of the ellipse of which μ and ν are conjugate semi-diameters. This ellipse we may call the *directional ellipse* of the bivector. In the case of a real vector, or of a vector having a real direction, it reduces to a straight line. In any other case, the angular direction from the imaginary to the real part of the bivector is to be regarded as positive in the ellipse, and the specification of the ellipse must be considered incomplete without the indication of this direction.

Parallelism of bivectors, then, signifies the similarity and similar position of their directional ellipses. Similar position includes identity of the angular directions mentioned above.

6. To reduce a given bivector $\mathfrak{r}$ to the above form, we may set

$$\begin{aligned}\mathfrak{r}.\mathfrak{r} &= (\cos q + \iota \sin q)^2 [\alpha + \iota\beta].[\alpha + \iota\beta] \\ &= (\cos 2q + \iota \sin 2q)(\alpha.\alpha - \beta.\beta) \\ &= a + \iota b,\end{aligned}$$

where a and b are scalars, which we may regard as known. The value of q may be determined by the equation

$$\tan 2q = \frac{b}{a},$$

the quadrant to which $2q$ belongs being determined so as to give $\sin 2q$ and $\cos 2q$ the same signs as b and a. Then α and β will be given by the equation

$$\alpha + \iota\beta = (\cos q - \iota \sin q)\mathfrak{r}.$$

The solution is indeterminate when the real and imaginary parts of the given bivector are perpendicular and equal in magnitude. In this case the directional ellipse is a circle, and the bivector may be called *circular*. The criterion of a circular bivector is

$$\mathfrak{r}.\mathfrak{r} = 0.$$

It is especially to be noticed that from this equation we cannot conclude that

$$\mathfrak{r} = 0,$$

as in the analysis of real vectors. This may also be shown by expressing $\mathfrak{r}$ in the form $xi + yj + zk$, in which x, y, z are biscalars. The equation then becomes

$$x^2 + y^2 + z^2 = 0,$$

which evidently does not require x, y, and z to vanish, as would be the case if only real values are considered.

7. *Def.*—We call two vectors ρ and σ perpendicular when $\rho.\sigma = 0$. Following the same analogy, we shall call two bivectors $\mathfrak{r}$ and $\mathfrak{s}$ perpendicular, when

$$\mathfrak{r}.\mathfrak{s} = 0.$$

In considering the geometrical signification of this equation, we shall first suppose that the real and imaginary components of $\mathfrak{r}$ and $\mathfrak{s}$ lie in the same plane, and that both $\mathfrak{r}$ and $\mathfrak{s}$ have not real directions. It is then evidently possible to express them in the form

$$m[\alpha + \iota\beta], \qquad m'[\alpha' + \iota\beta'],$$

where m and m' are biscalar, α and β are at right angles, and α' parallel with β. Then the equation $\mathfrak{r}.\mathfrak{s} = 0$ requires that

$$\beta.\beta' = 0, \quad \text{and} \quad \alpha.\beta' + \beta.\alpha' = 0.$$

This shows that the directional ellipses of the two bivectors are similar and the angular direction from the real to the imaginary component is the same in both, but the major axes of the ellipses are perpendicular. The case in which the directions of $\mathfrak{r}$ and $\mathfrak{s}$ are real, forms no exception to this rule.

It will be observed that every circular bivector is perpendicular to itself, and to every parallel bivector.

If two bivectors, $\mu+\iota\nu$, $\mu'+\iota\nu'$, which do not lie in the same plane are perpendicular, we may resolve μ and ν into components parallel and perpendicular to the plane of μ' and ν'. The components perpendicular to the plane evidently contribute nothing to the value of

$$[\mu+\iota\nu].[\mu'+\iota\nu'].$$

Therefore the components of μ and ν parallel to the plane of μ', ν', form a bivector which is perpendicular to $\mu'+\iota\nu'$. That is, if two bivectors are perpendicular, the directional ellipse of either, projected upon the plane of the other and rotated through a quadrant in that plane, will be similar and similarly situated to the directional ellipse of the second.

8. A bivector may be divided in one and only one way into parts parallel and perpendicular to another, provided that the second is not circular. If $\mathfrak{a}$ and $\mathfrak{b}$ are the bivectors, the parts of $\mathfrak{a}$ will be

$$\frac{\mathfrak{b}.\mathfrak{a}}{\mathfrak{b}.\mathfrak{b}}\mathfrak{b} \quad \text{and} \quad \mathfrak{a}-\frac{\mathfrak{b}.\mathfrak{a}}{\mathfrak{b}.\mathfrak{b}}\mathfrak{b}.$$

If $\mathfrak{b}$ is circular, the resolution of $\mathfrak{a}$ is impossible, unless it is perpendicular to $\mathfrak{b}$. In this case the resolution is indeterminate.

9. Since $\mathfrak{a}\times\mathfrak{b}.\mathfrak{a}=0$, and $\mathfrak{a}\times\mathfrak{b}.\mathfrak{b}=0$, $\mathfrak{a}\times\mathfrak{b}$ is perpendicular to $\mathfrak{a}$ and $\mathfrak{b}$. We may regard the plane of the product as determined by the condition that the directional ellipses of the factors projected upon it become similar and similarly situated. The directional ellipse of the product is similar to these projections, but its orientation is different by 90°. It may easily be shown that $\mathfrak{a}\times\mathfrak{b}$ vanishes only with $\mathfrak{a}$ or $\mathfrak{b}$, or when $\mathfrak{a}$ and $\mathfrak{b}$ are parallel.

10. The bivector equation

$$(\mathfrak{a}\times\mathfrak{b}.\mathfrak{c})\mathfrak{d}-(\mathfrak{b}.\mathfrak{c}\times\mathfrak{d})\mathfrak{a}+(\mathfrak{c}.\mathfrak{d}\times\mathfrak{a})\mathfrak{b}-(\mathfrak{d}.\mathfrak{a}\times\mathfrak{b})\mathfrak{c}=0$$

is identical, as may be verified by substituting expressions of the form $xi+yj+zk$ (x, y, z being biscalars), for each of the bivectors. (Compare No. 37.) This equation shows that if the product $\mathfrak{a}\times\mathfrak{b}$ of any two bivectors vanishes, one of these will be equal to the other with a biscalar coefficient, that is, they will be parallel, according to the definition given above. If the product $\mathfrak{a}.\mathfrak{b}\times\mathfrak{c}$ of any three bivectors vanishes, the equation shows that one of these may be expressed as a sum of the other two with biscalar coefficients. In this case, we may say (from the analogy of the scalar analysis) that the three bivectors are complanar. (This does not imply that they lie in any same *real* plane.) If $\mathfrak{a}.\mathfrak{b}\times\mathfrak{c}$ is not equal to zero, the equation shows that any fourth bivector may be expressed as a sum of $\mathfrak{a}$, $\mathfrak{b}$, and $\mathfrak{c}$ with biscalar coefficients, and indicates how these coefficients may be determined.

11. The equation

$$(\mathfrak{r}.\mathfrak{a})\mathfrak{b}\times\mathfrak{c}+(\mathfrak{r}.\mathfrak{b})\mathfrak{c}\times\mathfrak{a}+(\mathfrak{r}.\mathfrak{c})\mathfrak{a}\times\mathfrak{b}=(\mathfrak{a}\times\mathfrak{b}.\mathfrak{c})\mathfrak{r}$$

is also identical, as may easily be verified. If we set

$$\mathfrak{c}=\mathfrak{a}\times\mathfrak{b},$$

and suppose that

$$\mathfrak{r}.\mathfrak{a}=0, \quad \mathfrak{r}.\mathfrak{b}=0,$$

the equation becomes

$$(\mathfrak{r}.\mathfrak{a}\times\mathfrak{b})\mathfrak{a}\times\mathfrak{b}=(\mathfrak{a}\times\mathfrak{b}.\mathfrak{a}\times\mathfrak{b})\mathfrak{r}.$$

This shows that if a bivector $\mathfrak{r}$ is perpendicular to two bivectors $\mathfrak{a}$ and $\mathfrak{b}$, which are not parallel, $\mathfrak{r}$ will be parallel to $\mathfrak{a}\times\mathfrak{b}$. Therefore all bivectors which are perpendicular to two given bivectors are parallel to each other, unless the given two are parallel.

[*Note by Editors.*—The notation $|\Phi|\,\Phi_C^{-1}$, used on page 64, was later improved by the author by the introduction of his Double Multiplication, according to which the above expression is represented by Φ_2, and $|\Phi|$ by Φ_3. See this volume, pages 112, 160, and 181. For an extended treatment of Professor Gibbs's researches on Double Multiplication in their application to Vector Analysis see pp. 306-321, and 333 of "Vector Analysis," by E. B. Wilson, Chas. Scribner's Sons, New York, 1901.]

IV.

ON MULTIPLE ALGEBRA.

Address before the Section of Mathematics and Astronomy of the American Association for the Advancement of Science, by the Vice-President.

[*Proceedings of the American Association for the Advancement of Science*, vol. xxxv. pp. 37-66, 1886.]

It has been said that "the human mind has never invented a labor-saving machine equal to algebra."* If this be true, it is but natural and proper that an age like our own, characterized by the multiplication of labor-saving machinery, should be distinguished by an unexampled development of this most refined and most beautiful of machines. That such has been the case, none will question. The improvement has been in every part. Even to enumerate the principal lines of advance would be a task for any one; for me an impossibility. But if we should ask, in what direction the advance has been made which is to characterize the development of algebra in our day, we may, I think, point to that broadening of its field and methods which gives us *multiple algebra*.

Of the importance of this change in the conception of the office of algebra, it is hardly necessary to speak: that it is really characteristic of our time will be most evident if we go back some two or three-score years, to the time when the seeds were sown which are now yielding so abundant a harvest. The failure of Möbius, Hamilton, Grassmann, Saint-Venant to make an immediate impression upon the course of mathematical thought in any way commensurate with the importance of their discoveries is the most conspicuous evidence that the times were not ripe for the methods which they sought to introduce. A satisfactory theory of the imaginary quantities of ordinary algebra, which is essentially a simple case of multiple algebra, with difficulty obtained recognition in the first third of this century. We must observe that this *double algebra*, as it has been called, was not sought for or invented;—it forced itself, unbidden, upon the attention of mathematicians, and with its rules already formed.

* *The Nation*, vol. xxxiii, p. 237.

But the idea of double algebra, once received, although as it were unwillingly, must have suggested to many minds more or less distinctly the possibility of other multiple algebras, of higher orders, possessing interesting or useful properties.

The application of double algebra to the geometry of the plane suggested not unnaturally to Hamilton the idea of a triple algebra which should be capable of a similar application to the geometry of three dimensions. He was unable to find a satisfactory triple algebra, but discovered at length a quadruple algebra, *quaternions*, which answered his purpose, thus satisfying, as he says in one of his letters, an intellectual want which had haunted him at least fifteen years. So confident was he of the value of this algebra, that the same hour he obtained permission to lay his discovery before the Royal Irish Academy, which he did on November 13, 1843.* This system of multiple algebra is far better known than any other, except the ordinary double algebra of imaginary quantities,—far too well known to require any especial notice at my hands. All that here requires our attention is the close historical connection between the imaginaries of ordinary algebra and Hamilton's system, a fact emphasized by Hamilton himself and most writers on quaternions. It was quite otherwise with Möbius and Grassmann.

The point of departure of the *Barycentrischer Calcul* of Möbius, published in 1827,—a work of which Clebsch has said that it can never be admired enough,†—is the use of equations in which the terms consist of letters representing points with numerical coefficients, to express barycentric relations between the points. Thus, that the point S is the centre of gravity of weights, a, b, c, d, placed at the points A, B, C, D, respectively, is expressed by the equation

$$(a+b+c+d)S=aA+bB+cC+dD.$$

An equation of the more general form

$$aA+bB+cC+\text{etc.}=pP+qQ+rR+\text{etc.}$$

signifies that the weights a, b, c, etc., at the points A, B, C, etc., have the same sum and the same centre of gravity as the weights p, q, r, etc., at the points P, Q, R, etc., or, in other words, that the former are barycentrically equivalent to the latter. Such equations, of which each represents four ordinary equations, may evidently be multiplied or divided by scalars,‡ may be added or subtracted, and may have

* *Phil. Mag.* (3), vol. xxv, p. 490; *North British Review*, vol. xlv (1866), p. 57.

† See his eulogy on Plücker, p. 14, *Gött. Abhandl.*, vol. xvi.

‡ I use this term in Hamilton's sense, to denote the ordinary positive and negative quantities of algebra. It may, however, be observed that in most cases in which I shall have occasion to use it, the proposition would hold without exclusion of imaginary quantities,—that this exclusion is generally for simplicity and not from necessity.

their terms arranged and transposed, exactly like the ordinary equations of algebra. It follows that the elimination of letters representing points from equations of this kind is performed by the rules of ordinary algebra. This is evidently the beginning of a quadruple algebra, and is identical, as far as it goes, with Grassmann's marvellous geometrical algebra.

In the same work we find also, for the first time so far as I am aware, the distinction of positive and negative consistently carried out on the designation of segments of lines, of triangles, and of tetrahedra, viz., that a change in place of two letters, in such expressions as AB, ABC, $ABCD$, is equivalent to prefixing the negative sign. It is impossible to overestimate the importance of this step, which gives to designations of this kind the generality and precision of algebra.

Moreover, if A, B, C are three points in the same straight line, and D any point outside of that line, the author observes that we have

$$AB+BC+CA=0,$$

and also, with D prefixed,

$$DAB+DBC+DCA=0.$$

Again, if A, B, C, D are four points in the same plane, and E any point outside of that plane, we have

$$ABC-BCD+CDA-DAB=0,$$

and also, with E prefixed,

$$EABC-EBCD+ECDA-EDAB=0.$$

The similarity to multiplication in the derivation of these formulæ cannot have escaped the author's notice. Yet he does not seem to have been able to generalize these processes. It was reserved for the genius of Grassmann to see that AB might be regarded as the product of A and B, DAB as the product of D and AB, and $EABC$ as the product of E and ABC. That Möbius could not make this step was evidently due to the fact that he had not the conception of the addition of other multiple quantities than such as may be represented by masses situated at points. Even the addition of vectors (i.e., the fact that the composition of directed lines could be treated as an addition) seems to have been unknown to him at this time, although he subsequently discovered it, and used it in his *Mechanik des Himmels*, which was published in 1843. This addition of vectors, or *geometrical addition*, seems to have occurred independently to many persons.

Seventeen years after the *Barycentrischer Calcul*, in 1844, the year in which Hamilton's first papers on quaternions appeared in print, Grassmann published his *Lineale Ausdehnungslehre*, in which he developed the idea and the properties of the *external* or *combinatorial* *product*, a conception which is perhaps to be regarded as the greatest monument of the author's genius. This volume was to have been followed by another, of the nature of which some intimation was given in the preface and in the work itself. We are especially told that the *internal product*,* which for vectors is identical except in sign with the scalar part of Hamilton's product (just as Grassmann's external product of two vectors is practically identical with the vector part of Hamilton's product), and the *open product*,† which in the language of to-day would be called a matrix, were to be treated in the second volume. But both the internal product of vectors and the open product are clearly defined, and their fundamental properties indicated, in this first volume.

This remarkable work remained unnoticed for more than twenty years, a fact which was doubtless due in part to the very abstract and philosophical manner in which the subject was presented. In consequence of this neglect the author changed his plan, and instead of a supplementary volume published in 1862 a single volume entitled *Ausdehnungslehre*, in which were treated, in an entirely different style, the same topics as in the first volume, as well as those which he had reserved for the second.

Deferring for the moment the discussion of these topics in order to follow the course of events, we find in the year following the first *Ausdehnungslehre* a remarkable memoir of Saint-Venant ‡, in which are clearly described the addition both of vectors and of oriented areas, the differentiation of these with respect to a scalar quantity, and a multiplication of two vectors and of a vector and an oriented area. These multiplications, called by the author *geometrical*, are entirely identical with Grassmann's external multiplication of the same quantities.

It is a striking fact in the history of the subject, that the short period of less than two years was marked by the appearance of well-developed and valuable systems of multiple algebra by British, German, and French authors, working apparently entirely independently of one another. No system of multiple algebra had appeared before, so far as I know, except such as were confined to additive processes with multiplication by scalars, or related to the ordinary double algebra of imaginary quantities. But the appearance of a single one of these systems would have been sufficient to mark an epoch, perhaps the most important epoch in the history of the subject.

In 1853 and 1854, Cauchy published several memoirs on what he called *clefs algébriques*.§ These were units subject generally to

* See the preface.

† See § 172.

‡ *Comptes Rendus*, vol. xxi, p. 620.

§ *Comptes Rendus*, vols. xxxvi, ff.

combinatorial multiplication. His principal application was to the theory of elimination. In this application, as in the law of multiplication, he had been anticipated by Grassmann.

We come next to Cayley's celebrated *Memoir on the Theory of Matrices* * in 1858, of which Sylvester has said that it seems to him to have ushered in the reign of Algebra the Second. † I quote this dictum of a master as showing his opinion of the importance of the subject and of the memoir. But the foundations of the theory of matrices, regarded as multiple quantities, seem to me to have been already laid in the *Ausdehnungslehre* of 1844. To Grassmann's treatment of this subject we shall recur later.

After the *Ausdehnungslehre* of 1862, already mentioned, we come to Hankel's *Vorlesungen über die complexen Zahlen*, 1867. Under this title the author treats of the imaginary quantities of ordinary algebra, of what he calls *alternirende Zahlen*, and of quaternions. These alternate numbers, like Cauchy's *clefs*, are quantities subject to Grassmann's law of combinatorial multiplication. This treatise, published twenty-three years after the first *Ausdehnungslehre*, marks the first impression which we can discover of Grassmann's ideas upon the course of mathematical thought. The transcendent importance of these ideas was fully appreciated by the author, whose very able work seems to have had considerable influence in calling the attention of mathematicians to the subject.

In 1870, Professor Benjamin Peirce published his *Linear Associative Algebra*, subsequently developed and enriched by his son, Professor C. S. Peirce. The fact that the edition was lithographed seems to indicate that even at this late date a work of this kind could only be regarded as addressed to a limited number of readers. But the increasing interest in such subjects is shown by the republication of this memoir in 1881, ‡ as by that of the first *Ausdehnungslehre* in 1878.

The article on quaternions which has just appeared in the *Encyclopædia Britannica* mentions twelve treatises, including second editions and translations, besides the original treatises of Hamilton. That all the twelve are later than 1861 and all but two later than 1872 shows the rapid increase of interest in this subject in the last years.

Finally, we arrive at the *Lectures on the Principles of Universal Algebra* by the distinguished foreigner whose sojourn among us has given such an impulse to mathematical study in this country. The publication of these lectures, commenced in 1884 in the *American Journal of Mathematics*, has not as yet been completed,—a want but imperfectly supplied by the author's somewhat desultory publication

* *Phil. Trans.*, vol. cxlviii.

† *Amer. Journ. Math.*, vol. vi, p. 271.

‡ *Amer. Journ. Math.*, vol. iv.

of many remarkable papers on the same subject (which might be more definitely expressed as the algebra of matrices) in various foreign journals.

It is not an accident that this century has seen the rise of multiple algebra. The course of the development of ideas in algebra and in geometry, although in the main independent of any aid from this source, has nevertheless to a very large extent been of a character which can only find its natural expression in multiple algebra.

Our Modern Higher Algebra is especially occupied with the theory of linear transformations. Now what are the first notions which we meet in this theory? We have a set of n variables, say x, y, z, and another set, say x', y', z', which are homogeneous linear functions of the first, and therefore expressible in terms of them by means of a block of n^2 coefficients. Here the quantities occur by sets, and invite the notations of multiple algebra. It was in fact shown by Grassmann in his first *Ausdehnungslehre* and by Cauchy nine years later, that the notations of multiple algebra afford a natural key to the subject of elimination.

Now I do not merely mean that we may save a little time or space by writing perhaps ρ for x, y and z; ρ' for x', y' and z'; and Φ for a block of n^2 quantities. But I mean that the subject as usually treated under the title of determinants has a stunted and misdirected development on account of the limitations of single algebra. This will appear from a very simple illustration. After a little preliminary matter the student comes generally to a chapter entitled "Multiplication of Determinants," in which he is taught that the product of the determinants of two matrices may be found by performing a somewhat lengthy operation on the two matrices, by which he obtains a third matrix, and then taking the determinant of this. But what significance, what value has this theorem? For aught that appears in the majority of treatises which I have seen, we have only a complicated and lengthy way of performing a simple operation. The real facts of the case may be stated as follows:

Suppose the set of n quantities ρ' to be derived from the set ρ by the matrix Φ, which we may express by

$$\rho' = \Phi . \rho;$$

and suppose the set ρ'' to be derived from the set ρ' by the matrix Ψ, i.e.,

$$\rho'' = \Psi . \rho'.$$

and

$$\rho'' = \Psi . \Phi . \rho;$$

it is evident that ρ'' can be derived from ρ by the operation of a single matrix, say Θ, i.e.,

$$\rho'' = \Theta . \rho,$$

so that

$$\Theta = \Psi . \Phi.$$

In the language of multiple algebra Θ is called the product of Ψ and Φ. It is of course interesting to see how it is derived from the latter, and it is little more than a schoolboy's exercise to determine this. Now this matrix Θ has the property that its determinant is equal to the products of the determinants of Ψ and Φ. And this property is all that is generally stated in the books, and the fundamental property, which is all that gives the subject its interest, that Θ is itself the product of Ψ and Φ in the language of multiple algebra, i.e., that operating by Θ is equivalent to operating successively by Φ and Ψ, is generally omitted. The chapter on this subject, in most treatises which I have seen, reads very like the play of Hamlet with Hamlet's part left out.

And what is the cause of this omission? Certainly not ignorance of the property in question. The fact that it is occasionally given would be a sufficient bar to this answer. It is because the author fails to see that his real subject is matrices and not determinants. Of course, in a certain sense, the author has a right to choose his subject. But this does not mean that the choice is unimportant, or that it should be determined by chance or by caprice. The problem well put is half solved, as we all know. If one chooses the subject ill, it will develop itself in a cramped manner.

But the case is really much worse than I have stated it. Not only is the true significance of the formation of Θ from Ψ and Φ not given, but the student is often not taught to form the matrix which is the product of Ψ and Φ, but one which is the product of one of these matrices and the conjugate of the other. Thus the proposition which is proved loses all its simplicity and significance, and must be recast before the instructor can explain its true bearings to the student. This fault has been denounced by Sylvester, and if anyone thinks I make too much of the standpoint from which the subject is viewed, I will refer him to the opening paragraphs of the "Lectures on Universal Algebra" in the sixth volume of the *American Journal of Mathematics*, where, with a wealth of illustration and an energy of diction which I cannot emulate, the most eloquent of mathematicians expresses his sense of the importance of the substitution of the idea of the matrix for that of the determinant. If then so important, why was the idea of the matrix let slip? Of course the writers on this subject had it to commence with. One cannot even define a determinant without the idea of a matrix. The simple fact is that in general the writers on this subject have especially developed those ideas which are naturally expressed in simple algebra, and have postponed or slurred over or omitted altogether those ideas which find their natural expression in multiple algebra. But in this subject the latter happen to be the fundamental ideas, and those which ought to direct the whole course of thought.

I have taken a very simple illustration, perhaps the very first theorem which meets the student after those immediately connected with the introductory definitions, both because the simplest illustration is really the best, and because I am here most at home. But the principles of multiple algebra seem to me to shed a flood of light into every corner of the subjects usually treated under the title of determinants, the subject gaining as much in breadth from the new notions as in simplicity from the new notations; and in the more intricate subjects of invariants, covariants, etc., I believe that the principles of multiple algebra are ready to perform an equal service. Certainly they make many things seem very simple to me which I should otherwise find difficult of comprehension.

Let us turn to geometry.

If we were asked to characterize in a single word our modern geometry, we would perhaps say that it is a geometry of position. Now position is essentially a multiple quantity, or, if you prefer, is naturally represented in algebra by a multiple quantity. And the growth in this century of the so-called synthetic as opposed to analytical geometry seems due to the fact that by the ordinary analysis geometers could not easily express, except in a cumbersome and unnatural manner, the sort of relations in which they were particularly interested. With the introduction of the notations of multiple algebra, this difficulty falls away, and with it the opposition between synthetic and analytical geometry.

It is, however, interesting and very instructive to observe how the ingenuity of mathematicians has often triumphed over the limitations of ordinary algebra. A conspicuous example and one of the simplest is seen in the *Mécanique Analytique*, where the author, by the use of what are sometimes called indeterminate equations, is able to write in one equation the equivalent of an indefinite number. Thus the equation

$$X\,dx+Y\,dy+Z\,dz=0,$$

by the indeterminateness of the values of dx, dy, dz, is made equivalent to the three equations

$$X=0,\quad Y=0,\quad Z=0.$$

It is instructive to compare this with

$$Xi+Yj+Zk=0,$$

which is the form that Hamilton or Grassmann would have used. The use of this analytical artifice, if such it can be called, runs all through the work and is fairly characteristic of it.

Again, the introduction of the potential in the theory of gravity, or electricity, or magnetism, gives us a scalar quantity instead of a vector as the subject of study; and in mechanics generally the use of the force-function substitutes a simple quantity for a complex. This method is in reality not different from that just mentioned, since Lagrange's indeterminate equation expresses, at least in its origin, the variation of the force-function. It is indeed the real beauty of Lagrange's method that it is not so much an analytical artifice, as the natural development of the subject.

In modern analytical geometry we find methods in use which are exceedingly ingenious, and give forms curiously like those of multiple algebra, but which, at least if logically carried out very far, are excessively artificial, and that for the expression of the simplest things. The simplest conceptions of the geometry of three dimensions are points and planes, and the simplest relation between these is that a point lies in a plane. Let us see how these notions have been handled by means of ordinary algebra, and by multiple algebra. It will illustrate the characteristic difference of the methods, perhaps as well as the reading of an elaborate treatise.

In multiple algebra a point is designated by a single letter, just as it is in what is called synthetic geometry, and as it generally is by the ordinary analyst when he is not writing equations. But in his equations, instead of a single letter the analyst introduces several letters (coordinates) to represent the point.

A plane may be represented in multiple algebra as in synthetic geometry by a single letter; in the ordinary algebra it is sometimes represented by three coordinates, for which it is most convenient to take the reciprocals of the segments cut off by the plane on three axes. But the modern analyst has a more ingenious method of representing the plane. He observes that the equation of the plane may be written

$$\xi x + \eta y + \zeta z = 1, \tag{1}$$

where ξ, η, ζ are the reciprocals of the segments, and x, y, z are the coordinates of any point in the plane. Now if we set

$$p = \xi x + \eta y + \zeta z, \tag{2}$$

this letter will represent an expression which represents the plane. In fact, we may say that p implicitly contains ξ, η, and ζ, which are the coordinates of the plane. We may therefore speak of the plane p, and for many purposes can introduce the letter p into our equations instead of ξ, η, ζ. For example, the equation

$$p''' = \frac{p' + p''}{2} \tag{3}$$

is equivalent to the three equations

$$\xi''' = \frac{\xi' + \xi''}{2}, \qquad \eta''' = \frac{\eta' + \eta''}{2}, \qquad \zeta''' = \frac{\zeta' + \zeta''}{2}. \tag{4}$$

It is to be noticed that on account of the indeterminateness of the x, y, and z, this method, regarded as an analytical artifice, is identical with that of Lagrange, also that in multiple algebra we should have an equation of precisely the same form as (3) to express the same relation between the planes, but that the equation would be explained to the student in a totally different manner. This we shall see more particularly hereafter.

It is curious that we have thus a simpler notation for a plane than for a point. This however may be reversed. If we commence with the notion of the coordinates of a plane, ξ, η, ζ, the equation of a point (i.e., the equation between ξ, η, ζ which will hold for every plane passing through the point) will be

$$x\xi+y\eta+z\zeta=1, \tag{5}$$

where x, y, z are the coordinates of the point. Now if we set

$$q=x\xi+y\eta+z\zeta, \tag{6}$$

we may regard the single letter q as representing the point, and use it, in many cases, instead of the coordinates x, y, z, which indeed it implicitly contains. Thus we may write

$$q'''=\frac{q'+q''}{2} \tag{7}$$

for the three equations

$$x'''=\frac{x'+x''}{2}, \qquad y'''=\frac{y'+y''}{2}, \qquad z'''=\frac{z'+z''}{2}. \tag{8}$$

Here, by an analytical artifice, we come to equations identical in form and meaning with those used by Hamilton, Grassmann, and even by Möbius in 1827. But the explanations of the formulæ would differ widely. The methods of the founders of multiple algebra are characterized by a bold simplicity, that of the modern geometry by a somewhat bewildering ingenuity. That p and q represent the same expression (in one case x, y, z, and in the other ξ, η, ζ being indeterminate) is a circumstance which may easily become perplexing. I am not quite certain that it would be convenient to use both of these abridged notations at the same time. In fact, if the geometer using these methods were asked to express by an equation in p and q that the point q lies in the plane p, he might find himself somewhat entangled in the meshes of his own ingenuity, and need some new artifice to extricate himself. I do not mean that his genius might not possibly be equal to the occasion, but I do mean very seriously that it is a vicious method which requires any ingenuity or any artifice to express so simple a relation.

If we use the methods of multiple algebra which are most comparable to those just described, a point is naturally represented by a vector (ρ) drawn to it from the origin, a plane by a vector (σ) drawn from the origin perpendicularly toward the plane and in length equal to the reciprocal of the distance of the plane from the origin. The equation

$$\sigma''' = \frac{\sigma' + \sigma''}{2} \tag{9}$$

will have precisely the same meaning as equation (3), and

$$\rho''' = \frac{\rho' + \rho''}{2} \tag{10}$$

will have precisely the same meaning as equation (7), viz., that the point ρ''' is in the middle between ρ' and ρ''. That the point ρ lies in the plane σ is expressed by equating to unity the product of ρ and σ called by Grassmann internal, or by Hamilton called the scalar part of the product taken negatively. By whatever name called, the quantity in question is the product of the lengths of the vectors and the cosine of the included angle. It is of course immaterial what particular sign we use to express this product, as whether we write

$$\rho . \sigma = 1, \qquad \text{or} \qquad S \rho \sigma = -1. \tag{11}$$

I should myself prefer the simplest possible sign for so simple a relation. It may be observed that ρ and σ may be expressed as the geometrical sum of their components parallel to a set of perpendicular axes, viz.,

$$\rho = xi + yj + zk, \qquad \sigma = \xi i + \eta j + \zeta k. \tag{12}$$

By substitution of these values, equation (11) becomes by the laws of this kind of multiplication

$$x\xi + y\eta + z\zeta = 1. \tag{13}$$

My object in going over these elementary matters is to call attention to the very roundabout way in which the ordinary analysis makes out to represent a point or a plane by a single letter, as distinguished from the directness and simplicity of the notations of multiple algebra, and also to the fact that the representations of points and planes by single letters in the ordinary analysis are not, when obtained, as amenable to analytical treatment as are the notations of multiple algebra.

I have compared that form of the ordinary analysis which relates to Cartesian axes with a vector analysis. But the case is essentially the same if we compare the form of ordinary analysis which relates to a fundamental tetrahedron with Grassmann's geometrical analysis, founded on the point as the elementary quantity.

In the method of ordinary analysis a point is represented by four coordinates, of which each represents the distance of the point from a plane of the tetrahedron divided by the distance of the opposite vertex from the same plane. The equation of a plane may be put in the form

$$\xi x + \eta y + \zeta z + \omega w = 0, \tag{14}$$

where ξ, η, ζ, ω are the distances of the plane from the four points, and x, y, z, w are the coordinates of any point in the plane. Here we may set

$$p=\xi x+\eta y+\zeta z+\omega w, \tag{15}$$

and say that p represents the plane. To some extent we can introduce this letter into equations instead of ξ, η, ζ, ω. Thus the equation

$$lp'+mp''+np'''=0 \tag{16}$$

(which denotes that the planes p', p'', p''', meet in a common line, making angles of which the sines are proportional to l, m, and n) is equivalent to the four equations

$$l\xi'+m\xi''+n\xi'''=0, \qquad l\eta'+m\eta''+n\eta'''=0, \quad \text{etc.} \tag{17}$$

Again, we may regard ξ, η, ζ, ω as the coordinates of a plane. The equation of a point will then be

$$x\xi+y\eta+z\zeta+w\omega=0. \tag{18}$$

If we set

$$q=x\xi+y\eta+z\zeta+w\omega, \tag{19}$$

we may say that q represents the point. The equation

$$q'''=\frac{q'+q''}{2}, \tag{20}$$

which indicates that the point q''' bisects the line between q' and q'', is equivalent to the four equations

$$\xi'=\frac{\xi''+\xi'''}{2}, \qquad \eta'=\frac{\eta''+\eta'''}{2}, \quad \text{etc.} \tag{21}$$

To express that the point q lies in the plane p does not seem easy, without going back to the use of coordinates.

The form of multiple algebra which is to be compared to this is the geometrical algebra of Möbius and Grassmann, in which points without reference to any origin are represented by single letters, say by Italic capitals, and planes may also be represented by single letters, say by Greek capitals. An equation like

$$Q'''=\frac{Q'+Q''}{2}, \tag{22}$$

has exactly the same meaning as equation (20) of ordinary algebra. So

$$l\Pi'+m\Pi''+n\Pi'''=0 \tag{23}$$

has precisely the same meaning as equation (16) of ordinary algebra. That the point Q lies in the plane Π is expressed by equating to zero the product of Q and Π which is called by Grassmann external and which might be defined as the distance of the point from the plane. We may write this

$$Q\times\Pi=0. \tag{24}$$

To show that so simple an expression is really amenable to analytical treatment, I observe that Q may be expressed in terms of any four points (not in the same plane) on the barycentric principle explained above, viz.,

$$Q = xA + yB + zC + wD, \tag{25}$$

and Π may be expressed in terms of combinatorial products of A, B, C, and D, viz.,

$$\Pi = \xi B \times C \times D + \eta C \times A \times D + \zeta D \times A \times B + \omega A \times C \times B, \tag{26}$$

and by these substitutions, by the laws of the combinatorial product to be mentioned hereafter, equation (24) is transformed into

$$w\omega + x\xi + y\eta + z\zeta = 0, \tag{27}$$

which is identical with the formula of ordinary analysis.*

I have gone at length into this very simple point in order to illustrate the fact, which I think is a general one, that the modern geometry is not only tending to results which are appropriately expressed in multiple algebra, but that it is actually striving to clothe itself in forms which are remarkably similar to the notations of multiple algebra, only less simple and general and far less amenable to analytical treatment, and therefore, that a certain logical necessity calls for throwing off the yoke under which analytical geometry has so long labored. And lest this should seem to be the utterance of an uninformed enthusiasm, or the echoing of the possibly exaggerated claims of the devotees of a particular branch of mathematical study, I will quote a sentence from Clebsch and one from Clifford, relating to the past and to the future of multiple algebra. The former in his eulogy on Plücker,† in 1871, speaking of recent advances in geometry, says that "in a certain sense the coordinates of a straight line, and in general a great part of the fundamental conceptions of the newer algebra, are contained in the *Ausdehnungslehre* of 1844," and Clifford ‡ in the last year of his life, speaking of the *Ausdehnungslehre,* with which he had but recently become acquainted, expresses "his profound admiration of that extraordinary work, and his conviction that its principles will exercise a vast influence upon the future of mathematical science."

Another subject in which we find a tendency toward the forms and methods of multiple algebra, is the calculus of operations. Our ordinary analysis introduces operators, and the successive operations A and B may be equivalent to the operation C. To express this in an equation we may write

$$BA(x) = C(x),$$

* The letters ξ, η, ζ, ω, here denote the distances of the plane Π from the points A, B, C, D, divided by six times the volume of the tetrahedron, A, B, C, D. The letters x, y, z, w, denote the tetrahedral coordinates as above.

† *Gött. Abhandl.*, vol. xvi, p. 28. ‡ *Amer. Journ. Math.*, vol. i, p. 350.

where x is any quantity or function. We may also have occasion to write

$$A(x)+B(x)=D(x), \quad \text{or} \quad (A+B)(x)=D(x).$$

But it is almost impossible to resist the tendency to express these relations in the form

$$BA=C,$$

$$A+B=D,$$

in which the operators appear in a sense as quantities, i.e., as subjects of functional operation. Now since these operators are often of such nature that they cannot be perfectly specified by a single numerical quantity, when we treat them as quantities they must be regarded as multiple quantities. In this way certain formulæ which essentially belong to multiple algebra get a precarious footing where they are only allowed because they are regarded as abridged notations for equations in ordinary algebra. Yet the logical development of such notations would lead a good way in multiple algebra, and doubtless many investigators have entered the field from this side.

One might also notice, to show how the ordinary algebra is becoming saturated with the notions and notations which seem destined to turn it into a multiple algebra, the notation so common in the higher algebra

$$(a, b, c)(x, y, z)$$

for

$$ax+by+cz.$$

This is evidently the same as Grassmann's internal product of the multiple quantities (a, b, c) and (x, y, z), or, in the language of quaternions, the scalar part, taken negatively, of the product of the vectors of which a, b, c and x, y, z are the components. A similar correspondence with Grassmann's methods might, I think, be shown in such notations as, for example,

$$(a, b, c, d)(x, y)^3.$$

The free admission of such notations is doubtless due to the fact that they are regarded simply as abridged notations.

The author of the celebrated "Memoir on the Theory of Matrices" goes much farther than this in his use of the forms of multiple algebra. Thus he writes explicitly one equation to stand for several, without the use of any of the analytical artifices which have been mentioned. This work has indeed, as we have seen, been characterized as marking the commencement of multiple algebra,—a view to which we can only take exception as not doing justice to earlier writers.

But the significance of this memoir with regard to the point which I am now considering is that it shows that the chasm so marked in the second quarter of this century is destined to be closed up. Notions and notations for which a Cayley is sponsor will not be excluded from good society among mathematicians. And if we admit as suitable the notations used in this memoir (where it is noticeable that the author rather avoids multiple algebra, and only uses it very sparingly), we shall logically be brought to use a great deal more. For example, if it is a good thing to write in our equations a single letter to represent a matrix of n^2 numerical quantities, why not use a single letter to represent the n quantities operated upon, as Grassmann and Hamilton have done? Logical consistency seems to demand it. And if we may use the sign)(to denote an operation by which two sets of quantities are combined to form a third set, as is the case in this memoir, why not use other signs to denote other functional operations of which the result is a multiple quantity? If it be conceded that this is the proper method to follow where simplicity of conception, or brevity of expression, or ease of transformation is served thereby, our algebra will become in large part a multiple algebra.

We have considered the subject a good while from the outside; we have glanced at the principal events in the history of multiple algebra; we have seen how the course of modern thought seems to demand its aid, how it is actually leaning toward it, and beginning to adopt its methods. It may be worth while to direct our attention more critically to multiple algebra itself, and inquire into its essential character and its most important principles.

I do not know that anything useful or interesting, which relates to multiple quantity, and can be symbolically expressed, falls outside of the domain of multiple algebra. But if it is asked, what notions are to be regarded as fundamental, we must answer, here as elsewhere, those which are most simple and fruitful. Unquestionably, no relations are more so than those which are known by the names of addition and multiplication.

Perhaps I should here notice the essentially different manner in which the multiplication of multiple quantities has been viewed by different writers. Some, as Hamilton, or De Morgan, or Peirce, speak of the product of two multiple quantities, as if only one product could exist, at least in the same algebra. Others, as Grassmann, speak of various kinds of products for the same multiple quantities. Thus Hamilton seems for many years to have agitated the question, what he should regard as the product of each pair of a set of triplets, or in the geometrical application of the subject, what he should regard as the product of each pair of a system of perpendicular directed lines.* Grassmann asks, What products, i.e., what distributive functions of the multiple quantities, are most important?

---

* *Phil. Mag.* (3), vol. xxv, p. 490; *North British Review*, vol. xlv, (1866), p. 57.

It may be that in some cases the fact that only one kind of product is known in ordinary algebra has led those to whom the problem presented itself in the form of finding a new algebra to adopt this characteristic derived from the old. Perhaps the reason lies deeper in a distinction like that in arithmetic between concrete and abstract numbers or quantities. The multiple quantities corresponding to concrete quantities such as ten apples or three miles are evidently such combinations as ten apples + seven oranges, three miles northward + five miles eastward, or six miles in a direction fifty degrees east of north. Such are the fundamental multiple quantities from Grassmann's point of view. But if we ask what it is in multiple algebra which corresponds to an abstract number like twelve, which is essentially an operator, which changes one mile into twelve miles, and $1,000 into $12,000, the most general answer would evidently be: an operator which will work such changes as, for example, that of ten apples + seven oranges into fifty apples + 100 oranges, or that of one vector into another.

Now an operator has, of course, one characteristic relation, viz., its relation to the operand. This needs no especial definition, since it is contained in the definition of the operator. If the operation is distributive, it may not inappropriately be called multiplication, and the result is *par excellence* the product of the operator and operand. The sum of operators *quâ* operators, is an operator which gives for the product the sum of the products given by the operators to be added. The product of two operators is an operator which is equivalent to the successive operations of the factors. This multiplication is necessarily associative, and its definition is not really different from that of the operators themselves. And here I may observe that Professor C. S. Peirce has shown that his father's associative algebras may be regarded as operational and matricular.*

Now the calculus of distributive operators is a subject of great extent and importance, but Grassmann's view is the more comprehensive, since it embraces the other with something besides. For every quantitative operator may be regarded as a quantity, i.e., as the subject of mathematical operation, but every quantity cannot be regarded as an operator; precisely as in grammar every verb may be taken as substantive, as in the infinitive, while every substantive does not give us a verb.

Grassmann's view seems also the most practical and convenient. For we often use many functions of the same pair of multiple quantities, which are distributive with respect to both, and we need some simple designation to indicate a property of such fundamental

* *Amer. Journ. Math.*, vol. iv, p. 221.

importance in the algebra of such functions, and no advantage appears in singling out a particular function to be alone called the product. Even in quaternions, where Hamilton speaks of only one product of two vectors (regarding it as a special case of the product of quaternions, i.e., of operators), he nevertheless comes to use the scalar part of this product and the vector part separately. Now the distributive law is satisfied by each of these, which therefore may conveniently be called products. In this sense we have three kinds of products of vectors in Hamilton's analysis.

Let us then adopt the more general view of multiplication, and call any function of two or more multiple quantities, which is distributive with respect to all, a product, with only this limitation, that when one of the factors is simply an ordinary algebraic quantity, its effect is to be taken in the ordinary sense.

It is to be observed that this definition of multiplication implies that we have an addition both of the kind of quantity to which the product belongs, and of the kinds to which the factors belong. Of course, these must be subject to the general formal laws of addition. I do not know that it is necessary for the purposes of a general discussion to stop to define these operations more particularly, either on their own account or to complete the definition of multiplication. Algebra, as a formal science, may rest on a purely formal foundation. To take our illustration again from mechanics, we may say that if a man is inventing a particular machine,—a sewing machine, a reaper,—nothing is more important than that he should have a precise idea of the operation which his machine is to perform, yet when he is treating the general principles of mechanics he may discuss the lever, or the form of the teeth of wheels which will transmit uniform motion, without inquiring the purpose to which the apparatus is to be applied; and in like manner that if we were forming a particular algebra,—a geometrical algebra, a mechanical algebra, an algebra for the theory of elimination and substitution, an algebra for the study of quantics,—we should commence by asking, What are the multiple quantities, or sets of quantities, which we have to consider? What are the additive relations between them? What are the multiplicative relations between them? etc., forming a perfectly defined and complete idea of these relations as we go along; but in the development of a general algebra no such definiteness of conception is requisite. Given only the purely formal law of the distributive character of multiplication,—this is sufficient for the foundation of a science. Nor will such a science be merely a pastime for an ingenious mind. It will serve a thousand purposes in the formation of particular algebras. Perhaps we shall find that in the most important cases the particular algebra is little more than an application or interpretation of the general.

Grassmann observes that any kind of multiplication of n-fold quantities is characterized by the relations which hold between the products of n independent units. In certain kinds of multiplication these characteristic relations will hold true of the products of any of the quantities.

Thus if the value of a product is independent of the order of the factors when these belong to the system of units, it will always be independent of the order of the factors. The kind of multiplication characterized by this relation and no other between the products is called by Grassmann *algebraic*, because its rules coincide with those of ordinary algebra. It is to be observed, however, that it gives rise to multiple quantities of higher orders. If n independent units are required to express the original quantities, $n\frac{n+1}{2}$ units will be required for the products of two factors, $n\frac{(n+1)(n+2)}{2.3}$ for the products of three factors, etc.

Again, if the value of a product of factors belonging to a system of units is multiplied by -1 when two factors change places, the same will be true of the product of any factors obtained by addition of the units. The kind of multiplication characterized by this relation and no other is called by Grassmann *external* or *combinatorial*. For our present purpose we may denote it by the sign $\times$. It gives rise to multiple quantities of higher orders, $n\frac{n-1}{2}$ units being required to express the products of two factors, $n\frac{(n-1)(n-2)}{2.3}$ units for products of three factors, etc. All products of more than n factors are zero. The products of n factors may be expressed by a single unit, viz., the product of the n original units taken in a specified order, which is generally set equal to 1. The products of $n-1$ factors are expressed in terms of n units, those of $n-2$ factors in terms of $n\frac{n-1}{2}$ units, etc. This kind of multiplication is associative, like the algebraic.

Grassmann observes, with respect to binary products, that these two kinds of multiplication are the only kinds characterized by laws which are the same for any factors as for particular units, except indeed that characterized by no special laws, and that for which all products are zero.* The last we may evidently reject as nugatory. That for which there are no special laws, i.e., in which no equations

* Crelle's *Journ. f. Math.*, vol. xlix, p. 138.

subsist between the products of a system of independent units, is also rejected by Grassmann, as not appearing to afford important applications. I shall, however, have occasion to speak of it, and shall call it the indeterminate product. In this kind of multiplication, n^2 units are required to express the products of two factors, and n^3 units for products of three factors, etc. It evidently may be regarded as associative.

Another very important kind of multiplication is that called by Grassmann *internal.* In the form in which I shall give it, which is less general than Grassmann's, it is in one respect the most simple of all, since its only result is a numerical quantity. It is essentially binary and characterized by laws of the form

$$i.i=1, \quad j.j=1, \quad k.k=1, \quad \text{etc.,}$$
$$i.j=0, \quad j.i=0, \quad \text{etc.,}$$

where i, j, k, etc., represent a system of independent units. I use the dot as significant of this kind of multiplication.

Grassmann derives this kind of multiplication from the combinatorial by the following process. He defines the complement (Ergänzung) of a unit as the combinatorial product of all the other units, taken with such a sign that the combinatorial product of the unit and its complement shall be positive. The combinatorial product of a unit and its complement is therefore unity, and that of a unit and the complement of any other unit is zero. The internal product of two units is the combinatorial product of the first and the complement of the second.

It is important to observe that any scalar product of two factors of the same kind of multiple quantities, which is positive when the factors are identical, may be regarded as an internal product, i.e., we may always find such a system of units, that the characteristic equations of the product will reduce to the above form. The nature of the subject may afford a definition of the product independent of any reference to a system of units. Such a definition will then have obvious advantages. An important case of this kind occurs in geometry in that product of two vectors which is obtained by multiplying the products of their lengths by the cosine of the angle which they include. This is an internal product in Grassmann's sense.

Let us now return to the indeterminate product, which I am inclined to regard as the most important of all, since we may derive from it the algebraic and the combinatorial. For this end we will prefix Σ to an indeterminate product to denote the sum of all the terms obtained by taking the factors in every possible order. Then,

$$\Sigma\, a|\beta|\gamma,$$

for instance, where the vertical line is used to denote the

indeterminate product,* is a distributive function of α, β, and γ. It is evidently not affected by changing the order of the letters. It is, therefore, an algebraic product in the sense in which the term has been defined.

So, again, if we prefix $\Sigma\pm$ to an indeterminate product to denote the sum of all terms obtained by giving the factors every possible order, those terms being taken negatively which are obtained by an odd number of simple permutations,

$$\Sigma \pm \alpha|\beta|\gamma,$$

for instance, will be a distributive function of α, β, γ, which is multiplied by -1 when two of these letters change places. It will therefore be a combinatorial product.

It is a characteristic and very important property of an indeterminate product that every product of all its factors with any other quantities is also a product of the indeterminate product and the other quantities. We need not stop for a formal proof of this proposition, which indeed is an immediate consequence of the definitions of the terms.

These considerations bring us naturally to what Grassmann calls *regressive multiplication*, which I will first illustrate by a very simple example. If n, the degree of multiplicity of our original quantities, is 4, the combinatorial product of $\alpha\times\beta\times\gamma$ and $\delta\times\epsilon$, viz.,

$$\alpha\times\beta\times\gamma\times\delta\times\epsilon,$$

is necessarily zero, since the number of factors exceeds four. But if for $\delta\times\epsilon$ we set its equivalent

$$\delta|\epsilon-\epsilon|\delta,$$

we may multiply the first factor in each of these indeterminate products combinatorially by $\alpha\times\beta\times\gamma$, and prefix the result, which is a numerical quantity, as coefficient to the second factor. This will give

$$(\alpha\times\beta\times\gamma\times\delta)\epsilon-(\alpha\times\beta\times\gamma\times\epsilon)\delta.$$

Now, the first term of this expression is a product of $\alpha\times\beta\times\gamma$, δ, and ϵ, and therefore, by the principle just stated, a product of $\alpha\times\beta\times\gamma$ and $\delta|\epsilon$. The second term is a similar product of $\alpha\times\beta\times\gamma$ and $\epsilon|\delta$. Therefore the whole expression is a product of $\alpha\times\beta\times\gamma$ and $\delta|\epsilon-\epsilon|\delta$, that is, of $\alpha\times\beta\times\gamma$ and $\delta\times\epsilon$. That is, except in sign, what Grassmann calls the *regressive product* of $\alpha\times\beta\times\gamma$ and $\delta\times\epsilon$.

To generalize this process, we first observe that an expression of the form

$$\Sigma \pm \alpha\times\beta|\gamma\times\delta,$$

in which each term is an indeterminate product of two combinatorial products, and in which $\Sigma\pm$ denotes the sum of all terms obtained by

* This notation must not be confounded with Grassmann's use of the vertical line.

putting every different pair of the letters before the dividing line, the negative sign being used for any terms which may be obtained by an odd number of simple permutations of the letters,—in other words, the expression

$$\alpha\times\beta|\gamma\times\delta-\alpha\times\gamma|\beta\times\delta-\alpha\times\delta|\gamma\times\beta+\beta\times\gamma|\alpha\times\delta$$
$$-\beta\times\delta|\alpha\times\gamma+\gamma\times\delta|\alpha\times\beta,$$

is a distributive function of α, β, γ, and δ, which is multiplied by -1 when two of these letters change places, and may, therefore, be regarded as equivalent to the combinatorial product $\alpha\times\beta\times\gamma\times\delta$. Now, if $n=5$, the combinatorial product of

$$\rho\times\sigma\times\tau \qquad \text{and} \qquad \alpha\times\beta\times\gamma\times\delta$$

is zero. But if we multiply the first member of each of the above indeterminate products by $\rho\times\sigma\times\tau$, and prefix the result as coefficient to the second member, we obtain

$$(\rho\times\sigma\times\tau\times\alpha\times\beta)\gamma\times\delta-(\rho\times\sigma\times\tau\times\alpha\times\gamma)\beta\times\delta+\text{etc.},$$

which is what Grassmann calls the regressive product of $\rho\times\sigma\times\tau$ and $\alpha\times\beta\times\gamma\times\delta$. It is easy to see that the principle may be extended so as to give a regressive product in any case in which the total number of factors of two combinatorial products is greater than n. Also, that we might form a regressive product by treating the first of the given combinatorials as we have treated the second. It may easily be shown that this would give the same result, except in some cases with a difference of sign. To avoid this inconvenience, we may make the rule, that whenever in the substitution of a sum of indeterminate products for a combinatorial, both factors of the indeterminate products are of odd degree, we change the sign of the whole expression. With this understanding, the results which we obtain will be identical with Grassmann's regressive product. The propriety of the name consists in the fact that the product is of less degree than either of the factors. For the contrary reason, the ordinary external or combinatorial multiplication is sometimes called by Grassmann *progressive*.

Regressive multiplication is associative and exhibits a very remarkable analogy with the progressive. This analogy I have not time here to develop, but will only remark that in this analogy lies in its most general form that celebrated *principle of duality*, which appears in various forms in geometry and certain branches of analysis.

To fix our ideas, I may observe that in geometry the progressive multiplication of points gives successively lines, planes and volumes; the regressive multiplication of planes gives successively lines, points and scalar quantities.

The indeterminate product affords a natural key to the subject of matrices. In fact, a sum of indeterminate products of the second degree represents n^2 scalars, which constitute an ordinary or quadratic matrix; a sum of indeterminate products of the third degree represents n^3 scalars, which constitute a cubic matrix, etc. I shall confine myself to the simplest and most important case, that of quadratic matrices.

An expression of the form

$$\alpha(\lambda.\rho)$$

being a product of α, λ, and ρ, may be regarded as a product of $\alpha|\lambda$ and ρ, by a principle already stated. Now if Φ denotes a sum of indeterminate products, of second degree, say $\alpha|\lambda+\beta|\mu+$etc., we may write

$$\Phi.\rho$$

for

$$\alpha(\lambda.\rho)+\beta(\mu.\rho)+\text{etc.}$$

This is like ρ, a quantity of the first degree, and it is a homogeneous linear function of ρ. It is easy to see that the most general form of such a function may be expressed in this way. An equation like

$$\sigma=\Phi.\rho$$

represents n equations in ordinary algebra, in which n variables are expressed as linear functions of n others by means of n^2 coefficients.

The internal product of two indeterminate products may be defined by the equation

$$(\alpha|\beta).(\gamma|\delta)=(\beta.\gamma)\,\alpha|\delta.$$

This defines the internal product of matrices, as

$$\Psi.\Phi.$$

This product evidently gives a matrix, the operation of which is equivalent to the successive operations of Φ and Ψ; i.e.,

$$(\Psi.\Phi).\rho=\Psi.(\Phi.\rho).$$

We may express this a little more generally by saying that internal multiplication is associative when performed on a series of matrices, or on such a series terminated by a quantity of the first degree.

Another kind of multiplication of binary indeterminate products is that in which the preceding factors are multiplied combinatorially, and also the following. It may be defined by the equation

$$(\alpha|\lambda)\overset{\times}{\times}(\beta|\mu)\overset{\times}{\times}(\gamma|\nu)=\alpha\times\beta\times\gamma|\lambda\times\mu\times\nu.$$

This defines a multiplication of matrices denoted by the same symbol, as

$$\Phi\overset{\times}{\times}\Psi\overset{\times}{\times}\Omega, \qquad \Phi\overset{\times}{\times}\Psi\overset{\times}{\times}\Omega\overset{\times}{\times}\Theta.$$

This multiplication, which is associative and commutative, is of great importance in the theory of determinants. In fact,

$$\frac{1}{\underline{|n}}\Phi_{\times}^{\times n}$$

is the determinant of the matrix Φ. A lower power, as the mth, with the divisor $n(n-1)\ldots(n-m+1)$ would express as multiple quantity all the subdeterminants of order m.*

It is evident that by the combination of the operations of indeterminate, algebraic, and combinatorial multiplication we obtain multiple quantities of a more complicated nature than by the use of only one of these kinds of multiplication. The indeterminate product of combinatorial products we have already mentioned. The combinatorial product of algebraic products, and the indeterminate product of algebraic products, are also of great importance, especially in the theory of quantics. These three multiplications, with the internal, especially in connection with the general property of the indeterminate product given above, and the derivation of the algebraic and combinatorial products from the indeterminate, which affords a generalization of that property, give rise to a great wealth of multiplicative relations between these multiple quantities. I say "*wealth* of multiplicative relations" designedly, for there is hardly any kind of relations between things which are the objects of mathematical study, which add so much to the resources of the student as those which we call multiplicative, except perhaps the simpler class which we call additive, and which are presupposed in the multiplicative. This is a truth quite independent of our using any of the notations of multiple algebra, although a suitable notation for such relations will of course increase their value.

Perhaps, before closing, I ought to say a few words on the applications of multiple algebra.

First of all, geometry, and the geometrical sciences which treat of things having position in space, kinematics, mechanics, astronomy physics, crystallography, seem to demand a method of this kind, for position in space is essentially a multiple quantity and can only be represented by simple quantities in an arbitrary and cumbersome manner. For this reason, and because our spatial intuitions are more developed than those of any other class of mathematical relations, these subjects are especially adapted to introduce the student to the methods of multiple algebra. Here, Nature herself takes us by the hand and leads us along by easy steps, as a mother teaches her child to walk. In the contemplation of such subjects, Möbius, Hamilton,

---

* Quadratic matrices may also be represented by a sum of indeterminate products of a quantity of the first degree with a combinatorial product of $(n-1)$st degree, as, for example, when $n=4$, by a sum of products of the form

$$\alpha|\beta\times\gamma\times\delta.$$

The theory of such matrices is almost identical with that of those of the other form, except that the external multiplication takes the place of the internal, in the multiplication of the matrices with each other and with quantities of the first degree.

and Grassmann formed their algebras, although the philosophical mind of the last was not satisfied until he had produced a system unfettered by any spatial relations. It is probably in connection with some of these subjects that the notions of multiple algebra are most widely disseminated.

Maxwell's *Treatise on Electricity and Magnetism* has done so much to familiarize students of physics with quaternion notations, that it seems impossible that this subject should ever again be entirely divorced from the methods of multiple algebra.

I wish that I could say as much of astronomy. It is, I think, to be regretted, that the oldest of the scientific applications of mathematics, the most dignified, the most conservative, should keep so far aloof from the youngest of mathematical methods; and standing as I do to-day, by some chance, among astronomers, although not of the guild, I cannot but endeavor to improve the opportunity by expressing my conviction of the advantages which astronomers might gain by employing some of the methods of multiple algebra. A very few of the fundamental notions of a vector analysis, the addition of vectors and what quaternionists would call the scalar part and the vector part of the product of two vectors (which may be defined without the notion of the quaternion),—these three notions with some four fundamental properties relating to them are sufficient to reduce enormously the labor of mastering such subjects as the elementary theory of orbits, the determination of an orbit from three observations, the differential equations which are used in determining the best orbit from an indefinite number of observations by the method of least squares, or those which give the perturbations when the elements are treated as variable. In all these subjects the analytical work is greatly simplified, and it is far easier to find the best form for numerical calculation than by the use of the ordinary analysis.

I may here remark that in its geometrical applications multiple algebra will naturally take one of two principal forms, according as vectors or points are taken as elementary quantities, i.e., according as something having magnitude and direction, or something having magnitude and position at a point, is the fundamental conception. These forms of multiple algebra may be distinguished as *vector analysis* and *point analysis*. The former we may call a triple, the latter a quadruple algebra, if we determine the degree of the algebra from the degree of multiplicity of the fundamental conception. The former is included in the latter, since the subtraction of points gives us vectors, and in this way Grassmann's vector analysis is included in his point analysis. Hamilton's system, in which the vector is the fundamental idea, is nevertheless made a quadruple algebra by the addition of ordinary numerical quantities. For practical purposes we may regard Hamilton's system as equivalent to Grassmann's algebra of vectors. Such practical equivalence is of course consistent with great differences of notation, and of the point of view from which the subject is regarded.

Perhaps I should add a word in regard to the nature of the problems which require a vector analysis, or the more general form of Grassmann's point analysis. The distinction of the problems is very marked, and corresponds precisely to the distinction familiar to all analysts between problems which are suitable for Cartesian coordinates, and those which are suitable for the use of tetrahedral, or, in plane geometry, triangular coordinates. Thus, in mechanics, kinematics, astronomy, physics, or crystallography, Grassmann's point analysis will rarely be wanted. One might teach these subjects for years by a vector analysis, and never perhaps feel the need of any of the notions or notations which are peculiar to the point analysis, precisely as in ordinary algebra one might use the Cartesian coordinates in teaching these subjects, without any occasion for the use of tetrahedral coordinates. I think of one exception, which, however, confirms the rule. The very important theory of forces acting on a rigid body is much better treated by point analysis than by vector analysis, exactly as in ordinary algebra it is much better treated by tetrahedral coordinates than by Cartesian,—I mean for the purpose of the elegant development of general propositions. A sufficient theory for the purposes of numerical calculations can easily enough be given by any method, and the most familiar to the student is for such practical purposes of course the best. On the other hand, the projective properties of bodies, the relations of collinearity, and similar subjects, seem to demand the point analysis for their adequate treatment.

If I have said that the algebra of vectors is contained in the algebra of points, it does not follow that in a certain sense the algebra of points is not deducible from the algebra of vectors. In mathematics, a part often contains the whole. If we represent points by vectors drawn from a common origin, and then develop those relations between such vectors representing points, which are independent of the position of the origin,—by this simple process we may obtain a large part, possibly all, of an algebra of points. In this way the vector analysis may be made to serve very conveniently for many of those subjects which I have mentioned as suitable for point analysis. The vector analysis, thus enlarged, is hardly to be distinguished from a point analysis, but the treatment of the subject in this way has somewhat of a makeshift character, as distinguished from the unity and simplicity of the subject when developed directly from the idea of something situated at a point.

Of those subjects which have no relations to space, the elementary theory of eliminations and substitutions, including the theory of matrices and determinants, seems to afford the most simple application of multiple algebra. I have already indicated what seems to me the appropriate foundation for the theory of matrices. The method is essentially that which Grassmann has sketched in his first *Ausdehnungslehre* under the name of the *open product* and has developed at length in the second.

In the theory of quantics Grassmann's algebraic product finds an application, the quantic appearing as a sum of algebraic products in Grassmann's sense of the term. As it has been stated that these products are subject to the same laws as the ordinary products of algebra, it may seem that we have here a distinction without an important difference. If the quantics were to be subject to no farther multiplications, except the algebraic in Grassmann's sense, such an objection would be valid. But quantics regarded as sums of algebraic products, in Grassmann's sense, are multiple quantities and subject to a great variety of other multiplications than the algebraic, by which they were formed. Of these the most important are doubtless the combinatorial, the internal, and the indeterminate. The combinatorial and the internal may be applied, not only to the quantic as a whole or to the algebraic products of which it consists, but also to the individual factors in each term, in accordance with the general principle which has been stated with respect to the indeterminate product and which will apply also to the algebraic, since the algebraic may be regarded as a sum of indeterminate products.

In the differential and integral calculus it is often advantageous to regard as multiple quantities various sets of variables, especially the independent variables, or those which may be taken as such. It is often convenient to represent in the form of a single differential coefficient, as

$$\frac{d\tau}{d\rho},$$

a block or matrix of ordinary differential coefficients. In this expression, ρ may be a multiple quantity representing say n independent variables, and τ another representing perhaps the same number of dependent variables. Then $d\rho$ represents the n differentials of the former, and $d\tau$ the n differentials of the latter. The whole expression represents an operator which turns $d\rho$ into $d\tau$, so that we may write identically

$$d\tau = \frac{d\tau}{d\rho} d\rho.$$

Here we see a matrix of n^2 differential coefficients represented by a quotient. This conception is due to Grassmann, as well as the representation of the matrix by a sum of products, which we have already considered. It is to be observed that these multiple differential coefficients are subject to algebraic laws very similar to those which relate to ordinary differential coefficients when there is a single independent variable, e.g.,

$$\frac{d\sigma}{d\tau}\,\frac{d\tau}{d\rho}=\frac{d\sigma}{d\rho},$$

$$\frac{d\rho}{d\tau}\,\frac{d\tau}{d\rho}=1.$$

In the integral calculus, the transformation of multiple integrals by change of variables is made very simple and clear by the methods of multiple algebra.

In the geometrical applications of the calculus, there is a certain class of theorems, of which Green's and Poisson's are the most notable examples, which seem to have been first noticed in connection with certain physical theories, especially those of electricity and magnetism, and which have only recently begun to find their way into treatises on the calculus. These not only find simplicity of expression and demonstration in the infinitesimal calculus of multiple quantities, but also their natural position, which they hardly seem to find in the ordinary treatises.

But I do not so much desire to call your attention to the diversity of the applications of multiple algebra, as to the simplicity and unity of its principles. The student of multiple algebra suddenly finds himself freed from various restrictions to which he has been accustomed. To many, doubtless, this liberty seems like an invitation to license. Here is a boundless field in which caprice may riot. It is not strange if some look with distrust for the result of such an experiment. But the farther we advance, the more evident it becomes that this too is a realm subject to law. The more we study the subject, the more we find all that is most useful and beautiful attaching itself to a few central principles. We begin by studying *multiple algebras;* we end, I think, by studying MULTIPLE ALGEBRA.

V.

ON THE DETERMINATION OF ELLIPTIC ORBITS FROM THREE COMPLETE OBSERVATIONS.

[*Memoirs of the National Academy of Sciences*, vol. IV. part II. pp. 79–104, 1889.]

THE determination of an orbit from three complete observations by the solution of the equations which represent elliptic motion presents so great difficulties in the general case, that in the first solution of the problem we must generally limit ourselves to the case in which the intervals between the observations are not very long. In this case we substitute some comparatively simple relations between the unknown quantities of the problem, which have an approximate validity for short intervals, for the less manageable relations which rigorously subsist between these quantities. A comparison of the approximate solution thus obtained with the exact laws of elliptic motion will always afford the means of a closer approximation, and by a repetition of this process we may arrive at any required degree of accuracy.

It is therefore a problem not without interest—it is, in fact, the natural point of departure in the study of the determination of orbits—to express in a manner combining as far as possible simplicity and accuracy the relations between three positions in an orbit separated by small or moderate intervals. The problem is not entirely determinate, for we may lay the greater stress upon simplicity or upon accuracy; we may seek the most simple relations which are sufficiently accurate to give us any approximation to an orbit, or we may seek the most exact expression of the real relations, which shall not be too complex to be serviceable.

Derivation of the Fundamental Equation.

The following very simple considerations afford a vector equation, not very complex and quite amenable to analytical transformation, which expresses the relations between three positions in an orbit separated by small or moderate intervals, with an accuracy far exceeding that of the approximate relations generally used in the determination of orbits.

If we adopt such a unit of time that the acceleration due to the sun's action is unity at a unit's distance, and denote the vectors* drawn from the sun to the body in its three positions by $\mathfrak{R}_1$, $\mathfrak{R}_2$, $\mathfrak{R}_3$, and the lengths of these vectors (the heliocentric distances) by r_1, r_2, r_3, the accelerations corresponding to the three positions will be represented by $-\frac{\mathfrak{R}_1}{r_1^{\,3}}$, $-\frac{\mathfrak{R}_2}{r_2^{\,3}}$, $-\frac{\mathfrak{R}_3}{r_3^{\,3}}$. Now the motion between the positions considered may be expressed with a high degree of accuracy by an equation of the form

$$\mathfrak{R}=\mathfrak{A}+t\mathfrak{B}+t^2\mathfrak{C}+t^3\mathfrak{D}+t^4\mathfrak{E},$$

having five vector constants. The actual motion rigorously satisfies six conditions, viz., if we write τ_3 for the interval of time between the

---

* Vectors, or *directed quantities*, will be represented in this paper by German capitals. The following notations will be used in connection with them :

The sign = denotes identity in direction as well as length.

The sign + denotes geometrical addition, or what is called composition in mechanics.

The sign − denotes reversal of direction, or composition after reversal.

The notation $\mathfrak{A}.\mathfrak{B}$ denotes the product of the lengths of the vectors and the cosine of the angle which they include. It will be called the *direct product* of $\mathfrak{A}$ and $\mathfrak{B}$. If x, y, z are the rectangular components of $\mathfrak{A}$, and x', y', z' those of $\mathfrak{B}$,

$$\mathfrak{A}.\mathfrak{B}=xx'+yy'+zz'.$$

$\mathfrak{A}.\mathfrak{A}$ may be written $\mathfrak{A}^2$ and called the square of $\mathfrak{A}$.

The notation $\mathfrak{A}\times\mathfrak{B}$ will be used to denote a vector of which the length is the product of the lengths of $\mathfrak{A}$ and $\mathfrak{B}$ and the sine of the angle which they include. Its direction is perpendicular to $\mathfrak{A}$ and $\mathfrak{B}$, and on that side on which a rotation from $\mathfrak{A}$ to $\mathfrak{B}$ appears counter-clockwise. It will be called the *skew product* of $\mathfrak{A}$ and $\mathfrak{B}$. If the rectangular components of $\mathfrak{A}$ and $\mathfrak{B}$ are x, y, z, and x', y', z', those of $\mathfrak{A}\times\mathfrak{B}$ will be

$$yz'-zy', \qquad zx'-xz', \qquad xy'-yx'.$$

The notation $(\mathfrak{A}\mathfrak{B}\mathfrak{C})$ denotes the volume of the parallelopiped of which three edges are obtained by laying off the vectors $\mathfrak{A}$, $\mathfrak{B}$, and $\mathfrak{C}$ from any same point, which volume is to be taken positively or negatively, according as the vector $\mathfrak{C}$ falls on the side of the plane containing $\mathfrak{A}$ and $\mathfrak{B}$, on which a rotation from $\mathfrak{A}$ to $\mathfrak{B}$ appears counter-clockwise, or on the other side. If the rectangular components of $\mathfrak{A}$, $\mathfrak{B}$, and $\mathfrak{C}$ are x, y, z; x', y', z'; and x'', y'', z'',

$$(\mathfrak{A}\mathfrak{B}\mathfrak{C})=\begin{vmatrix} x & y & z \\ x' & y' & z' \\ x'' & y'' & z'' \end{vmatrix}.$$

It follows, from the above definitions, that for any vectors $\mathfrak{A}$, $\mathfrak{B}$, and $\mathfrak{C}$

$$\mathfrak{A}.\mathfrak{B}=\mathfrak{B}.\mathfrak{A}, \qquad \mathfrak{A}\times\mathfrak{B}=-\mathfrak{B}\times\mathfrak{A},$$

$$(\mathfrak{A}\mathfrak{B}\mathfrak{C})=(\mathfrak{B}\mathfrak{C}\mathfrak{A})=(\mathfrak{C}\mathfrak{A}\mathfrak{B})=-(\mathfrak{A}\mathfrak{C}\mathfrak{B})=-(\mathfrak{C}\mathfrak{B}\mathfrak{A})=-(\mathfrak{B}\mathfrak{A}\mathfrak{C}),$$

and $$(\mathfrak{A}\mathfrak{B}\mathfrak{C})=\mathfrak{A}.(\mathfrak{B}\times\mathfrak{C})=\mathfrak{B}.(\mathfrak{C}\times\mathfrak{A})=\mathfrak{C}.(\mathfrak{A}\times\mathfrak{B})\,;$$

also that $\mathfrak{A}.\mathfrak{B}$, $\mathfrak{A}\times\mathfrak{B}$, are distributive functions of $\mathfrak{A}$ and $\mathfrak{B}$, and $(\mathfrak{A}\mathfrak{B}\mathfrak{C})$ a distributive function of $\mathfrak{A}$, $\mathfrak{B}$, and $\mathfrak{C}$, for example, that if $\mathfrak{A}=\mathfrak{L}+\mathfrak{M}$,

$$\mathfrak{A}.\mathfrak{B}=\mathfrak{L}.\mathfrak{B}+\mathfrak{M}.\mathfrak{B}, \qquad \mathfrak{A}\times\mathfrak{B}=\mathfrak{L}\times\mathfrak{B}+\mathfrak{M}\times\mathfrak{B}, \qquad (\mathfrak{A}\mathfrak{B}\mathfrak{C})=(\mathfrak{L}\mathfrak{B}\mathfrak{C})+(\mathfrak{M}\mathfrak{B}\mathfrak{C}),$$

and so for $\mathfrak{B}$ and $\mathfrak{C}$.

The notation $(\mathfrak{A}\mathfrak{B}\mathfrak{C})$ is identical with that of Lagrange in the *Mécanique Analytique*, except that there its use is limited to unit vectors. The signification of $\mathfrak{A}\times\mathfrak{B}$ is closely related to, but not identical with, that of the notation $[r_1 r_2]$ commonly used to denote the double area of a triangle determined by two positions in an orbit.

first and second positions, and τ_1 for that between the second and third, and set $t=0$ for the second position,

for $t=-\tau_3$,

$$\mathfrak{R}=\mathfrak{R}_1, \qquad \frac{d^2\mathfrak{R}}{dt^2}=-\frac{\mathfrak{R}_1}{r_1^{\,3}};$$

for $t=0$,

$$\mathfrak{R}=\mathfrak{R}_2, \qquad \frac{d^2\mathfrak{R}}{dt^2}=-\frac{\mathfrak{R}_2}{r_2^{\,3}};$$

for $t=\tau_1$,

$$\mathfrak{R}=\mathfrak{R}_3, \qquad \frac{d^2\mathfrak{R}}{dt^2}=-\frac{\mathfrak{R}_3}{r_3^{\,3}}.$$

We may therefore write with a high degree of approximation

$$\begin{aligned}
&\mathfrak{R}_1=\mathfrak{A}-\tau_3\mathfrak{B}+\tau_3^{\,2}\mathfrak{C}-\tau_3^{\,3}\mathfrak{D}+\tau_3^{\,4}\mathfrak{E}\\
&\mathfrak{R}_2=\mathfrak{A}\\
&\mathfrak{R}_3=\mathfrak{A}+\tau_1\mathfrak{B}+\tau_1^{\,2}\mathfrak{C}+\tau_1^{\,3}\mathfrak{D}-\tau_1^{\,4}\mathfrak{E}\\
&-\frac{\mathfrak{R}_1}{r_1^{\,3}}=2\mathfrak{C}-6\tau_3\mathfrak{D}+12\tau_3^{\,2}\mathfrak{E}\\
&-\frac{\mathfrak{R}_2}{r_2^{\,3}}=2\mathfrak{C}\\
&-\frac{\mathfrak{R}_3}{r_3^{\,3}}=2\mathfrak{C}+6\tau_1\mathfrak{D}+12\tau_1^{\,2}\mathfrak{E}.
\end{aligned}$$

From these six equations the five constants $\mathfrak{A}$, $\mathfrak{B}$, $\mathfrak{C}$, $\mathfrak{D}$, $\mathfrak{E}$ may be eliminated, leaving a single equation of the form

$$A_1\Big(1+\frac{B_1}{r_1^{\,3}}\Big)\mathfrak{R}_1-\Big(1-\frac{B_2}{r_2^{\,3}}\Big)\mathfrak{R}_2+A_3\Big(1+\frac{B_3}{r_3^{\,3}}\Big)\mathfrak{R}_3=0, \tag{1}$$

where

$$A_1=\frac{\tau_1}{\tau_1+\tau_3}, \quad A_3=\frac{\tau_3}{\tau_1+\tau_3},$$

$$B_1=\tfrac{1}{12}(-\tau_1^{\,2}+\tau_1\tau_3+\tau_3^{\,2}), \quad B_2=\tfrac{1}{12}(\tau_1^{\,2}+3\tau_1\tau_3+\tau_3^{\,2})$$

$$B_3=\tfrac{1}{12}(\tau_1^{\,2}+\tau_1\tau_3-\tau_3^{\,2}).$$

This we shall call our fundamental equation. In order to discuss its geometrical signification, let us set

$$n_1=A_1\Big(1+\frac{B_1}{r_1^{\,3}}\Big), \quad n_2=\Big(1-\frac{B_2}{r_2^{\,3}}\Big), \quad n_3=A_3\Big(1+\frac{B_3}{r_3^{\,3}}\Big), \tag{2}$$

so that the equation will read

$$n_1\mathfrak{R}_1-n_2\mathfrak{R}_2+n_3\mathfrak{R}_3=0. \tag{3}$$

This expresses that the vector $n_2\mathfrak{R}_2$ is the diagonal of a parallelogram of which $n_1\mathfrak{R}_1$ and $n_3\mathfrak{R}_3$ are sides. If we multiply by $\mathfrak{R}_3$ and by $\mathfrak{R}_1$, *in skew multiplication*, we get

$$n_1\mathfrak{R}_1\times\mathfrak{R}_3-n_2\mathfrak{R}_2\times\mathfrak{R}_3=0, \quad -n_2\mathfrak{R}_1\times\mathfrak{R}_2+n_3\mathfrak{R}_1\times\mathfrak{R}_3=0, \tag{4}$$

whence

$$\frac{\mathfrak{R}_2\times\mathfrak{R}_3}{n_1}=\frac{\mathfrak{R}_1\times\mathfrak{R}_3}{n_2}=\frac{\mathfrak{R}_1\times\mathfrak{R}_2}{n_3}. \tag{5}$$

Our equation may therefore be regarded as signifying that the three vectors $\mathfrak{R}_1$, $\mathfrak{R}_2$, $\mathfrak{R}_3$ lie in one plane, and that the three triangles determined each by a pair of these vectors, and usually denoted by $[r_2 r_3]$, $[r_1 r_3]$, $[r_1 r_2]$, are proportional to

$$A_1\left(1+\frac{B_1}{r_1^3}\right), \quad \left(1-\frac{B_2}{r_2^3}\right), \quad A_3\left(1+\frac{B_3}{r_3^3}\right).$$

Since this vector equation is equivalent to three ordinary equations, it is evidently sufficient to determine the three positions of the body in connection with the conditions that these positions must lie upon the lines of sight of three observations. To give analytical expression to these conditions, we may write $\mathfrak{E}_1$, $\mathfrak{E}_2$, $\mathfrak{E}_3$ for the vectors drawn from the sun to the three positions of the earth (or, more exactly, of the observatories where the observations have been made), $\mathfrak{F}_1$, $\mathfrak{F}_2$, $\mathfrak{F}_3$ for unit vectors drawn in the directions of the body, as observed, and ρ_1, ρ_2, ρ_3 for the three distances of the body from the places of observation. We have then

$$\mathfrak{R}_1 = \mathfrak{E}_1 + \rho_1 \mathfrak{F}_1, \quad \mathfrak{R}_2 = \mathfrak{E}_2 + \rho_2 \mathfrak{F}_2, \quad \mathfrak{R}_3 = \mathfrak{E}_3 + \rho_3 \mathfrak{F}_3. \tag{6}$$

By substitution of these values our fundamental equation becomes

$$A_1\left(1+\frac{B_1}{r_1^3}\right)(\mathfrak{E}_1+\rho_1\mathfrak{F}_1) - \left(1-\frac{B_2}{r_2^3}\right)(\mathfrak{E}_2+\rho_2\mathfrak{F}_2) + A_3\left(1+\frac{B_3}{r_3^3}\right)(\mathfrak{E}_3+\rho_3\mathfrak{F}_3) = 0, \tag{7}$$

where ρ_1, ρ_2, ρ_3, r_1, r_2, r_3 (the geocentric and heliocentric distances) are the only unknown quantities. From equations (6) we also get, by squaring both members in each,

$$\left.\begin{aligned} r_1^2 = \mathfrak{E}_1^2 + 2(\mathfrak{E}_1.\mathfrak{F}_1)\rho_1 + \rho_1^2, \quad r_2^2 = \mathfrak{E}_2^2 + 2(\mathfrak{E}_2.\mathfrak{F}_2)\rho_2 + \rho_2^2, \\ r_3^2 = \mathfrak{E}_3^2 + 2(\mathfrak{E}_3.\mathfrak{F}_3)\rho_3 + \rho_3^2, \end{aligned}\right\} \tag{8}$$

by which the values of r_1, r_2, r_3 may be derived from those of ρ_1, ρ_2, ρ_3, or *vice versâ*. Equations (7) and (8), which are equivalent to six ordinary equations, are sufficient to determine the six quantities r_1, r_2, r_3, ρ_1, ρ_2, ρ_3; or, if we suppose the values of r_1, r_2, r_3 in terms of ρ_1, ρ_2, ρ_3 to be substituted in equation (7), we have a single vector equation, from which we may determine the three geocentric distances ρ_1, ρ_2, ρ_3.

It remains to be shown, first, how the numerical solution of the equation may be performed, and secondly, how such an approximate solution of the actual problem may furnish the basis of a closer approximation.

Solution of the Fundamental Equation.

The relations with which we have to do will be rendered a little more simple if instead of each geocentric distance we introduce the distance of the body from the foot of the perpendicular from the sun upon the line of sight. If we set

$$q_1=\rho_1+(\mathfrak{E}_1.\mathfrak{F}_1), \qquad q_2=\rho_2+(\mathfrak{E}_2.\mathfrak{F}_2), \qquad q_3=\rho_3+(\mathfrak{E}_3.\mathfrak{F}_3), \tag{9}$$

$$p_1^2=\mathfrak{E}_1^2-(\mathfrak{E}_1.\mathfrak{F}_1)^2, \quad p_2^2=\mathfrak{E}_2^2-(\mathfrak{E}_2.\mathfrak{F}_2)^2, \quad p_3=\mathfrak{E}_3^2-(\mathfrak{E}_3.\mathfrak{F}_3)^2, \tag{10}$$

equations (8) become

$$r_1^2=q_1^2+p_1^2, \qquad r_2^2=q_2^2+p_2^2, \qquad r_3^2=q_3^2+p_3^2. \tag{11}$$

Let us also set, for brevity,

$$\left.\begin{aligned}\mathfrak{S}_1=A_1\Big(1+\frac{B_1}{r_1^3}\Big)(\mathfrak{E}_1+\rho_1\mathfrak{F}_1), \quad \mathfrak{S}_2=-\Big(1-\frac{B_2}{r_2^3}\Big)(\mathfrak{E}_2+\rho_2\mathfrak{F}_2),\\ \mathfrak{S}_3=A_3\Big(1+\frac{B_3}{r_3^3}\Big)(\mathfrak{E}_3+\rho_3\mathfrak{F}_3).\end{aligned}\right\} \tag{12}$$

Then $\mathfrak{S}_1$, $\mathfrak{S}_2$, $\mathfrak{S}_3$ may be regarded as functions respectively of ρ_1, ρ_2, ρ_3, therefore of q_1, q_2, q_3, and if we set

$$\mathfrak{S}'=\frac{d\mathfrak{S}_1}{dq_1}, \quad \mathfrak{S}''=\frac{d\mathfrak{S}_2}{dq_2}, \quad \mathfrak{S}'''=\frac{d\mathfrak{S}_3}{dq_3}, \tag{13}$$

and

$$\mathfrak{S}=\mathfrak{S}_1+\mathfrak{S}_2+\mathfrak{S}_3, \tag{14}$$

we shall have

$$d\mathfrak{S}=\mathfrak{S}'dq_1+\mathfrak{S}''dq_2+\mathfrak{S}'''dq_3. \tag{15}$$

To determine the value of $\mathfrak{S}'$, we get by differentiation

$$\mathfrak{S}'=A_1\Big(1+\frac{B_1}{r_1^3}\Big)\mathfrak{F}_1-A_1\frac{3B_1}{r_1^4}\frac{dr_1}{dq_1}(\mathfrak{E}_1+\rho_1\mathfrak{F}_1). \tag{16}$$

But by (11)

$$\frac{dr_1}{dq_1}=\frac{q_1}{r_1}. \tag{17}$$

Therefore

$$\left.\begin{aligned}\mathfrak{S}'&=A_1\Big(1+\frac{B_1}{r_1^3}\Big)\mathfrak{F}_1-\frac{3B_1q_1}{r_1^5(1+B_1r_1^{-3})}\mathfrak{S}_1\\ \mathfrak{S}''&=-\Big(1-\frac{B_2}{r_2^3}\Big)\mathfrak{F}_2+\frac{3B_2q_2}{r_2^5(1-B_2r_2^{-3})}\mathfrak{S}_2\\ \mathfrak{S}'''&=A_3\Big(1+\frac{B_3}{r_3^3}\Big)\mathfrak{F}_3-\frac{3B_3q_3}{r_3^5(1+B_3r_3^{-3})}\mathfrak{S}_3\end{aligned}\right\} \tag{18}$$

Now if any values of q_1, q_2, q_3 (either assumed or obtained by a previous approximation) give a certain residual $\mathfrak{S}$ (which would be zero if the values of q_1, q_2, q_3 satisfied the fundamental equation), and we wish to find the corrections Δq_1, Δq_2, Δq_3, which must be added to q_1, q_2, q_3 to reduce the residual to zero, we may apply equation (15) to these finite differences, and will have approximately, when these differences are not very large,

$$-\mathfrak{S}=\mathfrak{S}'\Delta q_1+\mathfrak{S}''\Delta q_2+\mathfrak{S}'''\Delta q_3. \tag{19}$$

This gives *

$$\Delta q_1 = -\frac{(\mathfrak{S}\mathfrak{S}''\mathfrak{S}''')}{(\mathfrak{S}'\mathfrak{S}''\mathfrak{S}''')}\quad \Delta q_2 = -\frac{(\mathfrak{S}\mathfrak{S}'''\mathfrak{S}')}{(\mathfrak{S}'\mathfrak{S}''\mathfrak{S}''')},\quad \Delta q_3 = -\frac{(\mathfrak{S}\mathfrak{S}'\mathfrak{S}'')}{(\mathfrak{S}'\mathfrak{S}''\mathfrak{S}''')}. \tag{20}$$

From the corrected values of q_1, q_2, q_3 we may calculate a new residual $\mathfrak{S}$, and from that determine another correction for each of the quantities q_1, q_2, q_3.

It will sometimes be worth while to use formulæ a little less simple for the sake of a more rapid approximation. Instead of equation (19) we may write, with a higher degree of accuracy,

$$-\mathfrak{S} = \mathfrak{S}'\Delta q_1 + \mathfrak{S}''\Delta q_2 + \mathfrak{S}'''\Delta q_3 + \tfrac{1}{2}\mathfrak{T}'(\Delta q_1)^2 + \tfrac{1}{2}\mathfrak{T}''(\Delta q_2)^2 + \tfrac{1}{2}\mathfrak{T}'''(\Delta q_3)^2, \tag{21}$$

where

$$\left.\begin{aligned}
\mathfrak{T}' &= \frac{d^2\mathfrak{S}_1}{dq_1^2} = 2A_1B_1\frac{d(r_1^{-3})}{dq_1}\mathfrak{F}_1 + \frac{B_1}{1+B_1r_1^{-3}}\frac{d^2(r_1^{-3})}{dq_1^2}\mathfrak{S}_1\\
\mathfrak{T}'' &= \frac{d^2\mathfrak{S}_2}{dq_2^2} = \quad 2B_2\frac{d(r_2^{-3})}{dq_2}\mathfrak{F}_2 - \frac{B_2}{1-B_2r_2^{-3}}\frac{d^2(r_2^{-3})}{dq_2^2}\mathfrak{S}_2\\
\mathfrak{T}''' &= \frac{d^2\mathfrak{S}_3}{dq_3^2} = 2A_3B_3\frac{d(r_3^{-3})}{dq_3}\mathfrak{F}_3 + \frac{B_3}{1+B_3r_3^{-3}}\frac{d^2(r_3^{-3})}{dq_3^2}\mathfrak{S}_3
\end{aligned}\right\} \tag{22}$$

It is evident that $\mathfrak{T}''$ is generally many times greater than $\mathfrak{T}'$ or $\mathfrak{T}'''$, the factor B_2, in the case of equal intervals, being exactly ten times as great as A_1B_1 or A_3B_3. This shows, in the first place, that the accurate determination of Δq_2 is of the most importance for the subsequent approximations. It also shows that we may attain nearly the same accuracy in writing

$$-\mathfrak{S} = \mathfrak{S}'\Delta q_1 + \mathfrak{S}''\Delta q_2 + \mathfrak{S}'''\Delta q_3 + \tfrac{1}{2}\mathfrak{T}''\Delta q_2^2. \tag{23}$$

We may, however, often do a little better than this without using a more complicated equation. For $\mathfrak{T}' + \mathfrak{T}'''$ may be estimated very roughly as equal to $\frac{1}{5}\mathfrak{T}''$. Whenever, therefore, Δq_1 and Δq_3 are about as large as Δq_2, as is often the case, it may be a little better to use the coefficient $\frac{6}{10}$ instead of $\frac{1}{2}$ in the last term.

For Δq_2, then, we have the equation

$$-(\mathfrak{S}\mathfrak{S}'''\mathfrak{S}') = (\mathfrak{S}'\mathfrak{S}''\mathfrak{S}''')\Delta q_2 + \tfrac{6}{10}(\mathfrak{T}''\mathfrak{S}'''\mathfrak{S}')\Delta q_2^2. \tag{24}$$

$(\mathfrak{T}''\mathfrak{S}'''\mathfrak{S}')$ is easily computed from the formula

$$\left.\begin{aligned}
(\mathfrak{T}''\mathfrak{S}'''\mathfrak{S}') = \frac{1}{q_2}\left(1 - 5\frac{q_2^2}{r_2^2}\right)\left((\mathfrak{S}'\mathfrak{S}''\mathfrak{S}''') + (\mathfrak{F}_2\mathfrak{S}'''\mathfrak{S}')\right)\\
- \frac{B_2}{q_2 r_2^3}\left(1 + \frac{q_2^2}{r_2^2}\right)(\mathfrak{F}_2\mathfrak{S}'''\mathfrak{S}'),
\end{aligned}\right\} \tag{25}$$

which may be derived from equations (18) and (22).

---

* These equations are obtained by taking the direct products of both members of the preceding equation with $\mathfrak{S}'' \times \mathfrak{S}'''$, $\mathfrak{S}''' \times \mathfrak{S}'$, and $\mathfrak{S}' \times \mathfrak{S}''$, respectively. See footnote on page 119.

The quadratic equation (24) gives two values of the correction to be applied to the position of the body. When they are not too large, they will belong to two different solutions of the problem, generally to the two least removed from the values assumed. But a very large value of Δq_2 must not be regarded as affording any trustworthy indication of a solution of the problem. In the majority of cases we only care for one of the roots of the equation, which is distinguished by being very small, and which will be most easily calculated by a small correction to the value which we get by neglecting the quadratic term.*

When a comet is somewhat near the earth we may make use of the fact that the earth's orbit is one solution of the problem, i.e., that $-\rho_2$ is one value of Δq_2, to save the trifling labor of computing the value of $(\mathfrak{T}''\mathfrak{S}'''\mathfrak{S}')$. For it is evident from the theory of equations that if $-\rho_2$ and z are the two roots,

$$\rho_2 - z = \frac{(\mathfrak{S}'\mathfrak{S}''\mathfrak{S}''')}{\frac{3}{5}(\mathfrak{T}''\mathfrak{S}'''\mathfrak{S}')} \qquad -\rho_2 z = \frac{(\mathfrak{S}\mathfrak{S}'''\mathfrak{S}')}{\frac{3}{5}(\mathfrak{T}''\mathfrak{S}'''\mathfrak{S}')}.$$

Eliminating $(\mathfrak{T}''\mathfrak{S}'''\mathfrak{S}')$, we have

$$(\rho_2 - z)(\mathfrak{S}\mathfrak{S}'''\mathfrak{S}') = -\rho_2 z(\mathfrak{S}'\mathfrak{S}''\mathfrak{S}'''),$$

whence

$$\frac{1}{z} = \frac{1}{\rho_2} - \frac{(\mathfrak{S}'\mathfrak{S}''\mathfrak{S}''')}{(\mathfrak{S}\mathfrak{S}'''\mathfrak{S}')}.$$

Now $-\dfrac{(\mathfrak{S}\mathfrak{S}'''\mathfrak{S}')}{(\mathfrak{S}'\mathfrak{S}''\mathfrak{S}''')}$ is the value of Δq_2, which we obtain if we neglect the quadratic term in equation (24). If we call this value $[\Delta q_2]$, we have for the more exact value †

$$\Delta q_2 = \frac{[\Delta q_2]}{1 + \frac{[\Delta q_2]}{\rho_2}}. \tag{26}$$

The quantities Δq_1 and Δq_3 might be calculated by the equations

$$\left.\begin{aligned} -(\mathfrak{S}\mathfrak{S}''\mathfrak{S}''') &= (\mathfrak{S}'\mathfrak{S}''\mathfrak{S}''')\Delta q_1 + \tfrac{6}{10}(\mathfrak{T}''\mathfrak{S}''\mathfrak{S}''')\Delta q_2^2 \\ -(\mathfrak{S}\mathfrak{S}'\mathfrak{S}'') &= (\mathfrak{S}'\mathfrak{S}''\mathfrak{S}''')\Delta q_3 + \tfrac{6}{10}(\mathfrak{T}''\mathfrak{S}'\mathfrak{S}'')\Delta q_2^2 \end{aligned}\right\} \tag{27}$$

* In the case of Swift's comet (V, 1880), the writer found by the quadratic equation -·247 and -·116 for corrections of the assumed geocentric distance ·250. The first of these numbers gives an approximation to the position of the earth; the second to that of the comet, viz., the geocentric distance ·134 instead of the true value ·1333. The coefficient $\frac{6}{10}$ was used in the quadratic equation; with the coefficient $\frac{1}{2}$ the approximations would not be quite so good. The value of the correction obtained by neglecting the quadratic term was ·079, which indicates that the approximations (in this very critical case) would be quite tedious without the use of the quadratic term.

† In the case mentioned in the preceding footnote, from $[\Delta q_2] = -·079$ and $\rho_2 = ·25$, we get $\Delta q_2 = -·1155$, which is sensibly the same value as that obtained by calculating the quadratic term.

But a little examination will show that the coefficients of Δq_2^2 in these equations will not generally have very different values from the coefficient of the same quantity in equation (24). We may therefore write with sufficient accuracy

$$\Delta q_1 = [\Delta q_1] + \Delta q_2 - [\Delta q_2], \quad \Delta q_3 = [\Delta q_3] + \Delta q_2 - [\Delta q_2], \qquad (28)$$

where $[\Delta q_1]$, $[\Delta q_2]$, $[\Delta q_3]$ denote the values obtained from equations (20).

In making successive corrections of the distances q_1, q_2, q_3, it will not be necessary to recalculate the values of $\mathfrak{S}'$, $\mathfrak{S}''$, $\mathfrak{S}'''$, when these have been calculated from fairly good values of q_1, q_2, q_3. But when, as is generally the case, the first assumption is only a rude guess, the values of $\mathfrak{S}'$, $\mathfrak{S}''$, $\mathfrak{S}'''$ should be recalculated after one or two corrections of q_1, q_2, q_3. To get the best results when we do not recalculate $\mathfrak{S}'$, $\mathfrak{S}''$, $\mathfrak{S}'''$, we may proceed as follows: Let $\mathfrak{S}'$, $\mathfrak{S}''$, $\mathfrak{S}'''$ denote the values which have been calculated; Dq_1, Dq_2, Dq_3, respectively, the sum of the corrections of each of the quantities q_1, q_2, q_3, which have been made since the calculation of $\mathfrak{S}'$, $\mathfrak{S}''$, $\mathfrak{S}'''$; $\mathfrak{S}$ the residual after all the corrections of q_1, q_2, q_3, which have been made; and Δq_1, Δq_2, Δq_3 the remaining corrections which we are seeking. We have, then, very nearly

$$\left.\begin{aligned} -\mathfrak{S} = \{\mathfrak{S}' + \mathfrak{T}'(Dq_1 + \tfrac{1}{2}\Delta q_1)\}\Delta q_1 + \{\mathfrak{S}'' + \mathfrak{T}''(Dq_2 + \tfrac{1}{2}\Delta q_2)\}\Delta q_2 \\ + \{\mathfrak{S}''' + \mathfrak{T}'''(Dq_3 + \tfrac{1}{2}\Delta q_3)\}\Delta q_3. \end{aligned}\right\} \qquad (29)$$

The same considerations which we applied to equation (21) enable us to simplify this equation also, and to write with a fair degree of accuracy

$$-(\mathfrak{S}\mathfrak{S}'''\mathfrak{S}') = \{(\mathfrak{S}'\mathfrak{S}''\mathfrak{S}''') + \tfrac{6}{5}(\mathfrak{T}''\mathfrak{S}'''\mathfrak{S}')(Dq_2 + \tfrac{1}{2}\Delta q_2)\}\Delta q_2, \qquad (30)$$

$$\Delta q_1 = [\Delta q_1] + \Delta q_2 - [\Delta q_2], \quad \Delta q_3 = [\Delta q_3] + \Delta q_2 - [\Delta q_2], \qquad (31)$$

where

$$[\Delta q_1] = -\frac{(\mathfrak{S}\mathfrak{S}''\mathfrak{S}''')}{(\mathfrak{S}'\mathfrak{S}''\mathfrak{S}''')}, \quad [\Delta q_2] = -\frac{(\mathfrak{S}\mathfrak{S}'''\mathfrak{S}')}{(\mathfrak{S}'\mathfrak{S}''\mathfrak{S}''')}, \quad [\Delta q_3] = -\frac{(\mathfrak{S}\mathfrak{S}'\mathfrak{S}'')}{(\mathfrak{S}'\mathfrak{S}''\mathfrak{S}''')}. \qquad (32)$$

Correction of the Fundamental Equation.

When we have thus determined, by the numerical solution of our fundamental equation, approximate values of the three positions of the body, it will always be possible to apply a small numerical correction to the equation, so as to make it agree exactly with the laws of elliptic motion in a fictitious case differing but little from the actual. After such a correction the equation will evidently apply to the actual case with a much higher degree of approximation.

There is room for great diversity in the application of this principle. The method which appears to the writer the most simple and direct is the following, in which the correction of the intervals for aberration is combined with the correction required by the approximate nature of the equation.*

The solution of the fundamental equation gives us three points, which must necessarily lie in one plane with the sun, and in the lines of sight of the several observations. Through these points we may pass an ellipse, and calculate the intervals of time required by the exact laws of elliptic motion for the passage of the body between them. If these calculated intervals should be identical with the given intervals, corrected for aberration, we would evidently have the true solution of the problem. But suppose, to fix our ideas, that the calculated intervals are a little too long. It is evident that if we repeat our calculations, using in our fundamental equation intervals shortened in the same ratio as the calculated intervals have come out too long, the intervals calculated from the second solution of the fundamental equation must agree almost exactly with the desired values. If necessary, this process may be repeated, and thus any required degree of accuracy may be obtained, whenever the solution of the uncorrected equation gives an approximation to the true positions. For this it is necessary that the intervals should not be too great. It appears, however, from the results of the example of Ceres, given hereafter, in which the heliocentric motion exceeds 62° but the calculated values of the intervals of time differ from the given values by little more than one part in two thousand, that we have here not approached the limit of the application of our formula.

In the usual terminology of the subject, the fundamental equation with intervals uncorrected for aberration represents the *first hypothesis;* the same equation with the intervals affected by certain numerical coefficients (differing little from unity) represents the *second hypothesis;* the *third hypothesis*, should such be necessary, is represented by a similar equation with corrected coefficients, etc.

In the process indicated there are certain economies of labor which should not be left unmentioned, and certain precautions to be observed in order that the neglected figures in our computations may not unduly influence the result.

It is evident, in the first place, that for the correction of our fundamental equation we need not trouble ourselves with the position of the orbit in the solar system. The intervals of time, which determine this correction, depend only on the three heliocentric distances r_1, r_2, r_3 and the two heliocentric angles, which will be represented by $v_2 - v_1$ and $v_3 - v_2$, if we write v_1, v_2, v_3 for the true anomalies. These angles ($v_2 - v_1$ and $v_3 - v_2$) may be determined from r_1, r_2, r_3 and n_1, n_2, n_3,

* When an approximate orbit is known in advance, we may correct the fundamental equation at once. The formulæ will be given in the Summary, § xii.

and therefore from r_1, r_2, r_3 and the given intervals. For our fundamental equation, which may be written

$$n_1\mathfrak{R}_1 - n_2\mathfrak{R}_2 + n_3\mathfrak{R}_3 = 0, \tag{33}$$

indicates that we may form a triangle in which the lengths of the sides shall be n_1r_1, n_2r_2, and n_3r_3 (let us say for brevity, s_1, s_2, s_3), and the directions of the sides parallel with the three heliocentric directions of the body. The angles opposite s_1 and s_3 will be respectively $v_3 - v_2$ and $v_2 - v_1$. We have, therefore, by a well-known formula,

$$\left.\begin{aligned} \tan\frac{v_3-v_2}{2} &= \sqrt{\frac{(s_1-s_2+s_3)(s_1+s_2-s_3)}{(s_1+s_2+s_3)(-s_1+s_2+s_3)}} \\ \tan\frac{v_2-v_1}{2} &= \sqrt{\frac{(-s_1+s_2+s_3)(s_1-s_2-s_3)}{(s_1+s_2+s_3)(s_1+s_2-s_3)}} \end{aligned}\right\}. \tag{34}$$

As soon, therefore, as the solution of our fundamental equation has given a sufficient approximation to the values of r_1, r_2, r_3 (say five- or six-figure values, if our final result is to be as exact as seven-figure logarithms can make it), we calculate n_1, n_2, n_3 with seven-figure logarithms by equations (2), and the heliocentric angles by equations (34).

The semi-parameter corresponding to these values of the heliocentric distances and angles is given by the equation

$$p = \frac{n_1r_1 - n_2r_2 + n_3r_3}{n_1 - n_2 + n_3}. \tag{35}$$

The expression $n_1 - n_2 + n_3$, which occurs in the value of the semi-parameter, and the expression $n_1r_1 - n_2r_2 + n_3r_3$, or $s_1 - s_2 + s_3$, which occurs both in the value of the semi-parameter and in the formulæ for determining the heliocentric angles, represent small quantities of the second order (if we call the heliocentric angles small quantities of the first order), and cannot be very accurately determined from approximate numerical values of their separate terms. The first of these quantities may, however, be determined accurately by the formula

$$n_1 - n_2 + n_3 = \frac{A_1B_1}{r_1^{\,3}} + \frac{B_2}{r_2^{\,3}} + \frac{A_3B_3}{r_3^{\,3}}. \tag{36}$$

With respect to the quantity $s_1 - s_2 + s_3$, a little consideration will show that if we are careful to use the same value wherever the expression occurs, both in the formulæ for the heliocentric angles and for the semi-parameter, the inaccuracy of the determination of this value from the cause mentioned will be of no consequence in the process of correcting the fundamental equation. For although the logarithm of $s_1 - s_2 + s_3$ as calculated by seven-figure logarithms from r_1, r_2, r_3 may be accurate only to four or five figures, we may regard it as absolutely correct if we make a very small change in the value of one of the heliocentric distances (say r_2). We need not trouble ourselves farther about this change, for it will be of a magnitude which we neglect in computations with seven-figure tables. That the heliocentric angles thus determined may not agree as closely as they might with the positions on the lines of sight determined by the first solution of the fundamental equation is of no especial consequence in the correction of the fundamental equation, which only requires the exact fulfilment of two conditions, viz., that our values of the heliocentric distances and angles shall have the relations required by the fundamental equation to the given intervals of time, and that they shall have the relations required by the exact laws of elliptic motion to the calculated intervals of time. The third condition, that none of these values shall differ too widely from the actual values, is of a looser character.

After the determination of the heliocentric angles and the semi-parameter, the eccentricity and the true anomalies of the three positions may next be determined, and from these the intervals of time. These processes require no especial notice. The appropriate formulæ will be given in the Summary of Formulæ.

Determination of the Orbit from the Three Positions and the Intervals of Time.

The values of the semi-parameter and the heliocentric angles as given in the preceding paragraphs depend upon the quantity $s_1 - s_2 + s_3$, the numerical determination of which from s_1, s_2, and s_3 is critical to the second degree when the heliocentric angles are small. This was of no consequence in the process which we have called the *correction of the fundamental equation.* But for the actual determination of the orbit from the positions given by the corrected equation—or by the uncorrected equation, when we judge that to be sufficient—a more accurate determination of this quantity will generally be necessary. This may be obtained in different ways, of which the following is perhaps the most simple. Let us set

$$\mathfrak{S}_4 = \mathfrak{S}_3 - \mathfrak{S}_1, \tag{37}$$

and s_4 for the length of the vector $\mathfrak{S}_4$, obtained by taking the square root of the sum of the squares of the components of the vector. It is evident that s_2 is the longer and s_4 the shorter diagonal of a parallelogram of which the sides are s_1 and s_3. The area of the triangle having the sides s_1, s_2, s_3 is therefore equal to that of the triangle having the sides s_1, s_3, s_4, each being one-half of the parallelogram. This gives

$$\begin{aligned}(s_1+s_2+s_3)(-s_1+s_2+s_3)(s_1-s_2+s_3)(s_1+s_2-s_3)\\ =(s_1+s_4+s_3)(-s_1+s_4+s_3)(s_1-s_4+s_3)(s_1+s_4-s_3),\end{aligned} \tag{38}$$

and

$$s_1-s_2+s_3=\frac{(s_1+s_4+s_3)(-s_1+s_4+s_3)(s_1-s_4+s_3)(s_1+s_4-s_3)}{(s_1+s_2+s_3)(-s_1+s_2+s_3)(s_1+s_2-s_3)}. \qquad (39)$$

The numerical determination of this value of $s_1-s_2+s_3$ is critical only to the first degree.

The eccentricity and the true anomalies may be determined in the same way as in the correction of the formula. The position of the orbit in space may be derived from the following considerations. The vector $-\mathfrak{S}_2$ is directed from the sun toward the second position of the body; the vector $\mathfrak{S}_4$ from the first to the third position. If we set

$$\mathfrak{S}_5=\mathfrak{S}_4-\frac{\mathfrak{S}_4.\mathfrak{S}_2}{s_2^2}\mathfrak{S}_2, \qquad (40)$$

the vector $\mathfrak{S}_5$ will be in the plane of the orbit, perpendicular to $-\mathfrak{S}_2$ and on the side toward which anomalies increase. If we write s_5 for the length of $\mathfrak{S}_5$,

$$-\frac{\mathfrak{S}_2}{s_2} \text{ and } \frac{\mathfrak{S}_5}{s_5}$$

will be unit vectors. Let $\mathfrak{I}$ and $\mathfrak{I}'$ be unit vectors determining the position of the orbit, $\mathfrak{I}$ being drawn from the sun toward the perihelion, and $\mathfrak{I}'$ at right angles to $\mathfrak{I}$, in the plane of the orbit, and on the side toward which anomalies increase. Then

$$\mathfrak{I}=-\cos v_2\frac{\mathfrak{S}_2}{s_2}-\sin v_2\frac{\mathfrak{S}_5}{s_5}, \qquad (41)$$

$$\mathfrak{I}'=-\sin v_2\frac{\mathfrak{S}_2}{s_2}+\cos v_2\frac{\mathfrak{S}_5}{s_5}. \qquad (42)$$

The time of perihelion passage (T) may be determined from any one of the observations by the equation

$$\frac{k}{a^{\frac{3}{2}}}(t-T)=E-e\sin E, \qquad (43)$$

the eccentric anomaly E being calculated from the true anomaly v. The interval $t-T$ in this equation is to be measured in days. A better value of T may be found by averaging the three values given by the separate observations, with such weights as the circumstances may suggest. But any considerable differences in the three values of T would indicate the necessity of a second correction of the formula, and furnish the basis for it.

For the calculation of an ephemeris we have

$$\mathfrak{R}=-ae\mathfrak{I}+\cos E\, a\mathfrak{I}+\sin E\, b\mathfrak{I}' \qquad (44)$$

in connection with the preceding equation.

Sometimes it may be worth while to make the calculations for the correction of the formula in the slightly longer form indicated for the determination of the orbit. This will be the case when we wish simultaneously to correct the formula for its theoretical imperfection, and to correct the observations by comparison with others not too remote. The rough approximation to the orbit given by the uncorrected formula may be sufficient for this purpose. In fact, for observations separated by very small intervals, the imperfection of the uncorrected formula will be likely to affect the orbit less than the errors of the observations.

The computer may prefer to determine the orbit from the first and third heliocentric positions with their times. This process, which has certain advantages, is perhaps a little longer than that here given, and does not lend itself quite so readily to successive improvements of the hypothesis. When it is desired to derive an improved hypothesis from an orbit thus determined, the formulæ in § XII of the summary may be used.

SUMMARY OF FORMULÆ

WITH DIRECTIONS FOR USE.

(For the case in which an approximate orbit is known in advance, see XII.)

I.

Preliminary computations relating to the intervals of time.

t_1, t_2, t_3 = times of the observations in days.

$\log k = 8{\cdot}2355814$ (after Gauss)

$$\tau_1 = k(t_3 - t_2) \qquad \tau_3 = k(t_2 - t_1)$$

$$A_1 = \frac{t_3 - t_2}{t_3 - t_1} \qquad A_3 = \frac{t_2 - t_1}{t_3 - t_1}$$

$$B_1 = \frac{-\tau_1^2 + \tau_1\tau_3 + \tau_3^2}{12} \qquad B_2 = \frac{\tau_1^2 + 3\tau_1\tau_3 + \tau_3^2}{12} \qquad B_3 = \frac{\tau_1^2 + \tau_1\tau_3 - \tau_3^2}{12}$$

For control: $\qquad A_1B_1 + B_2 + A_3B_3 = \frac{1}{2}\tau_1\tau_3.$

II.

Preliminary computations relating to the first observation.

X_1, Y_1, Z_1 (components of $\mathfrak{E}_1$) = the heliocentric coordinates of the earth, increased by the geocentric coordinates of the observatory.

ξ_1, η_1, ζ_1 (components of $\mathfrak{F}_1$) = the direction-cosines of the observed position, corrected for the aberration of the fixed stars.

$$\mathfrak{E}_1^2 = X_1^2 + Y_1^2 + Z_1^2 \quad (\mathfrak{E}_1.\mathfrak{F}_1) = X_1\xi_1 + Y_1\eta_1 + Z_1\zeta_1 \quad p_1^2 = \mathfrak{E}_1^2 - (\mathfrak{E}_1.\mathfrak{F}_1)^2$$

Preliminary computations relating to the second and third observations.

The formulæ are entirely analogous to those relating to the first observation, the quantities being distinguished by the proper suffixes.

III.

Equations of the first hypothesis.

When the preceding quantities have been computed, their numerical values (or their logarithms, when more convenient for computation,) are to be substituted in the following equations:

Components of $\mathfrak{S}_1$

$$q_1=\rho_1+(\mathfrak{E}_1.\mathfrak{F}_1) \qquad \alpha_1=A_1\xi_1(1+R_1)\left(q_1+\frac{X_1}{\xi_1}-(\mathfrak{E}_1.\mathfrak{F}_1)\right)$$

$$r_1^2=q_1^2+p_1^2 \qquad \beta_1=A_1\eta_1(1+R_1)\left(q_1+\frac{Y_1}{\eta_1}-(\mathfrak{E}_1.\mathfrak{F}_1)\right) \quad \text{III}_1$$

$$R_1=\frac{B_1}{r_1^3} \qquad \gamma_1=A_1\zeta_1(1+R_1)\left(q_1+\frac{Z_1}{\zeta_1}-(\mathfrak{E}_1.\mathfrak{F}_1)\right)$$

For control: $s_1^2=\alpha_1^2+\beta_1^2+\gamma_1^2=A_1^2(1+R_1)^2r_1^2$

Components of $\mathfrak{S}'$

$$P'=\frac{3R_1q_1}{(1+R_1)r_1^2} \qquad \left.\begin{aligned}\alpha'&=A_1\xi_1+A_1\xi_1R_1-P'\alpha_1\\ \beta'&=A_1\eta_1+A_1\eta_1R_1-P'\beta_1\\ \gamma'&=A_1\zeta_1+A_1\zeta_1R_1-P'\gamma_1\end{aligned}\right\}\text{III}$$

Components of $\mathfrak{S}_2$

$$q_2=\rho_2+(\mathfrak{E}_2.\mathfrak{F}_2) \qquad \alpha_2=-\xi_2(1-R_2)\left(q_2+\frac{X_2}{\xi_2}-(\mathfrak{E}_2.\mathfrak{F}_2)\right)$$

$$r_2^2=q_2^2+p_2^2 \qquad \beta_2=-\eta_2(1-R_2)\left(q_2+\frac{Y_2}{\eta_2}-(\mathfrak{E}_2.\mathfrak{F}_2)\right) \quad \text{III}_2$$

$$R_2=\frac{B_2}{r_2^3} \qquad \gamma_2=-\zeta_2(1-R_2)\left(q_2+\frac{Z_2}{\zeta_2}-(\mathfrak{E}_2.\mathfrak{F}_2)\right)$$

For control: $s_2^2=\alpha_2^2+\beta_2^2+\gamma_2^2=(1-R_2)^2r_2^2$

Components of $\mathfrak{S}''$

$$P''=\frac{3R_2q_2}{(1-R_2)r_2^2} \qquad \left.\begin{aligned}\alpha''&=-\xi_2+\xi_2R_2+P''\alpha_2\\ \beta''&=-\eta_2+\eta_2R_2+P''\beta_2\\ \gamma''&=-\zeta_2+\zeta_2R_2+P''\gamma_2\end{aligned}\right\}\text{III}''$$

Components of $\mathfrak{S}_3$

$$q_3=\rho_3+(\mathfrak{E}_3.\mathfrak{F}_3) \qquad \alpha_3=A_3\xi_3(1+R_3)\left(q_3+\frac{X_3}{\xi_3}-(\mathfrak{E}_3.\mathfrak{F}_3)\right)$$

$$r_3^2=q_3^2+p_3^2 \qquad \beta_3=A_3\eta_3(1+R_3)\left(q_3+\frac{Y_3}{\eta_3}-(\mathfrak{E}_3.\mathfrak{F}_3)\right) \quad \text{III}_3$$

$$R_3=\frac{B_3}{r_3^3} \qquad \gamma_3=A_3\zeta_3(1+R_3)\left(q_3+\frac{Z_3}{\zeta_3}-(\mathfrak{E}_3.\mathfrak{F}_3)\right)$$

For control: $s_3^2 = a_3^2 + \beta_3^2 + \gamma_3^2 = A_3^2(1+R_3)^2 r_3^2$

Components of $\mathfrak{S}'''$

$$P''' = \frac{3R_3 q_3}{(1+R_3) r_3^2} \qquad \left.\begin{aligned} a''' &= A_3\xi_3 + A_3\xi_3 R_3 - P''' a_3 \\ \beta''' &= A_3\eta_3 + A_3\eta_3 R_3 - P'''\beta_3 \\ \gamma''' &= A_3\zeta_3 + A_3\zeta_3 R_3 - P'''\gamma_3 \end{aligned}\right\} \text{III}'''$$

The computer is now to assume any reasonable values either of the geocentric distances, ρ_1, ρ_2, ρ_3, or of the heliocentric distances, r_1, r_2, r_3 (the former in the case of a comet, the latter in the case of an asteroid), and from these assumed values to compute the rest of the following quantities:

By equations III_1, III′.	By equations III_2, III″.	By equations III_3, III‴.
q_1	q_2	q_3
$\log r_1$	$\log r_2$	$\log r_3$
$\log R_1$	$\log R_2$	$\log R_3$
$\log(1+R_1)$	$\log(1-R_2)$	$\log(1+R_3)$
$\log P'$	$\log P''$	$\log P'''$
a_1	a_2	a_3
β_1	β_2	β_3
γ_1	γ_2	γ_3
a'	a''	a'''
β'	β''	β'''
γ'	γ''	γ'''

IV.

Calculations relating to differential coefficients.

Components of $\mathfrak{S}''\times\mathfrak{S}'''$	Components of $\mathfrak{S}'''\times\mathfrak{S}'$	Components of $\mathfrak{S}'\times\mathfrak{S}''$
$a_1 = \beta''\gamma''' - \gamma''\beta'''$	$a_2 = \beta'''\gamma' - \gamma'''\beta'$	$a_3 = \beta'\gamma'' - \gamma'\beta''$
$b_1 = \gamma''a''' - a''\gamma'''$	$b_2 = \gamma'''a' - a'''\gamma'$	$b_3 = \gamma'a'' - a'\gamma''$
$c_1 = a''\beta''' - \beta''a'''$	$c_2 = a'''\beta' - \beta'''a'$	$c_3 = a'\beta'' - \beta'a''$

$$G = (\mathfrak{S}'\mathfrak{S}''\mathfrak{S}''') = a_1 a' + b_1\beta' + c_1\gamma' = a_2 a'' + b_2\beta'' + c_2\gamma'' = a_3 a''' + b_3\beta''' + c_3\gamma'''.$$

These computations are controlled by the agreement of the three values of G.

The following are not necessary except when the corrections to be made are large:

$$H = (\mathfrak{F}_2\mathfrak{S}'''\mathfrak{S}') = a_2\xi_2 + b_2\eta_2 + c_2\zeta_2$$

$$L = \frac{1}{q_2}\left(1+\frac{H}{G}\right)\left(1-5\frac{q_2^2}{r_2^2}\right) - \frac{R_2 H}{q_2 G}\left(1+\frac{q_2^2}{r_2^2}\right)$$

V.

Corrections of the geocentric distances.

Components of $\mathfrak{S}$.

$$\alpha=\alpha_1+\alpha_2+\alpha_3 \qquad C_1=-\frac{a_1\alpha+b_1\beta+c_1\gamma}{G}$$

$$\beta=\beta_1+\beta_2+\beta_3 \qquad C_2=-\frac{a_2\alpha+b_2\beta+c_2\gamma}{G}$$

$$\gamma=\gamma_1+\gamma_2+\gamma_3 \qquad C_3=-\frac{a_3\alpha+b_3\beta+c_3\gamma}{G}$$

$$\Delta q_2=C_2-\tfrac{6}{10}L(\Delta q_2)^2.$$

(This equation will generally be most easily solved by repeated substitutions.)

$$\Delta q_1=C_1-\tfrac{6}{10}L(\Delta q_2)^2 \qquad \Delta q_3=C_3-\tfrac{6}{10}L(\Delta q_2)^2.$$

VI.

Successive corrections.

Δq_1, Δq_2, Δq_3 are to be added as corrections to q_1, q_2, q_3. With the new values thus obtained the computation by equations III_1, III_2, III_3 are to be recommenced. Two courses are now open:

(*a*) The work may be carried on exactly as before to the determination of new corrections for q_1, q_2, q_3.

(*b*) The computations by equations III′, III″, III‴, and IV may be omitted, and the old values of a_1, b_1, c_1, a_2, etc., G, and L may be used with the new residuals α, β, γ to get new corrections for q_1, q_2, q_3 by the equations

$$\Delta q_2=\frac{C_2}{1+\frac{6}{5}L(Dq_2+\frac{1}{2}C_2)},$$

$$\Delta q_1=C_1+\Delta q_2-C_2, \qquad \Delta q_3=C_3+\Delta q_2-C_2,$$

where Dq_2 denotes the former correction of q_2. (More generally, at any stage of the work, Dq_2 will represent the sum of all the corrections of q_2 which have been made since the last computation of a_1, b_1, etc.)

So far as any general rule can be given, it is advised to recompute a_1, b_1, etc., and G *once*, perhaps after the second corrections of q_1, q_2, q_3, unless the assumed values represent a fair approximation. Whether L is also to be recomputed, depends on its magnitude, and on that of the correction of q_2, which remains to be made. In the later stages of the work, when the corrections are small, the terms containing L may be neglected altogether.

The corrections of q_1, q_2, q_3 should be repeated until the equations

$$\alpha=0 \qquad \beta=0 \qquad \gamma=0$$

are nearly satisfied. Approximate values of r_1, r_2, r_3 may suffice for the following computations, which, however, must be made with the greatest exactness.

VII.

Test of the first hypothesis.

$\log r_1$, $\log r_2$, $\log r_3$ (approximate values from the preceding computations).

$$N = A_1B_1r_1^{-3} + B_2r_2^{-3} + A_3B_3r_3^{-3}$$
$$s_1 = A_1r_1 + A_1B_1r_1^{-2}$$
$$s_2 = r_2 - B_2r_2^{-2}$$
$$s_3 = A_3r_3 + A_3B_3r_3^{-2}$$
$$s = \tfrac{1}{2}(s_1 + s_2 + s_3)$$
$$s - s_1,\ s - s_2,\ s - s_3.$$

The value of $s - s_2$ may be very small, and its logarithm in consequence ill determined. This will do no harm if the computer is careful to use the same value—computed, of course, as carefully as possible—wherever the expression occurs in the following formulæ:

$$\mathrm{R} = \sqrt{\frac{(s-s_1)(s-s_2)(s-s_3)}{s}} \qquad \tan\tfrac{1}{2}(v_2 - v_1) = \frac{\mathrm{R}}{s - s_3}$$

$$p = \frac{2(s - s_2)}{N} \qquad \tan\tfrac{1}{2}(v_3 - v_2) = \frac{\mathrm{R}}{s - s_1}$$

$$\tan\tfrac{1}{2}(v_3 - v_1) = \frac{s - s_2}{\mathrm{R}}$$

For adjustment of values: $\tfrac{1}{2}(v_3 - v_1) = \tfrac{1}{2}(v_2 - v_1) + \tfrac{1}{2}(v_3 - v_2)$

$$e \sin\tfrac{1}{2}(v_3 + v_1) = \frac{\dfrac{p}{r_1} - \dfrac{p}{r_3}}{2\sin\tfrac{1}{2}(v_3 - v_1)}$$

$$e \cos\tfrac{1}{2}(v_3 + v_1) = \frac{\dfrac{p}{r_1} + \dfrac{p}{r_3} - 2}{2\cos\tfrac{1}{2}(v_3 - v_1)}$$

$$\tan\tfrac{1}{2}(v_3 + v_1) \qquad e^2$$

For control: $$e \cos v_2 = \frac{p}{r_2} - 1$$

$$\epsilon = \sqrt{\frac{1-e}{1+e}} \qquad a = \frac{p}{1 - e^2}$$

$$\tan\tfrac{1}{2}E_1 = \epsilon \tan\tfrac{1}{2}v_1 \qquad \tan\tfrac{1}{2}E_2 = \epsilon \tan\tfrac{1}{2}v_2 \qquad \tan\tfrac{1}{2}E_3 = \epsilon \tan\tfrac{1}{2}v_3$$

$$\tau_{1\ \text{calc.}} = a^{\frac{3}{2}}(E_3 - E_2) + ea^{\frac{3}{2}} \sin E_2 - ea^{\frac{3}{2}} \sin E_3$$
$$\tau_{3\ \text{calc.}} = a^{\frac{3}{2}}(E_2 - E_1) + ea^{\frac{3}{2}} \sin E_1 - ea^{\frac{3}{2}} \sin E_2$$

VIII.

For the second hypothesis.

$$\delta\tau_1 = {\cdot}0057613k(\rho_2 - \rho_3) \qquad \text{(aberration-constant after Struve.)}$$

$$\delta\tau_3 = {\cdot}0057613k(\rho_1 - \rho_2) \qquad \log({\cdot}0057613k) = 5{\cdot}99610$$

$$\Delta \log \tau_1 = \log \tau_1 - \log(\tau_{1\,\text{calc.}} - \delta\tau_1)$$

$$\Delta \log \tau_3 = \log \tau_3 - \log(\tau_{3\,\text{calc.}} - \delta\tau_3)$$

$$\Delta \log(\tau_1\tau_3) = \Delta \log \tau_1 + \Delta \log \tau_3$$

$$\Delta \log \frac{\tau_1}{\tau_3} = \Delta \log \tau_1 - \Delta \log \tau_3$$

$$\Delta \log A_1 = -A_3 \Delta \log \frac{\tau_1}{\tau_3}$$

$$\Delta \log A_3 = -A_1 \Delta \log \frac{\tau_1}{\tau_3}$$

$$\Delta \log B_1 = \Delta \log(\tau_1\tau_3) - \frac{\tau_1^2 + \tau_3^2}{12B_1} \Delta \log \frac{\tau_1}{\tau_3}$$

$$\Delta \log B_2 = \Delta \log(\tau_1\tau_3) + \frac{\tau_1^2 - \tau_3^2}{12B_2} \Delta \log \frac{\tau_1}{\tau_3}$$

$$\Delta \log B_3 = \Delta \log(\tau_1\tau_3) + \frac{\tau_1^2 + \tau_3^2}{12B_3} \Delta \log \frac{\tau_1}{\tau_3}$$

These corrections are to be added to the logarithms of A_1, A_3, B_1, B_2, B_3, in equations III_1, III_2, III_3, and the corrected equations used to correct the values of q_1, q_2, q_3, until the residuals α, β, γ vanish. The new values of A_1, A_3 must satisfy the relation $A_1 + A_3 = 1$, and the corrections $\Delta \log A_1$, $\Delta \log A_3$ must be adjusted, if necessary, for this end.

Third hypothesis.

A second correction of equations III_1, III_2, III_3 may be obtained in the same manner as the first, but this will rarely be necessary.

IX.

Determination of the ellipse.

It is supposed that the values of

$$\alpha_1,\ \beta_1,\ \gamma_1, \qquad \alpha_2,\ \beta_2,\ \gamma_2, \qquad \alpha_3,\ \beta_3,\ \gamma_3,$$

$$r_1,\ r_2,\ r_3, \qquad R_1,\ R_2,\ R_3, \qquad s_1,\ s_2,\ s_3,$$

have been computed by equations III_1, III_2, III_3 with the greatest exactness, so as to make the residuals α, β, γ vanish, and that the two formulæ for each of the quantities s_1, s_2, s_3 give sensibly the same value.

Components of $\mathfrak{S}_4$ | Components of $\mathfrak{S}_5$

$$\alpha_4=\alpha_3-\alpha_1 \qquad \alpha_5=\alpha_4-\frac{\alpha_4\alpha_2+\beta_4\beta_2+\gamma_4\gamma_2}{s_2^2}\alpha_2$$

$$\beta_4=\beta_3-\beta_1 \qquad \beta_5=\beta_4-\frac{\alpha_4\alpha_2+\beta_4\beta_2+\gamma_4\gamma_2}{s_2^2}\beta_2$$

$$\gamma_4=\gamma_3-\gamma_1 \qquad \gamma_5=\gamma_4-\frac{\alpha_4\alpha_2+\beta_4\beta_2+\gamma_4\gamma_2}{s_2^2}\gamma_2$$

$$s_4^2=\alpha_4^2+\beta_4^2+\gamma_4^2 \qquad s_5^2=\alpha_5^2+\beta_5^2+\gamma_5^2$$

$$s=\tfrac{1}{2}(s_1+s_2+s_3) \qquad S=\tfrac{1}{2}(s_1+s_4+s_3)$$

For control only:

$$s-s_2=\frac{S(S-s_1)(S-s_4)(S-s_3)}{s(s-s_1)(s-s_3)}$$

$$\mathrm{R}^2=\frac{S(S-s_1)(S-s_4)(S-s_3)}{s_2^2} \qquad \tan\tfrac{1}{2}(v_2-v_1)=\frac{\mathrm{R}}{s-s_3}$$

$$N=A_1R_1+R_2+A_3R_3 \qquad \tan\tfrac{1}{2}(v_3-v_2)=\frac{\mathrm{R}}{s-s_1}$$

$$p=\frac{2\mathrm{R}^2s}{N(s-s_1)(s-s_3)} \qquad \tan\tfrac{1}{2}(v_3-v_1)=\frac{\mathrm{R}s}{(s-s_1)(s-s_3)}$$

The computer should be careful to use the corrected values of A_1, A_3. (See VIII.) Trifling errors in the angles should be distributed.

$$e\sin\tfrac{1}{2}(v_3+v_1)=\frac{\dfrac{p}{r_1}-\dfrac{p}{r_3}}{2\sin\tfrac{1}{2}(v_3-v_1)}$$

$$e\cos\tfrac{1}{2}(v_3+v_1)=\frac{\dfrac{p}{r_1}+\dfrac{p}{r_3}-2}{2\cos\tfrac{1}{2}(v_3-v_1)}$$

$$\tan\tfrac{1}{2}(v_3+v_1) \qquad e^2$$

For control: $$e\cos v_2=\frac{p}{r_2}-1$$

$$\epsilon=\sqrt{\frac{1-e}{1+e}} \qquad a=\frac{p}{1-e^2} \qquad b=\sqrt{(ap)}$$

Direction-cosines of semi-major axis.

$$l=-\frac{\cos v_2}{s_2}\alpha_2-\frac{\sin v_2}{s_5}\alpha_5$$

$$m=-\frac{\cos v_2}{s_2}\beta_2-\frac{\sin v_2}{s_5}\beta_5$$

$$n=-\frac{\cos v_2}{s_2}\gamma_2-\frac{\sin v_2}{s_5}\gamma_5$$

Direction-cosines of semi-minor axis.

$$\lambda = -\frac{\sin v_2}{s_2}\alpha_2 + \frac{\cos v_2}{s_5}\alpha_5$$

$$\mu = -\frac{\sin v_2}{s_2}\beta_2 + \frac{\cos v_2}{s_5}\beta_5$$

$$\nu = -\frac{\sin v_2}{s_2}\gamma_2 + \frac{\cos v_2}{s_5}\gamma_5$$

Components of the semi-axes.

$$a_x = al \qquad a_y = am \qquad a_z = an$$

$$b_x = b\lambda \qquad b_y = b\mu \qquad b_z = b\nu$$

X.

Time of perihelion passage.

Corrections for aberration.

$$\tan\tfrac{1}{2}E_1 = \epsilon \tan\tfrac{1}{2}v_1 \qquad \delta t_1 = -\cdot 0057613\rho_1$$

$$\tan\tfrac{1}{2}E_2 = \epsilon \tan\tfrac{1}{2}v_2 \qquad \delta t_2 = -\cdot 0057613\rho_2$$

$$\tan\tfrac{1}{2}E_3 = \epsilon \tan\tfrac{1}{2}v_3 \qquad \delta t_3 = -\cdot 0057613\rho_3$$

$$\log \cdot 0057613 = 7\cdot 76052$$

$$t_1 + \delta t_1 - T = k^{-1}a^{\frac{3}{2}}(E_1 - e\sin E_1)$$

$$t_2 + \delta t_2 - T = k^{-1}a^{\frac{3}{2}}(E_2 - e\sin E_2)$$

$$t_3 + \delta t_3 - T = k^{-1}a^{\frac{3}{2}}(E_3 - e\sin E_3)$$

The threefold determination of T affords a control of the exactness of the solution of the problem. If the discrepancies in the values of T are such as to require another correction of the formulæ (a third hypothesis), this may be based on the equations

$$\Delta \log \tau_1 = M\frac{T_{(3)} - T_{(2)}}{t_3 - t_2} \qquad \Delta \log \tau_3 = M\frac{T_{(2)} - T_{(1)}}{t_2 - t_1}$$

where $T_{(1)}$, $T_{(2)}$, $T_{(3)}$ denote respectively the values obtained from the first, second, and third observations, and M the modulus of common logarithms.

XI.

For an ephemeris.

$$\frac{k}{a^{\frac{3}{2}}}(t - T) = E - e\sin E$$

Heliocentric coordinates. (Components of $\mathfrak{R}$.)

$$x = -ea_x + a_x \cos E + b_x \sin E$$

$$y = -ea_y + a_y \cos E + b_y \sin E$$

$$z = -ea_z + a_z \cos E + b_z \sin E$$

These equations are completely controlled by the agreement of the computed and observed positions and the following relations between the constants:

$$a_x b_x + a_y b_y + a_z b_z = 0 \qquad a_x^2 + a_y^2 + a_z^2 = a^2 \qquad b_x^2 + b_y^2 + b_z^2 = (1 - e^2)a^2$$

XII.

When an approximate orbit is known in advance, we may use it to improve our fundamental equation. The following appears to be the most simple method:

Find the excentric anomalies E_1, E_2, E_3, and the heliocentric distances r_1, r_2, r_3, which belong in the approximate orbit to the times of observation corrected for aberration.

Calculate B_1, B_3, as in § I, using these corrected times.

Determine A_1, A_3 by the equation

$$\frac{A_1\left(1+\frac{B_1}{r_1^3}\right)}{\sin(E_3-E_2)-e\sin E_3+e\sin E_2}=\frac{A_3\left(1+\frac{B_3}{r_3^3}\right)}{\sin(E_2-E_1)-e\sin E_2+e\sin E_1}$$

in connection with the relation $A_1+A_3=1$.

Determine B_2 so as to make

$$\frac{A_1\frac{B_1}{r_1^3}+\frac{B_2}{r_2^3}+A_3\frac{B_3}{r_3^3}}{4\sin\frac{1}{2}(E_2-E_1)\sin\frac{1}{2}(E_3-E_2)\sin\frac{1}{2}(E_3-E_1)}$$

equal to either member of the last equation.

It is not necessary that the times for which E_1, E_2, E_3, r_1, r_2, r_3, are calculated should precisely agree with the times of observation corrected for aberration. Let the former be represented by t_1', t_2', t_3', and the latter by t_1'', t_2'', t_3''; and let

$$\Delta\log\tau_1=\log(t_3''-t_2'')-\log(t_3'-t_2'),$$
$$\Delta\log\tau_3=\log(t_2''-t_1'')-\log(t_2'-t_1').$$

We may find B_1, B_3, A_1, A_3, B_2, as above, using t_1', t_2', t_3', and then use $\Delta\log\tau_1$, $\Delta\log\tau_3$ to correct their values, as in § VIII.

Numerical Example.

To illustrate the numerical computations we have chosen the following example, both on account of the large heliocentric motion, and because Gauss and Oppolzer have treated the same data by their different methods.

The data are taken from the *Theoria Motus*, § 159, viz.,

Times, 1805, September	5·51336	139·42711	265·39813
Longitudes of Ceres	95° 32′ 18″·56	99° 49′ 5″·87	118° 5′ 28″·85
Latitudes of Ceres	−0° 59′ 34″·06	+7° 16′ 36″·80	+7° 38′ 49″·39
Longitudes of the Earth	342° 54′ 56″·00	117° 12′ 43″·25	241° 58′ 50″·71
Logs of the Sun's distance	0·0031514	9·9929861	0·0056974

The positions of Ceres have been freed from the effects of parallax and aberration.

I.

From the given times we obtain the following values:

	Numbers.	Logarithms.
t_2-t_1	133·91375	2·1268252
t_3-t_2	125·97102	2·1002706
t_3-t_1	259·88477	2·4147809
A_1	·4847187	9·6854897
A_3	·5152812	9·7120443
τ_1		·3358520
τ_3		·3624066
B_1		9·6692113
B_2		·3183722
B_3		9·5623916

Control:

$$A_1B_1+B_2+A_3B_3=2{\cdot}4959086$$
$$\tfrac{1}{2}\tau_1\tau_3=2{\cdot}4959081$$

II.

From the given positions we get:

$\log X_1$	9·9835515	+	$\log X_2$	9·6531725	−	$\log X_3$	9·6775810	−
$\log Y_1$	9·4711748	−	$\log Y_2$	9·9420444	+	$\log Y_3$	9·9515547	−
Z_1	0		Z_2	0		Z_3	0	
$\log \xi_1$	8·9845270	−	$\log \xi_2$	9·2282738	−	$\log \xi_3$	9·6690294	−
$\log \eta_1$	9·9979027	+	$\log \eta_2$	9·9900800	+	$\log \eta_3$	9·9416855	+
$\log \zeta_1$	8·2387150	−	$\log \zeta_2$	9·1026549	+	$\log \zeta_3$	9·1240813	+
$\mathfrak{E}_1.\mathfrak{F}_1$	·3874081	−	$\mathfrak{E}_2.\mathfrak{F}_2$	·9314223	+	$\mathfrak{E}_3.\mathfrak{F}_3$	·5599304	−
p_1^2	·8645336	+	p_2^2	·1006681	+	p_3^2	·7130624	+

III.

The preceding computations furnish the numerical values for the equations III_1, III′, III_2, III″, III_3, III‴, which follow. Brackets indicate that logarithms have been substituted for numbers.

We have now to assume some values for the heliocentric distances r_1, r_2, r_3. A mean proportional between the mean distances of Mars and Jupiter from the Sun suggests itself as a reasonable assumption. In order, however, to test the convergence of the computations, when the assumptions are not happy, we will make the much less probable assumption (actually much farther from the truth) that the heliocentric distances are an arithmetical mean between the distances of Mars and Jupiter. This gives ·526 for the logarithm of each of the distances r_1, r_2, r_3. From these assumed values we compute the first column of numbers in the three following tables:

$$\left.\begin{array}{ll} q_1=\rho_1-{\cdot}3874081 & \alpha_1=-[8{\cdot}6700167](q_1-9{\cdot}5901555)(1+R_1) \\ r_1^2=q_1^2+{\cdot}8645336 & \beta_1=[9{\cdot}6833924](q_1+{\cdot}0900552)(1+R_1) \\ R_1=[9{\cdot}6692113]r_1^{-3} & \gamma_1=-[7{\cdot}9242047](q_1+{\cdot}3874081)(1+R_1) \end{array}\right\}\text{III}_1$$

$$P'=\frac{[{\cdot}47712]R_1q_1}{(1+R_1)r_1^2}\qquad \left.\begin{array}{l} \alpha'=-{\cdot}046775-[8{\cdot}67002]R_1-P'\alpha_1 \\ \beta'={\cdot}482383+[9{\cdot}68339]R_1-P'\beta_1 \\ \gamma'=-{\cdot}008399-[7{\cdot}92420]R_1-P'\gamma_1 \end{array}\right\}\text{III}'$$

Δq_1			−·66731	−·04558	−·0010434	+·0000006
q_1	+	3·22606	2·55875	2·51317	2·5142134	2·5142140
$\log r_1$	+	·52600	·434960	·4280791	·4282376	·4282377
$\log R_1$	+	8·09121	8·364331	8·3849740	8·3844985	
$\log(1+R_1)$	+	·00533	·009934	·0104122	·0104010	
$\log P'$	+	8·01967	8·369626	8·3957468	8·3951457	
α_1	+	·30136	·336506	·3390605	·3390018	
β_1	+	1·61938	1·307304	1·286223	1·2867056	
γ_1	−	·03072	·025316	·0249518	·0249601	
α'	−	·050505		·0563438		
β'	+	·47139		·4620942		
γ'	−	·00818		·0079821		

$$\left.\begin{array}{ll} q_2=\rho_2+{\cdot}9314223 & \alpha_2=+[9{\cdot}2282738](q_2+1{\cdot}7286820)(1-R_2) \\ r_2^2=q_2^2+{\cdot}1006681 & \beta_2=-[9{\cdot}9900800](q_2-{\cdot}0361309)(1-R_2) \\ R_2=[0{\cdot}3183722]r_2^{-3} & \gamma_2=-[9{\cdot}1026549](q_2-{\cdot}9314223)(1-R_2) \end{array}\right\}\text{III}_2$$

$$P''=\frac{[{\cdot}47712]R_2q_2}{(1-R_2)r_2^2}\qquad \left.\begin{array}{l} \alpha''={\cdot}169151-[9{\cdot}22827]R_2+P''\alpha_2 \\ \beta''=-{\cdot}977417+[9{\cdot}99008]R_2+P''\beta_2 \\ \gamma''=-{\cdot}126664+[9{\cdot}10265]R_2+P''\gamma_2 \end{array}\right\}\text{III}''$$

Δq_2			−·77826	+·005042	+·0013222	+·0000021
q_2	+	3·34235	2·56409	2·569132	2·5704542	2·5704563
$\log r_2$	+	·52600	·412233	·4130733	·4132934	·4132937
$\log R_2$	+	8·74037	9·081673	9·0791524	9·0784920	
$\log(1-R_2)$	+	9·97543	9·944142	9·9444866	9·9445766	
$\log P''$	+	8·71411	9·199120	9·1954270	9·1944598	
α_2	+	·81059	·638489	·6397466	·6400760	
β_2	−	3·05379	2·172660	2·1787230	2·1803116	
γ_2	−	·28858	·181843	·1825486	·1827338	
α''	+	·20182		·2491854		
β''	−	1·08177		1·2018221		
γ''	−	·13464		·1400944		

$$\left.\begin{array}{ll} q_3=\rho_3-{\cdot}5599304 & \alpha_3=-[9{\cdot}3810737](q_3+1{\cdot}5798163)(1+R_3) \\ r_3^2=q_3^2+{\cdot}7130624 & \beta_3=[9{\cdot}6537308](q_3-{\cdot}4630521)(1+R_3) \\ R_3=[9{\cdot}5623916]r_3^{-3} & \gamma_3=[8{\cdot}8361256](q_3+{\cdot}5599304)(1+R_3) \end{array}\right\}\text{III}_3$$

$$P'''=\frac{[{\cdot}47712]R_3q_3}{(1+R_3)r_3^2}\qquad \left.\begin{array}{l} \alpha'''=-{\cdot}240477-[9{\cdot}38107]R_3-P'''\alpha_3 \\ \beta'''=+{\cdot}450537+[9{\cdot}65373]R_3-P'''\beta_3 \\ \gamma'''=+{\cdot}068569+[8{\cdot}83613]R_3-P'''\gamma_3 \end{array}\right\}\text{III}'''$$

Δq_3			$-\cdot80780$	$-\cdot04055$	$+\cdot0025316$	$+\cdot0000031$
q_3	+	3·24945	2·44165	2·40110	2·4036316	2·4036347
$\log r_3$	+	0·52600	·412217	·4057319	·4061394	·4061399
$\log R_3$	+	7·98439	8·325742	8·3451948	8·3439733	
$\log(1+R_3)$	+	·00417	·009099	·0095108	·0094843	
$\log P'''$	+	7·91715	8·357016	8·3817516	8·3801993	
α_3	−	1·17253	·987590	·9785152	·9790776	
β_3	+	1·26749	·910305	·8924956	·8936069	
γ_3	+	·26373	·210171	·2075292	·2076940	
α'''	−	·22847		·2222335		
β'''	+	·44441		·4390163		
γ'''	+	·06690		·0650888		

IV.

The values of α', β', etc., furnish the basis for the computation of the following quantities:

$$a_1=-\cdot01254 \qquad a_2=-\cdot03517 \qquad a_3=-\cdot07232$$
$$b_1=+\cdot01726 \qquad b_2=-\cdot00525 \qquad b_3=-\cdot00845$$
$$c_1=-\cdot15746 \qquad c_2=-\cdot08526 \qquad c_3=-\cdot04050$$

For G we get three values sensibly identical. Adopting the mean, we set

$$G=\cdot01006.$$

We also get $H=-\cdot00998, \qquad L=\cdot02322.$*

V.

Taking the values of a_1, a_2, etc., from the columns under III_1, III_2, III_3, we form the residuals

$$a=-\cdot06058, \qquad \beta=-\cdot16692, \qquad \gamma=-\cdot05557.$$

From these, with the numbers last computed, we get

$$C_1=-\cdot65888, \qquad C_2=-\cdot76983, \qquad C_3=-\cdot79939,$$

which might be used as corrections for our values of q_1, q_2, q_3. To get more accurate values for these corrections we set

$$\Delta q_2=C_2-\tfrac{6}{10}L(\Delta q_2)^2, \quad \text{or} \quad \Delta q_2=-\cdot76983-\cdot01393(\Delta q_2)^2,$$

which gives $\Delta q_2=-\cdot77826.$

The quadratic term diminishes the value of Δq_2 by ·00843. Subtracting the same quantity from C_1 and C_2 we get

$$\Delta q_1=-\cdot66731, \qquad \Delta q_3=-\cdot80780.$$

* It would have been better to omit altogether the calculation of H and L, if the small value of the latter could have been foreseen. In fact, it will be found that the terms containing L hardly improve the convergence, being smaller than quantities which have been neglected. Nevertheless, the use of these terms in this example will illustrate a process which in other cases may be beneficial.

VI.

Applying these corrections to the values of q_1, q_2, q_3 we compute the second numerical columns under equations III_1, III_2, and III_3. We do not go on to the computations by equations III′, etc., but content ourselves with the old values of a_1, b_1, etc., G, and L, which with the new residuals

$$\alpha = -\cdot 012595, \qquad \beta = \cdot 044949, \qquad \gamma = \cdot 003012,$$

give $$C_1 = -\cdot 04567, \qquad C_2 = \cdot 004952, \qquad C_3 = -\cdot 04064.$$

$$\Delta q_2 = C_2 - L(Dq_2 + \tfrac{1}{2}C_2)\Delta q_2 = \cdot 004952 - \cdot 02322(-\cdot 77826 + \cdot 00247)\Delta q_2.$$

This gives $$\Delta q_2 = \cdot 005042.$$

As the term containing L has increased the value of Δq_2 by ·00009, we add this quantity to C_1 and C_3, and get

$$\Delta q_1 = -\cdot 04558, \qquad \Delta q_3 = -\cdot 04055.$$

With these corrections we compute the third numerical columns under equations III_1, etc. This time we recompute the quantities α', etc., with which we repeat the principal computations of IV, and get the new values

$$\begin{array}{lll} a_1 = -\cdot 0167215 & a_2 = -\cdot 0335815 & a_3 = -\cdot 0743299 \\ b_1 = +\cdot 0149145 & b_2 = -\cdot 0054413 & b_3 = -\cdot 0098825 \\ c_1 = -\cdot 1576886 & c_2 = -\cdot 0779570 & c_3 = -\cdot 0474318 \end{array}$$

$$G = \cdot 0090929.$$

The quantities H and L we neglect as of no consequence at this stage of the approximation.

With these values the new residuals

$$\alpha = +\cdot 0002919, \qquad \beta = -\cdot 0000044, \qquad \gamma = +\cdot 0000288,$$

give $$\Delta q_1 = C_1 = +\cdot 0010434, \qquad \Delta q_2 = C_2 = +\cdot 0013222,$$

$$\Delta q_3 = C_3 = +\cdot 0025316.$$

These corrections furnish the basis for the fourth columns of numbers under equations III_1, etc., which give the residuals

$$\alpha = +\cdot 0000002, \qquad \beta = +\cdot 0000009, \qquad \gamma = +\cdot 0000001,$$

and the new corrections

$$\Delta q_1 = +\cdot 0000006, \qquad \Delta q_2 = +\cdot 0000021, \qquad \Delta q_3 = +\cdot 0000031.$$

The corrected values of q_1, q_2, q_3 give

$$\log r_1 = 0\cdot 4282377, \quad \log r_2 = 0\cdot 4132937, \quad \log r_3 = 0\cdot 4061399.$$

We have carried the approximation farther than is necessary for the following *correction of the formula*, in order to see exactly where the uncorrected formula would lead us, and for the control afforded by the fourth residuals.

VII.

The computations for the test of the uncorrected formula (the first hypothesis) are as follows:

		Number or arc.	Logarithm.
r_1			0·4282377
r_2			0·4132937
r_3			0·4061399
$A_1B_1r_1^{-3}$	+	·01174865	8·0699879
$B_2r_2^{-3}$	+	·11980944	9·0784911
$A_3B_3r_3^{-3}$	+	·01137670	8·0560162
N	+	·14293479	9·1551380
s_1	+	1·3308476	0·1241283
s_2	+	2·2796616	0·3578704
s_3	+	1·3417404	0·1276685
s	+	2·4761248	0·3937725
$s-s_1$	+	1·1452772	0·0589106
$s-s_2$	+	0·1964632	9·2932812
$s-s_3$	+	1·1343844	0·0547602
R	+		9·5065898
p	+		0·4391732
$\tan\frac{1}{2}(v_2-v_1)$	+	15° 48′ 10″·82	9·4518296
$\tan\frac{1}{2}(v_3-v_2)$	+	15° 39′ 36″·38	9·4476792
$\tan\frac{1}{2}(v_3-v_1)$	+	31° 27′ 47″·20	9·7866915
$e\sin\frac{1}{2}(v_3+v_1)$	−		8·7099387
$e\cos\frac{1}{2}(v_3+v_1)$	+		8·7872701
$\tan\frac{1}{2}(v_3+v_1)$	−	− 39° 55′ 32″·31	9·9226686
e	+		8·9025438
ϵ	+		9·9652259
a	+		0·4419546
$\tan\frac{1}{2}v_1$	−	− 35° 41′ 39″·75	9·8563809
$\tan\frac{1}{2}v_2$	−	− 19° 53′ 28″·93	9·5584981
$\tan\frac{1}{2}v_3$	−	− 4° 13′ 52″·55	8·8691380
$\tan\frac{1}{2}E_1$	−	− 33° 33′ 0″·17	9·8216068
$\tan\frac{1}{2}E_2$	−	− 18° 28′ 6″·35	9·5237240
$\tan\frac{1}{2}E_3$	−	− 3° 54′ 24″·21	8·8343639
$\sin E_1$	−	− 67° 6′ 0″·34	9·9643473
$\sin E_2$	−	− 36° 56′ 12″·70	9·7788272
$\sin E_3$	−	− 7° 48′ 48″·42	9·1333734
$ea^{\frac{3}{2}}\sin E_1$	−	·3387061	9·5298230
$ea^{\frac{3}{2}}\sin E_2$	−	·2209545	9·3443029
$ea^{\frac{3}{2}}\sin E_3$	−	·0499861	8·6988491
$a^{\frac{3}{2}}(E_2-E_1)$	+	2·4226307	0·3842872
$a^{\frac{3}{2}}(E_3-E_2)$	+	2·3391145	0·3690515
$\tau_{3\text{ calc.}}$	+	2·3048791	0·3626482
$\tau_{1\text{ calc.}}$	+	2·1681461	0·3360885

VIII.

The logarithms of the calculated values of the intervals of time exceed those of the given values by ·0002416 for the first interval (τ_3) and ·0002365 for the second (τ_1). Therefore, since the corrections for aberration have been incorporated in the data, we set for the correction of the formula (for the second hypothesis)

$$\Delta \log \tau_1 = -\cdot 0002365 \qquad \Delta \log \tau_3 = -\cdot 0002416$$

This gives $\Delta \log A_1 = \cdot 0000026 \qquad \Delta \log A_3 = -\cdot 0000025$

$\Delta \log B_1 = -\cdot 0004872 \qquad \Delta \log B_2 = -\cdot 0004782 \qquad \Delta \log B_3 = -\cdot 0004665$

The new values of the logarithms of A_1, A_3 are

$$\log A_1 = 9\cdot 6854923 \qquad \log A_3 = 9\cdot 7120418$$

Applying these corrections to equations III_1, III_2, III_3,* we get the following:

$$\left.\begin{aligned} r_1^2 &= q_1^2 + \cdot 8645336 \\ \alpha_1 &= -[8\cdot 6700193](q_1 - 9\cdot 5901555)(1+R_1) \\ R_1 &= [9\cdot 6687241]r_1^{-3} \\ \beta_1 &= +[9\cdot 6833950](q_1 + \cdot 0900552)(1+R_1) \\ \gamma_1 &= -[7\cdot 9242073](q_1 + \cdot 3874081)(1+R_1) \end{aligned}\right\} \text{III}_1 \text{ corrected.}$$

Δq_1			+ ·0002887	− ·0000217
q_1	+	2·5142140	2·5145027	2·5144810
$\log r_1$	+	·4282377	·4282816	·4282782
$\log R_1$	+	8·3838110	8·3838793	8·3838894
$\log(1+R_1)$	+	·0103847	·0103863	·0103865
α_1	+	·3389910	·3389784	·3389796
β_1	+	1·2866654	1·2868124	1·2868024
γ_1	−	·0249593	·0249619	·0249617
$\log s_1$	+			·1241571

$$\left.\begin{aligned} r_2^2 &= q_2^2 + \cdot 1006681 \\ \alpha_2 &= +[9\cdot 2282738](q_2 + 1\cdot 7286820)(1-R_2) \\ R_2 &= [0\cdot 3178940]r_2^{-3} \\ \beta_2 &= -[9\cdot 9900800](q_2 - \cdot 0361309)(1-R_2) \\ \gamma_2 &= -[9\cdot 1026549](q_2 - \cdot 9314223)(1-R_2) \end{aligned}\right\} \text{III}_2 \text{ corrected.}$$

Δq_2			− ·0000955	+ ·0000187
q_2	+	2·5704563	2·5703608	2·5703795
$\log r_2$	+	0·4132937	·4132778	·4132809
$\log R_2$	+	9·0780129	9·0780605	9·0780513
$\log(1-R_2)$	+	9·9446418	9·9446353	9·9446365
α_2	+	·6401725	·6401487	·6401532
β_2	−	2·1806412	2·1805261	2·1805482
γ_2	−	·1827615	·1827481	·1827507
$\log s_2$	+			·3579174

* The corrections may be made without rewriting the equations.

$$\left.\begin{aligned} r_3^2 &= q_3^2 + \cdot 7130624 \\ \alpha_3 &= -[9\cdot 3810712](q_3 + 1\cdot 5798163)(1+R_3) \\ R_3 &= [9\cdot 5619251] r_3^{-3} \\ \beta_3 &= +[9\cdot 6537283](q_3 - \cdot 4630521)(1+R_3) \\ \gamma_3 &= +[8\cdot 8361231](q_3 + \cdot 5599304)(1+R_3) \end{aligned}\right\} \text{III}_3 \text{ corrected.}$$

Δq_3			+ ·0003302	+ ·0000424
q_3	+	2·4036347	2·4039649	2·4040073
$\log r_3$	+	·4061399	·4061929	·4061998
$\log R_3$	+	8·3435055	8·3433463	8·3433257
$\log(1+R_3)$	+	·0094742	·0094708	·0094704
α_3	−	·9790500	·9791236	·9791329
β_3	+	·8935824	·8937277	·8937461
γ_3	+	·2076882	·2077097	·2077124
$\log s_3$	+			·1277120

With these corrected equations the last values of q_1, q_2, q_3 give the residuals

$$\alpha = \cdot 0001135 \qquad \beta = -\cdot 0003934 \qquad \gamma = -\cdot 0000326$$

These give the corrections

$$\Delta q_1 = \cdot 0002887 \qquad \Delta q_2 = -\cdot 0000955 \qquad \Delta q_3 = \cdot 0003302$$

The next residuals are

$$\alpha = \cdot 0000035 \qquad \beta = \cdot 0000140 \qquad \gamma = -\cdot 0000003$$

which give the corrections

$$\Delta q_1 = -\cdot 0000217 \qquad \Delta q_2 = \cdot 0000187 \qquad \Delta q_3 = \cdot 0000424$$

The next residuals are

$$\alpha = -\cdot 0000001 \qquad \beta = \cdot 0000003 \qquad \gamma = \cdot 0000000$$

which must be regarded as entirely insensible.

IX, X.

It remains to determine the ellipse which passes through the points to which the numbers relate in the last columns under the corrected equations III_1, III_2, III_3, and also the time of perihelion passage. The computations are as follows:

		Number or arc.	Logarithm.
α_4	−	1·3181125	0·1199525
β_4	−	·3930563	9·5944547
γ_4	+	·2326741	9·3667481
s_4^2	+	1·9460513	0·2891543
s_4	+	1·3950100	0·1445772
s_1	+	1·3309358	
s_3	+	1·3418749	
s_2	+	2·2799084	0·3579174
s	+	2·4763596	0·3938137
$s-s_1$	+	1·1454238	0·0589662
$s-s_3$	+	1·1344847	0·0547986
S	+	2·0339104	0·3083318
$S-s_1$	+	·7029746	9·8469397
$S-s_4$	+	·6389004	9·8054332
$S-s_3$	+	·6920355	9·8401284
$\mathfrak{S}_4 . \mathfrak{S}_2$*	−	·0292373	8·4659373
$\mathfrak{S}_4 . \mathfrak{S}_2 s_2^{-2}$	−		7·7501025
$\mathfrak{S}_4 . \mathfrak{S}_2 s_2^{-2} \alpha_2$	−	·003600696	7·5563864
$\mathfrak{S}_4 . \mathfrak{S}_2 s_2^{-2} \beta_2$	+	·012265017	8·0886682
$\mathfrak{S}_4 . \mathfrak{S}_2 s_2^{-2} \gamma_2$	+	·001027926	7·0119616
α_5	−	1·3145118	0·1187645
β_5	−	·4053213	9·6077994
γ_5	+	·2316462	9·3648252
s_5^2	+	1·9458866	0·2891176
R^2	+		9·0132057
R	+		9·5066028
N	+	·14278017	9·1546679
p	+	2·7517987	0·4396167
$\tan \frac{1}{2}(v_2 - v_1)$	+	15° 48′ 7″·67	9·4518042
$\tan \frac{1}{2}(v_3 - v_2)$	+	15° 39′ 31″·14	9·4476366
$\tan \frac{1}{2}(v_3 - v_1)$	+	31° 27′ 38″·81	9·7866517
$e \sin \frac{1}{2}(v_3 + v_1)$	−		8·7099782
$e \cos \frac{1}{2}(v_3 + v_1)$	+		8·7951055
$\tan \frac{1}{2}(v_3 + v_1)$	−	39° 25′ 12″·94	9·9148727

		Number or arc.	Logarithm.
e	+	·08076104	8·9072019
$\tan \frac{1}{2}v_1$	−	− 35° 26′ 25″·87	9·8523140
$\tan \frac{1}{2}v_2$	−	− 19° 38′ 18″·20	9·5524725
$\tan \frac{1}{2}v_3$	−	− 3° 58′ 47″·06	8·8424313
ϵ	+		9·9648493
a	+		0·4424586
b	+		0·4410376
l	−	·8139130	9·9105780
m	+	·5564152	9·7453990
n	+	·1671768	9·2231760
λ	−	·5517065	9·7417081
μ	−	·8304016	9·9192881
ν	+	·07780215	8·8909916
a_x	−		0·3530366
a_y	+		0·1878576
a_z	+		9·6656346
b_x	−		0·1827457
b_y	−		0·3603257
b_z	+		9·3320292
$\tan \frac{1}{2}E_1$	−	− 33° 16′ 50″·08	9·8171633
$\tan \frac{1}{2}E_2$	−	− 18° 12′ 58″·10	9·5173218
$\tan \frac{1}{2}E_3$	−	− 3° 40′ 16″·33	8·8072806
$k^{-1} a^{\frac{3}{2}} e \sin E_1$	−	19·85671	1·2979074
$k^{-1} a^{\frac{3}{2}} e \sin E_2$	−	12·85291	1·1090014
$k^{-1} a^{\frac{3}{2}} e \sin E_3$	−	2·76589	·4418347
$k^{-1} a^{\frac{3}{2}} E_1$	−	311·31839	2·4932048
$k^{-1} a^{\frac{3}{2}} E_2$	−	170·40027	2·2314703
$k^{-1} a^{\frac{5}{2}} E_3$	−	34·34174	1·5358223
$T_{(1)}$	+	296·97504	
$T_{(2)}$	+	296·97447	
$T_{(3)}$	+	296·97398	
T	+	296·97450	

* $\mathfrak{S}_4 . \mathfrak{S}_2 = \alpha_4 \alpha_2 + \beta_4 \beta_2 + \gamma_4 \gamma_2$.

XI.

This gives the following equations for an ephemeris:

$$T = 1806, \text{ June, } 23{\cdot}97450, \text{ Paris mean time}$$

$$[2{\cdot}8863186](t-T) = E_{\text{in seconds}} - [4{\cdot}2216270] \sin E$$

Heliocentric coordinates relating to the ecliptic.

$$x = +{\cdot}1820700 - [0{\cdot}3530366] \cos E - [0{\cdot}1827457] \sin E$$

$$y = -{\cdot}1244685 + [0{\cdot}1878576] \cos E - [0{\cdot}3603257] \sin E$$

$$z = -{\cdot}0373970 + [9{\cdot}6656346] \cos E + [9{\cdot}3320292] \sin E$$

The differences of the values of $T_{(1)}$, $T_{(2)}$, $T_{(3)}$, from their mean T, indicate the residual errors of this hypothesis. They indicate differences in the calculated and the observed geocentric positions which are represented by the geocentric angles subtended by the path described by the planet in the following fractions of a day: ·00054, ·00003, ·00052. Since the heliocentric motion of the planet is about one-fourth of a degree per day, and the planet is considerably farther from the earth than from the sun at the times of the first and third observations, the errors will be less than half a second in arc.

If we desire all the accuracy possible with seven-figure logarithms, we may form a *third hypothesis* based on the following corrections:

$$\Delta \log \tau_1 = M \frac{T_{(3)} - T_{(2)}}{t_3 - t_2} = -{\cdot}0000017,$$

$$\Delta \log \tau_3 = M \frac{T_{(2)} - T_{(1)}}{t_2 - t_1} = -{\cdot}0000018.$$

The equations for an ephemeris will then be:

$$T = 1806, \text{ June } 23{\cdot}96378, \text{ Paris mean time}$$

$$[2{\cdot}8863140](t-T) = E_{\text{in seconds}} - [4{\cdot}2216530] \sin E$$

Heliocentric coordinates relating to the ecliptic.

$$x = +{\cdot}1820765 - [0{\cdot}3530261] \cos E - [0{\cdot}1827783] \sin E$$

$$y = -{\cdot}1244853 + [0{\cdot}1878904] \cos E - [0{\cdot}3603153] \sin E$$

$$z = -{\cdot}0373987 + [9{\cdot}6656285] \cos E + [9{\cdot}3320758] \sin E$$

The agreement of the calculated geocentric positions with the data is shown in the following table:

Times, 1805, September	5·51336	139·42711	265·39813
Second hypothesis:			
longitudes - -	95° 32′ 18″·88	99° 49′ 5″·87	118° 5′ 28″·52
errors - - -	0″·32	0″·00	−0″·33
latitudes - -	−0° 59′ 34″·01	7° 16′ 36″·82	7° 38′ 49″·34
errors - - -	0″·05	0″·02	−0″·05
Third hypothesis:			
longitudes - -	95° 32′ 18″·65	99° 49′ 5″·82	118° 5′ 28″·79
errors - - -	0″·09	−0″·05	−0″·06
latitudes - -	−0° 59′ 34″·04	7° 16′ 36″·78	7° 38′ 49″·38
errors - - -	0″·02	−0″·02	−0″·01

The immediate result of each hypothesis is to give three positions of the planet, from which, with the times, the orbit may be calculated in various ways, and with different results, so far as the positions deviate from the truth on account of the approximate nature of the hypothesis. In some respects, therefore, the correctness of an hypothesis is best shown by the values of the geocentric or heliocentric distances which are derived directly from it. The logarithms of the heliocentric distances are brought together in the following table, and corresponding values from Gauss* and Oppolzer† are added for comparison. It is worthy of notice that the positions given by our second hypothesis are substantially correct, and if the orbit had been calculated from the first and third of these positions with the interval of time, it would have left little to be desired.

	$\log r_1$.	$\log r_2$.	$\log r_3$.
First hypothesis - -	·4282377	·4132937	·4061399
Second hypothesis - -	·4282782	·4132809	·4061998
Third hypothesis - -	·4282786	·4132808	·4062003
Gauss :			
First hypothesis -	·4323934	·4114726	·4094712
Second hypothesis -	·4291773	·4129371	·4071975
Third hypothesis -	·4284841	·4132107	·4064697
Fourth hypothesis -	·4282792	·4132817	·4062033
Oppolzer :			
First hypothesis -	·4281340	·413330	·4061699
Second hypothesis -	·4282794	·4132801	·4061976
Third hypothesis -	·4282787		·4062009

In comparing the different methods, it should be observed that the determination of the positions in any hypothesis by Gauss's method requires successive corrections of a single independent variable, a corresponding determination by Oppolzer's method requires the successive corrections of two independent variables, while the corresponding determination by the method of the present paper requires the successive corrections of three independent variables.

* *Theoria motus*, § 159.

† *Lehrbuch zur Bahnbestimmung der Kometen und Planeten*, 2nd ed., vol. i, p. 394.

VI.

ON THE USE OF THE VECTOR METHOD IN THE DETERMINATION OF ORBITS

LETTER TO DR. HUGO BUCHHOLZ, EDITOR OF KLINKERFUES' *Theoretische Astronomie.**

New Haven, *October*, 1898.

DR. HUGO BUCHHOLZ,

My dear Sir,—The opinion of Fabritius † on the comparative convenience of different methods is entitled to far more weight than mine, for I am no astronomer, and have calculated very few orbits, none, indeed, except for the trial of my own formulæ. The object of my paper was to show to astronomers, who are rather conservative (and with right, for astronomy is the oldest of the exact sciences), the advantage in the use of vector notations, which I had learned in Physics from Maxwell. This object could be best obtained, not by showing, as I might have done, that much in the classic methods could be conveniently and perspicuously represented by vector notations, but rather by showing that these notations so simplify the subject, that it is easy to construct a method for the complete solution of the problem. That the method given is the best possible, I certainly do not claim, but only that it is much better than I could have found without the use of vector notations. Some of the more obvious crudities in my paper have been corrected in that of Beebe and Phillips.‡ Doubtless many more remain, even if the general method be preserved.

My first efforts, however, to solve the fundamental approximative equation were along the same lines which Fabritius has followed:— to set $r_1 = r_2$ and $r_3 = r_2$ in equation second of (2) of Fabritius, which will give ρ_2 and r_2, then to get r_1 from the first of (3) of Fabritius, and then r_3 either from equation second of (3) or from some other

* [In which the preceding memoir, and also that of Beebe and Phillips referred to below, are translated.]

† [See Fabritius, W. "Ueber eine leichte Methode der Bahnbestimmung mit Zugrundelegung des Princips von Gibbs," also "Weitere Anwendungen des Gibbs'chen Princips," *Astronomische Nachrichten*, No. 3061, 3065 (1891)].

‡ ["The Orbit of Swift's comet, 1880 V, Determined by Gibbs's Vector Method," W. Beebe and A. W. Phillips. *Gould's Astronomical Journal*, vol. ix, Dec. 1889.]

which would serve the purpose, and then to find better values of ρ_2, r_2 by setting in equation second of (2)

$$r_1=\left[\frac{r_1}{r_2}\right]r_2, \quad r_3=\left[\frac{r_3}{r_2}\right]r_2,$$

the expressions in brackets denoting numbers derived from the approximate values already found. This is similar to or identical with the method of Fabritius, except that he combines with it the principle of interpolation (for the first value in the third "hypothesis"). As I found the approximation by this method sometimes slow or failing, notably in the case of Swift's comet, 1880 V, I tried the method published in my paper. Indeed, it may be said that the method of my paper was constructed to meet the exigencies of the case of the comet, 1880 V.

In ordinary cases I think that the method of Fabritius may very likely be better than that which I published. The equations are very simply and perspicuously represented in vector notations. I shall use the notations of my paper, writing $\overline{E}$, $\overline{F}$, etc., for German letters.* To eliminate ρ_1 and ρ_3 from equation (7) in my paper, multiply *directly* by $\mathfrak{F}_1\times\mathfrak{F}_3$. This gives

$$A_1\left(1+\frac{B_1}{r_1^{\,3}}\right)(\mathfrak{E}_1\mathfrak{F}_1\mathfrak{F}_3)-\left(1-\frac{B_2}{r_2^{\,3}}\right)[(\mathfrak{E}_2\mathfrak{F}_1\mathfrak{F}_3)+\rho_2(\mathfrak{F}_2\mathfrak{F}_1\mathfrak{F}_3)]$$
$$+A_3\left(1+\frac{B_3}{r_3^{\,3}}\right)(\mathfrak{E}_3\mathfrak{F}_1\mathfrak{F}_3)=0. \qquad (a)$$

To eliminate ρ_3 and r_3, multiply by $\mathfrak{E}_3\times\mathfrak{F}_3$ which gives

$$A_1\left(1+\frac{B_1}{r_1^{\,3}}\right)[(\mathfrak{E}_1\mathfrak{E}_3\mathfrak{F}_3)+\rho_1(\mathfrak{F}_1\mathfrak{E}_3\mathfrak{F}_3)]$$
$$-\left(1-\frac{B_2}{r_2^{\,3}}\right)[(\mathfrak{E}_1\mathfrak{E}_3\mathfrak{F}_3)+\rho_2(\mathfrak{F}_2\mathfrak{E}_3\mathfrak{F}_3)]=0. \qquad (b)$$

When we have found ρ_1, r_1, ρ_2, r_2 it is not necessary to eliminate any of them, and to save labor in forming the equation for ρ_3, r_3, I should be inclined to take the components in (7) in the direction of one of the coordinate axes, choosing that one which is most nearly directed towards the third observed position. However, I will write

$$A_1\left(1+\frac{B_1}{r_1^{\,3}}\right)[(\mathfrak{E}_1.\mathfrak{P})+\rho_1(\mathfrak{F}_1.\mathfrak{P})]-\left(1-\frac{B_2}{r_2^{\,3}}\right)[(\mathfrak{E}_2.\mathfrak{P})+\rho_2(\mathfrak{F}_2.\mathfrak{P})]$$
$$+A_3\left(1+\frac{B_3}{r_3^{\,3}}\right)[(\mathfrak{E}_3.\mathfrak{P})+\rho_3(\mathfrak{F}_3.\mathfrak{P})]=0, \qquad (c)$$

where $\mathfrak{P}$ may represent an axis of coordinates, or $(\mathfrak{E}_1\times\mathfrak{F}_1)$ which would give Fabritius' equation. It might be directed towards the pole

* [In the remainder of the letter as here printed German capitals have been substituted for the $\overline{E}$, $\overline{F}$, $\overline{P}$, etc. of the original, thus making the notation uniform with that of the paper referred to.]

of the ecliptic, which would make $(\mathfrak{E}_1.\mathfrak{P})$, $(\mathfrak{E}_2.\mathfrak{P})$, $(\mathfrak{E}_3.\mathfrak{P})$ vanish, except for exceedingly minute quantities depending on the latitude of the sun and the geocentric coordinates of the observatories, if these are included in $\mathfrak{E}_1$, $\mathfrak{E}_2$, $\mathfrak{E}_3$.

The equations (*a*), (*b*), (*c*), which are together equivalent to (7), I would solve as follows, almost in the same way as Fabritius, but relying a little more on *interpolation*, and less on the convergence of which he speaks, which in special cases may more or less fail.

Setting $r_1 = r_2$ and $r_3 = r_2$ in (*a*), which thus modified I shall call (*a'*), and solving this (*a'*) by "trial and error," using ρ_2 as the independent variable, as soon as I have a value of ρ_2 which I think will give a residual of (*a'*) of the same order of smallness as the effect of changing $\frac{1}{r_1^3}$ and $\frac{1}{r_3^3}$ into $\frac{1}{r_2^3}$, I determine from this value by (*b*) and (*c*), r_1 and r_3, and then find the residual of (*a*), using the values of r_1, r_2, r_3 derived all from the same assumed ρ_2. Now using the last value of $\frac{\Delta\,(\text{residual})}{\Delta\rho_2}$ in my previous calculations on (*a'*) which indeed applies only roughly to the (*a*), I would get a value ρ_2 which I would use for the second "hypothesis" in (*a*). This will give a second residual in (*a*), which will enable me to make a more satisfactory interpolation. As many more interpolations may be made as shall be found necessary.

Some such method, which should perhaps be called the method of Fabritius, would, I think, in most cases probably be the best for solution of equation (7).

Of course I am quite aware that the merit of my paper, if any, lies principally in the fundamental approximation (1). I will add a few words on this subject.

The equation may be written more symmetrically

$$\frac{\tau_1}{\tau_2}\left(1 + \frac{\tau_2^2 + \tau_3^2 - 3\tau_1^2}{24 r_1^3}\right)\mathfrak{R}_1 - \left(1 + \frac{\tau_3^2 + \tau_1^2 - 3\tau_2^2}{24 r_2^3}\right)\mathfrak{R}_2 + \frac{\tau_3}{\tau_2}\left(1 + \frac{\tau_1^2 + \tau_2^2 - 3\tau_3^2}{24 r_3^3}\right)\mathfrak{R}_3 = 0. \qquad \text{I}$$

It might be made entirely symmetrical by writing $-\tau_2$ for τ_2.

If an expression ending with t^3 had been used, we could still have satisfied two of the conditions relating to acceleration, and should have obtained

$$\frac{\tau_1}{\tau_2}\mathfrak{R}_1 - \left(1 + \frac{\tau_1^2 - \tau_2^2}{6 r_2^3}\right)\mathfrak{R}_2 + \frac{\tau_3}{\tau_2}\left(1 + \frac{\tau_1^2 - \tau_3^2}{6 r_3^3}\right)\mathfrak{R}_3 = 0, \qquad \text{II}a$$

or

$$\frac{\tau_1}{\tau_2}\left(1 + \frac{\tau_2^2 - \tau_1^2}{6 r_1^3}\right)\mathfrak{R}_1 - \mathfrak{R}_2 + \frac{\tau_3}{\tau_2}\left(1 + \frac{\tau_2^2 - \tau_3^2}{6 r_3^3}\right)\mathfrak{R}_3 = 0, \qquad \text{II}b$$

or

$$\frac{\tau_1}{\tau_2}\left(1 + \frac{\tau_3^2 - \tau_1^2}{6 r_1^3}\right)\mathfrak{R}_1 - \left(1 + \frac{\tau_3^2 - \tau_2^2}{6 r_2^3}\right)\mathfrak{R}_2 + \frac{\tau_3}{\tau_2}\mathfrak{R}_3 = 0. \qquad \text{II}c$$

Using an expansion ending with t^2 we can only satisfy one condition relating to acceleration, say the second. This will give

$$\frac{\tau_1}{\tau_2}\mathfrak{R}_1-\left(1-\frac{\tau_1\tau_3}{2r_2^{\,3}}\right)\mathfrak{R}_2+\frac{\tau_3}{\tau_2}\mathfrak{R}_3=0. \qquad \text{III}$$

(Gauss uses virtually

$$\frac{\tau_1}{\tau_2}\mathfrak{R}_1-\frac{\mathfrak{R}_2}{1+\frac{\tau_1\tau_3}{2r_2^{\,3}}}+\frac{\tau_3}{\tau_2}\mathfrak{R}_3=0,$$

which is a little more convenient, but not, I think, generally quite so accurate.)

Writing an equation analogous to III for the earth and subtracting from (7), *Mem. Nat. Acad.*, we have

$$\frac{\tau_1}{\tau_2}\rho_1\mathfrak{F}_1-\left(1-\frac{\tau_1\tau_3}{2r_2^{\,3}}\right)\rho_2\mathfrak{F}_2+\frac{\tau_3}{\tau_2}\rho_3\mathfrak{F}_3=\frac{\tau_1\tau_3}{2}\left(\frac{1}{\mathfrak{E}_2^{\,3}}-\frac{1}{r_2^{\,3}}\right)\mathfrak{E}_2,$$

which gives, on multiplication by $\mathfrak{F}_1\times\mathfrak{F}_3$ and $\mathfrak{F}_2\times\mathfrak{E}_2$, theorems of Olbers and Lambert.

It is evident that *in general* the error in I is of the fifth order, in II*a*, II*b*, II*c* of the fourth, and in III of the third. But for equal intervals, the error in I is of the sixth order, and in III of the fourth. And when $\tau_2^{\,2}+\tau_3^{\,2}-3\tau_1^{\,2}=0$, II*a* becomes identical with I, and its error is of the fifth order.

The same is true of II*c* in the corresponding case. It follows that when the intervals are nearly as 5 : 8 we should use II*a* or II*b* instead of I. This will evidently abbreviate the solution given above as only one of the quantities r_1, r_3 is to be used.

The formulæ II*a*, II*b*, II*c* may also be obtained by the following method, which will show their relative accuracy.

The interpolation formula

$$\frac{\tau_1}{\tau_2}\frac{\mathfrak{R}_1}{r_1^{\,3}}-\frac{\mathfrak{R}_2}{r_2^{\,3}}+\frac{\tau_3}{\tau_2}\frac{\mathfrak{R}_3}{r_3^{\,3}}=0$$

has an error evidently of the second order. If we multiply by $\frac{\tau_2^{\,2}+\tau_3^{\,2}-3\tau_1^{\,2}}{24}$ and subtract from I, we get II*a*. So if we multiply by

$$\frac{\tau_3^{\,2}+\tau_1^{\,2}-3\tau_2^{\,2}}{24} \quad \text{or} \quad \frac{\tau_1^{\,2}+\tau_2^{\,2}-3\tau_3^{\,2}}{24}$$

we get II*b* or II*c*. The errors due to using one of these equations instead of I are therefore proportional to these multipliers and very unequal.

Again, in case of equal intervals, II*a* and II*c* become identical with III. There is, therefore, no reason for using II*a* or II*c* when the intervals are nearly equal. II*b* is in this case much less accurate than III.

It will be observed that all the formulæ I, II*a*, II*b*, II*c*, III, may be expressed in the general form

$$\frac{\tau_1}{\tau_2}\left(1+\frac{B_1}{r_1^3}\right)\mathfrak{R}_1-\left(1+\frac{B_2}{r_2^3}\right)\mathfrak{R}_2+\frac{\tau_3}{\tau_2}\left(1+\frac{B_3}{r_3^3}\right)\mathfrak{R}_3=0,$$

except that the letters B_1, B_2, B_3 have different values in the different cases, some vanishing in the more simple formulæ. Moreover, if the values of B_1, B_2, B_3 have been calculated for I, the values for II*a*, II*b*, or II*c* are found simply by subtraction of one of the numbers from the three. It is evident that II*b* will hardly be useful except in special cases, as in the determination of a parabolic orbit in the failing case of Olbers' method, and then it would be a question whether it would not be better to determine the orbit from ρ_2 and ρ_3, or ρ_2 and ρ_1, using II*a* or II*c*.

Equations II*a* and II*c* are very appropriate for the determination of an elliptic orbit when the observed motion is nearly in the ecliptic, by means of four observations with intervals nearly in the ratio 5 : 8 : 5.

It is evident that the solution of (7) given above may be varied, in ways too numerous to mention, by the use of the simpler forms II*a*, II*c*, or III for I in the earlier stages of the work. This only involves changing the values of B_1, B_2, B_3, in (*a*), (*b*) and (*c*).

It is not correct to say that in my expressions for the ratios of the triangles the error is of the fifth order in general, or for equal intervals, of the sixth. If we write p_1, p_2, p_3, for the coefficients of $\mathfrak{R}_1$, $\mathfrak{R}_2$, $\mathfrak{R}_3$ in I, and $\mathfrak{T}$ for the error of the equation, we have exactly

$$p_1\mathfrak{R}_1-p_2\mathfrak{R}_2+p_3\mathfrak{R}_3=\mathfrak{T},$$

which gives

$$p_1\mathfrak{R}_1\times\mathfrak{R}_3-p_2\mathfrak{R}_2\times\mathfrak{R}_3=\mathfrak{T}\times\mathfrak{R}_3,$$

$$\frac{\mathfrak{R}_2\times\mathfrak{R}_3}{\mathfrak{R}_1\times\mathfrak{R}_3}=\frac{p_1}{p_2}-\frac{\mathfrak{T}\times\mathfrak{R}_3}{p_2\mathfrak{R}_1\times\mathfrak{R}_3}.$$

Now $\frac{p_1}{p_2}$ is my expression for the ratio of the triangles, and $\frac{\mathfrak{T}\times\mathfrak{R}_3}{p_2\mathfrak{R}_1\times\mathfrak{R}_3}$ is its error. This is of the fourth order in general (since the denominator is of the first), and for equal intervals, of the fifth. The same is true of the two other ratios. Thus we have

$$\frac{\mathfrak{R}_1\times\mathfrak{R}_2}{\mathfrak{R}_1\times\mathfrak{R}_3}=\frac{p_3}{p_2}-\frac{\mathfrak{R}_1\times\mathfrak{T}}{p_2\mathfrak{R}_1\times\mathfrak{R}_3}.$$

Adding these equations and subtracting 1 [from both sides] we have

$$\frac{\mathfrak{R}_1\times\mathfrak{R}_2+\mathfrak{R}_2\times\mathfrak{R}_3-\mathfrak{R}_1\times\mathfrak{R}_3}{\mathfrak{R}_1\times\mathfrak{R}_3}=\frac{p_1+p_3-p_2}{p_2}+\frac{(\mathfrak{R}_3-\mathfrak{R}_1)\times\mathfrak{T}}{p_2\mathfrak{R}_1\times\mathfrak{R}_3}.$$

Here the last term, which represents the error, is of the fifth order in general, or for equal intervals, of the sixth. But the quantity sought is of the second order, and the *relative* error is of the third order in the general case, or the fourth for equal intervals. It is precisely this error which is most important in the case of elliptic orbits.

It will be observed that the accuracy of the expressions for the ratios $[r_1r_2]:[r_2r_3]:[r_1r_3]$ affords no measure of the accuracy of the formula for the determination of elliptic orbits.

I think that this hasty sketch will illustrate the convenience and perspicuity of vector notations in this subject, quite independently of any particular method which is chosen for the determination of the orbit. What is the best method? is hardly, I think, a question which admits of a definite reply. It certainly depends upon the ratio of the time intervals, their absolute value, and many other things.

Yours very truly,

J. WILLARD GIBBS.

P.S.—If we wish to use the *curtate* distances, with reference to the ecliptic or the equator, let ρ_1 be defined as the distance multiplied by cosine (lat. or dec.), and $\mathfrak{F}_1$ as a vector of length secant (lat. or dec.). For the most part the formulæ will require no change, but the square of $\mathfrak{F}_1$ will be $\sec^2$(lat. or dec.) instead of unity, so that the last terms of (8) will have this factor. $(\mathfrak{F}_1\mathfrak{F}_2\mathfrak{F}_3)$ will then be Gauss' (0.1.2.), whereas in my paper $(\mathfrak{F}_1\mathfrak{F}_2\mathfrak{F}_3)$ is Lagrange's $(C'C''C''')$.

J. W. G.

VII.

ON THE RÔLE OF QUATERNIONS IN THE ALGEBRA OF VECTORS.

[*Nature*, vol. XLIII. pp. 511–513, April 2, 1891.]

THE following passage, which has recently come to my notice, in the preface to the third edition of Prof. Tait's *Quaternions* seems to call for some reply:

"Even Prof. Willard Gibbs must be ranked as one of the retarders of quaternion progress, in virtue of his pamphlet on *Vector Analysis*, a sort of hermaphrodite monster, compounded of the notations of Hamilton and of Grassmann."

The merits or demerits of a pamphlet printed for private distribution a good many years ago do not constitute a subject of any great importance, but the assumptions implied in the sentence quoted are suggestive of certain reflections and inquiries which are of broader interest, and seem not untimely at a period when the methods and results of the various forms of multiple algebra are attracting so much attention. It seems to be assumed that a departure from quaternionic usage in the treatment of vectors is an enormity. If this assumption is true, it is an important truth; if not, it would be unfortunate if it should remain unchallenged, especially when supported by so high an authority. The criticism relates particularly to notations, but I believe that there is a deeper question of notions underlying that of notations. Indeed, if my offence had been solely in the matter of notation, it would have been less accurate to describe my production as a monstrosity, than to characterize its dress as uncouth.

Now what are the fundamental notions which are germane to a vector analysis? (A vector analysis is of course an algebra for vectors, or something which shall be to vectors what ordinary algebra is to ordinary quantities.) If we pass over those notions which are so simple that they go without saying, geometrical addition (denoted by +) is, perhaps, first to be mentioned. Then comes the product of the lengths of two vectors and the cosine of the angle which they include. This, taken negatively, is denoted in quaternions by $S\alpha\beta$, where α and β are the vectors. Equally important is a vector at right angles to α and β (on a specified side of their plane), and representing in length the product of their lengths and the sine of the angle which they include. This is denoted by $V\alpha\beta$ in quaternions. How these notions are represented in my pamphlet is a question of very subordinate consequence, which need not be considered at present. The importance of these notions, and the importance of a suitable notation for them, is not, I suppose, a matter on which there is any difference of opinion. Another function of α and β, called their product and written $\alpha\beta$, is used in quaternions. In the general case, this is neither a vector, like $V\alpha\beta$, nor a scalar (or ordinary algebraic quantity), like $S\alpha\beta$, but a quaternion—that is, it is part vector and part scalar. It may be defined by the equation—

$$\alpha\beta = V\alpha\beta + S\alpha\beta.$$

The question arises, whether the quaternionic product can claim a prominent and fundamental place in a system of vector analysis. It certainly does not hold any such place among the fundamental geometrical conceptions as the geometrical sum, the scalar product, or the vector product. The geometrical sum $\alpha+\beta$ represents the third side of a triangle as determined by the sides α and β. $V\alpha\beta$ represents in magnitude the area of the parallelogram determined by the sides α and β, and in direction the normal to the plane of the parallelogram. $S\gamma V\alpha\beta$ represents the volume of the parallelopiped determined by the edges α, β, and γ. These conceptions are the very foundations of geometry.

We may arrive at the same conclusion from a somewhat narrower but very practical point of view. It will hardly be denied that sines and cosines play the leading parts in trigonometry. Now the notations $V\alpha\beta$ and $S\alpha\beta$ represent the sine and the cosine of the angle included between α and β, combined in each case with certain other simple notions. But the sine and cosine combined with these auxiliary notions are incomparably more amenable to analytical transformation than the simple sine and cosine of trigonometry, exactly as numerical quantities combined (as in algebra) with the notion of positive or negative quality are incomparably more amenable to analytical transformation than the simple numerical quantities of arithmetic.

I do not know of anything which can be urged in favor of the quaternionic product of two vectors as a *fundamental* notion in vector analysis, which does not appear trivial or artificial in comparison with the above considerations. The same is true of the quaternionic quotient, and of the quaternion in general.

How much more deeply rooted in the nature of things are the functions $S\alpha\beta$ and $V\alpha\beta$ than any which depend on the definition of a quaternion, will appear in a strong light if we try to extend our formulæ to space of four or more dimensions. It will not be claimed that the notions of quaternions will apply to such a space, except indeed in such a limited and artificial manner as to rob them of their value as a system of geometrical algebra. But vectors exist in such a space, and there must be a vector analysis for such a space. The notions of geometrical addition and the scalar product are evidently applicable to such a space. As we cannot define the direction of a vector in space of four or more dimensions by the condition of perpendicularity to two given vectors, the definition of $V\alpha\beta$, as given above, will not apply *totidem verbis* to space of four or more dimensions. But a little change in the definition, which would make no essential difference in three dimensions, would enable us to apply the idea at once to space of any number of dimensions.

These considerations are of a somewhat *a priori* nature. It may be more convincing to consider the use actually made of the quaternion as an instrument for the expression of spatial relations. The principal use seems to be the derivation of the functions expressed by $S\alpha\beta$ and $V\alpha\beta$. Each of these expressions is regarded by quaternionic writers as representing two distinct operations; first, the formation of the product $\alpha\beta$, which is the quaternion, and then the taking out of this quaternion the scalar or the vector part, as the case may be, this second process being represented by the selective symbol, S or V. This is, I suppose, the natural development of the subject in a treatise on quaternions, where the chosen subject seems to require that we should commence with the idea of a quaternion, or get there as soon as possible, and then develop everything from that particular point of view. In a system of vector analysis, in which the principle of development is not thus predetermined, it seems to me contrary to good method that the more simple and elementary notions should be defined by means of those which are less so.

The quaternion affords a convenient notation for rotations. The notation $q(\ )q^{-1}$, where q is a quaternion and the operand is to be written in the parenthesis, produces on all possible vectors just such changes as a (finite) rotation of a solid body. Rotations may also be represented, in a manner which seems to leave nothing to be desired, by linear vector functions. Doubtless each method has advantages in certain cases, or for certain purposes. But since nothing is more simple than the definition of a linear vector function, while the definition of a quaternion is far from simple, and since in any case linear vector functions must be treated in a system of vector analysis, capacity for representing rotations does not seem to me sufficient to entitle the quaternion to a place among the *fundamental* and *necessary* notions of a vector analysis.

Another use of the quaternionic idea is associated with the symbol ∇.

The quantities written $S\nabla\omega$ and $V\nabla\omega$, where ω denotes a vector having values which vary in space, are of fundamental importance in physics. In quaternions these are derived from the quaternion $\nabla\omega$ by selecting respectively the scalar or the vector part. But the most simple and elementary definitions of $S\nabla\omega$ and $V\nabla\omega$ are quite independent of the conception of a quaternion, and the quaternion $\nabla\omega$ is scarcely used except in combination with the symbols S and V, expressed or implied. There are a few formulæ in which there is a trifling gain in compactness in the use of the quaternion, but the gain is very trifling so far as I have observed, and generally, it seems to me, at the expense of perspicuity.

These considerations are sufficient, I think, to show that the position of the quaternionist is not the only one from which the subject of vector analysis may be viewed, and that a method which would be monstrous from one point of view, may be normal and inevitable from another.

Let us now pass to the subject of notations. I do not know wherein the notations of my pamphlet have any special resemblance to Grassmann's, although the point of view from which the pamphlet was written is certainly much nearer to his than to Hamilton's. But this a matter of minor consequence. It is more important to ask, What are the requisites of a good notation for the purposes of vector analysis? There is no difference of opinion about the representation of geometrical addition. When we come to functions having an analogy to multiplication, the products of the lengths of two vectors and the cosine of the angle which they include, from any point of view except that of the quaternionist, seems more simple than the same quantity taken negatively. Therefore we want a notation for what is expressed by $-S\alpha\beta$, rather than $S\alpha\beta$, in quaternions. Shall the symbol denoting this function be a letter or some other sign? and shall it precede the vectors or be placed between them? A little reflection will show, I think, that while we must often have recourse to letters to supplement the number of signs available for the expression of all kinds of operations, it is better that the symbols expressing the most fundamental and frequently recurring operations should not be letters, and that a sign between the vectors, and, as it were, uniting them, is better than a sign before them in a case having a formal analogy with multiplication. The case may be compared with that of addition, for which $\alpha+\beta$ is evidently more convenient than $\Sigma(\alpha, \beta)$ or $\Sigma\alpha\beta$ would be. Similar considerations will apply to the function written in quaternions $V\alpha\beta$. It would seem that we obtain the *ne plus ultra* of simplicity and convenience, if we express the two functions by uniting the vectors in each case with a sign suggestive of multiplication. The particular forms of the signs which we adopt is a matter of minor consequence. In order to keep within the resources of an ordinary printing office, I have used a dot and a cross, which are already associated with multiplication, but are not needed for ordinary multiplication, which is best denoted by the simple juxtaposition of the factors. I have no especial predilection for these particular signs. The use of the dot is indeed liable to the objection that it interferes with its use as a separatrix, or instead of a parenthesis.

If, then, I have written $\alpha.\beta$ and $\alpha\times\beta$ for what is expressed in quaternions by $-S\alpha\beta$ and $V\alpha\beta$, and in like manner $\nabla.\omega$ and $\nabla\times\omega$ for $-S\nabla\omega$ and $V\nabla\omega$ in quaternions, it is because the natural development of a vector analysis seemed to lead logically to some such notations. But I think that I can show that these notations have some substantial advantages over the quaternionic in point of convenience.

Any linear vector function of a variable vector ρ may be expressed in the form—

$$\alpha\lambda.\rho+\beta\mu.\rho+\gamma\nu.\rho=(\alpha\lambda+\beta\mu+\gamma\nu).\rho=\Phi.\rho,$$

where

$$\Phi=\alpha\lambda+\beta\mu+\gamma\nu;$$

or in quaternions

$$-\alpha S\lambda\rho-\beta S\mu\rho-\gamma S\nu\rho=-(\alpha S\lambda+\beta S\mu+\gamma S\nu)\rho=-\phi\rho,$$

where

$$\phi=\alpha S\lambda+\beta S\mu+\gamma S\nu.$$

If we take the scalar product of the vector $\Phi.\rho$, and another vector σ, we obtain the scalar quantity

$$\sigma.\Phi.\rho=\sigma.(\alpha\lambda+\beta\mu+\gamma\nu).\rho,$$

or in quaternions

$$S\sigma\phi\rho=S\sigma(\alpha S\lambda+\beta S\mu+\gamma S\nu)\rho.$$

This is a function of σ and of ρ, and it is exactly the same kind of function of σ that it is of ρ, a symmetry which is not so clearly exhibited in the quaternionic notation as in the other. Moreover, we can write $\sigma.\Phi$ for $\sigma.(\alpha\lambda+\beta\mu+\gamma\nu)$. This represents a vector which is a function of σ, viz., the function conjugate to $\Phi.\sigma$; and $\sigma.\Phi.\rho$ may be regarded as the product of this vector and ρ. This is not so clearly indicated in the quaternionic notation, where it would be straining things a little to call $S\sigma\phi$ a vector.

The combinations $\alpha\lambda$, $\beta\mu$, etc., used above, are distributive with regard to each of the two vectors, and may be regarded as a kind of product. If we wish to express everything in terms of i, j, and k, Φ will appear as a sum of ii, ij, ik, ji, jj, jk, ki, kj, kk, each with a numerical coefficient. These nine coefficients may be arranged in a square, and constitute a matrix; and the study of the properties of expressions like Φ is identical with the study of ternary matrices. This expression of the matrix as a sum of products (which may be extended to matrices of any order) affords a point of departure from which the properties of matrices may be deduced with the utmost facility. The ordinary matricular product is expressed by a dot, as $\Phi.\Psi$. Other important kinds of multiplication may be defined by the equations—

$$(\alpha\lambda)\overset{\times}{\times}(\beta\mu)=(\alpha\times\beta)(\lambda\times\mu), \qquad (\alpha\lambda):(\beta\mu)=(\alpha.\beta)(\lambda.\mu).$$

With these definitions $\frac{1}{6}\Phi\overset{\times}{\times}\Phi:\Phi$ will be the determinant of Φ, and $\Phi\overset{\times}{\times}\Phi$ will be the conjugate of the reciprocal of Φ multiplied by twice the determinant. If Φ represents the manner in which vectors are affected by a strain, $\frac{1}{2}\Phi\overset{\times}{\times}\Phi$ will represent the manner in which surfaces are affected, and $\frac{1}{6}\Phi\overset{\times}{\times}\Phi:\Phi$ the manner in which volumes are affected. Considerations of this kind do not attach themselves so naturally to the notation $\phi=\alpha S\lambda+\beta S\mu+\gamma S\nu$, nor does the subject admit so free a development with this notation, principally because the symbol S refers to a special use of the matrix, and is very much in the way when we want to apply the matrix to other uses, or to subject it to various operations.

VIII.

QUATERNIONS AND THE *AUSDEHNUNGSLEHRE.*

[*Nature*, vol. XLIV. pp. 79-82, May 28, 1891.]

THE year 1844 is memorable in the annals of mathematics on account of the first appearance on the printed page of Hamilton's *Quaternions* and Grassmann's *Ausdehnungslehre*. The former appeared in the July, October, and supplementary numbers of the *Philosophical Magazine*, after a previous communication to the Royal Irish Academy, November 13, 1843. This communication was indeed announced to the Council of the Academy four weeks earlier, on the very day of Hamilton's discovery of quaternions, as we learn from one of his letters. The author of the *Ausdehnungslehre,* although not unconscious of the value of his ideas, seems to have been in no haste to place himself on record, and published nothing until he was able to give the world the most characteristic and fundamental part of his system with considerable development in a treatise of more than 300 pages, which appeared in August 1844.

The doctrine of quaternions has won a conspicuous place among the various branches of mathematics, but the nature and scope of the *Ausdehnungslehre,* and its relation to quaternions, seem to be still the subject of serious misapprehension in quarters where we naturally look for accurate information. Historical justice, and the interests of mathematical science, seem to require that the allusions to the *Ausdehnungslehre* in the article on "Quaternions" in the last edition of the *Encyclopædia Britannica,* and in the third edition of Prof. Tait's *Treatise on Quaternions,* should not be allowed to pass without protest.

It is principally as systems of geometrical algebra that quaternions and the *Ausdehnungslehre* come into comparison. To appreciate the relations of the two systems, I do not see how we can proceed better than if we ask first what they have in common, then what either system possesses which is peculiar to itself. The relative extent and importance of the three fields, that which is common to the two systems, and those which are peculiar to each, will determine the relative rank of the geometrical algebras. Questions of priority can only relate to the field common to both, and will be much simplified by having the limits of that field clearly drawn.

Geometrical addition in three dimensions is common to the two systems, and seems to have been discovered independently both by Hamilton and Grassmann, as well as by several other persons about the same time. It is not probable that any especial claim for priority with respect to this principle will be urged for either of the two with which we are now concerned.

The functions of two vectors which are represented in quaternions by $S\alpha\beta$ and $V\alpha\beta$ are common to both systems as published in 1844, but the quaternion is peculiar to Hamilton's. The linear vector function is common to both systems as ultimately developed, although mentioned only by Grassmann as early as 1844.

To those already acquainted with quaternions, the first question will naturally be: To what extent are the geometrical methods which are usually called quaternionic peculiar to Hamilton, and to what extent are they common to Grassmann? This is a question which anyone can easily decide for himself. It is only necessary to run one's eye over the equations used by quaternionic writers in the discussion of geometrical or physical subjects, and see how far they necessarily involve the idea of the quaternion, and how far they would be intelligible to one understanding the functions $S\alpha\beta$ and $V\alpha\beta$, but having no conception of the quaternion $\alpha\beta$, or at least could be made so by trifling changes of notation, as by writing S or V in places where they would not affect the value of the expressions. For such a test the examples and illustrations in treatises on quaternions would be manifestly inappropriate, so far as they are chosen to illustrate quaternionic principles, since the object may influence the form of presentation. But we may use any discussion of geometrical or physical subjects, where the writer is free to choose the form most suitable to the subject. I myself have used the chapters and sections in Prof. Tait's *Quaternions* on the following subjects: Geometry of the straight line and plane, the sphere and cyclic cone, surfaces of the second degree, geometry of curves and surfaces, kinematics, statics and kinetics of a rigid system, special kinetic problems, geometrical and physical optics, electrodynamics, general expressions for the action between linear elements, application of ∇ to certain physical analogies, pp. 160-371, except the examples (not worked out) at the close of the chapters.

Such an examination will show that for the most part the methods of representing spatial relations used by quaternionic writers are common to the systems of Hamilton and Grassmann. To an extent comparatively limited, cases will be found in which the quaternionic idea forms an essential element in the signification of the equations.

The question will then arise with respect to the comparatively limited field which is the peculiar property of Hamilton, How important are the advantages to be gained by the use of the quaternion? This question, unlike the preceding, is one into which a personal equation will necessarily enter. Everyone will naturally prefer the methods with which he is most familiar; but I think that it may be safely affirmed that in the majority of cases in this field the advantage derived from the use of the quaternion is either doubtful or very trifling. There remains a residuum of cases in which a substantial advantage is gained by the use of the quaternionic method. Such cases, however, so far as my own observation and experience extend, are very exceptional. If a more extended and careful inquiry should show that they are ten times as numerous as I have found them, they would still be exceptional.

We have now to inquire what we find in the *Ausdehnungslehre* in the way of a geometrical algebra, that is wanting in quaternions. In addition to an algebra of vectors, the *Ausdehnungslehre* affords a system of geometrical algebra in which the point is the fundamental element, and which for convenience I shall call Grassmann's algebra of points. In this algebra we have first the addition of points, or quantities located at points, which may be explained as follows. The equation

$$a\mathrm{A}+b\mathrm{B}+c\mathrm{C}+\text{ etc.}=e\mathrm{E}+f\mathrm{F}+\text{ etc.},$$

in which the capitals denote points, and the small letters scalars (or ordinary algebraic quantities), signifies that

$$a+b+c+\text{ etc.}=e+f+\text{ etc.},$$

and also that the centre of gravity of the weights a, b, c, etc., at the points A, B, C, etc., is the same as that of the weights e, f, etc., at the points E, F, etc. (It will be understood that negative weights are allowed as well as positive.) The equation is thus equivalent to four equations of ordinary algebra. In this Grassmann was anticipated by Möbius (*Barycentrischer Calcul*, 1827).

We have next the addition of finite straight lines, or quantities located in straight lines (*Liniengrössen*). The meaning of the equation

$$\mathrm{AB}+\mathrm{CD}+\text{ etc.}=\mathrm{EF}+\mathrm{GH}+\text{ etc.}$$

will perhaps be understood most readily, if we suppose that each member represents a system of forces acting on a rigid body. The equation then signifies that the two systems are equivalent. An equation of this form is therefore equivalent to six ordinary equations. It will be observed that the *Liniengrössen* AB and CD are not simply vectors; they have not merely length and direction, but they are also located each in a given line, although their position within those lines is immaterial. In Clifford's terminology, AB is a *rotor*, AB+CD a *motor*. In the language of Prof. Ball's *Theory of Screws*, AB+CD represents either a *twist* or a *wrench*.

We have next the addition of plane surfaces (*Plangrössen*). The equation

$$\mathrm{ABC+DEF+GHI=JKL}$$

signifies that the plane JKL passes through the point common to the planes ABC, DEF, and GHI, and that the projection by parallel lines of the triangle JKL on any plane is equal to the sum of the projections of ABC, DEF, and GHI on the same plane, the areas being taken positively or negatively according to the cyclic order of the projected points. This makes the equation equivalent to four ordinary equations.

Finally, we have the addition of volumes, as in the equation

$$\mathrm{ABCD+EFGH=IJKL},$$

where there is nothing peculiar, except that each term represents the six-fold volume of the tetrahedron, and is to be taken positively or negatively according to the relative position of the points.

We have also multiplications as follows: The line (*Liniengrösse*) AB is regarded as the product of the points A and B. The *Plangrösse* ABC, which represents the double area of the triangle, is regarded as the product of the three points A, B, and C, or as the product of the line AB and the point C, or of BC and A, or indeed of BA and C. The volume ABCD, which represents six times the tetrahedron, is regarded as the product of the points A, B, C, and D, or as the product of the point A and the *Plangrösse* BCD, or as the product of the lines AB and BC, etc., etc.

This does not exhaust the wealth of multiplicative relations which Grassmann has found in the very elements of geometry. The following products are called *regressive,* as distinguished from the *progressive,* which have been described. The product of the *Plangrössen* ABC and DEF is a part of the line in which the planes ABC and DEF intersect, which is equal in numerical value to the product of the double areas of the triangles ABC and DEF multiplied by the sine of the angle made by the planes. The product of the *Liniengrösse* AB and the *Plangrösse* CDE is the point of intersection of the line and the plane with a numerical coefficient representing the product of the length of the line and the double area of the triangle multiplied by the sine of the angle made by the line and the plane. The product of three *Plangrössen* is consequently the point common to the three planes with a certain numerical coefficient. In plane geometry we have a regressive product of two *Liniengrössen,* which gives the point of intersection of the lines with a certain numerical coefficient.

The fundamental operations relating to the point, line, and plane are thus translated into analysis by multiplications. The immense flexibility and power of such an analysis will be appreciated by anyone who considers what generalized multiplication in connection with additive relations has done in other fields, as in quaternions, or in the theory of matrices, or in the algebra of logic. For a single example, if we multiply the equation

$$\mathrm{AB}+\mathrm{CD}+\text{etc.}=\mathrm{EF}+\mathrm{GH}+\text{etc.}$$

by PQ (P and Q being any two points), we have

$$\mathrm{ABPQ}+\mathrm{CDPQ}+\text{etc.}=\mathrm{EFPQ}+\mathrm{GHPQ}+\text{etc.},$$

which will be recognised as expressing an important theorem of statics.

The field in which Grassmann's algebra of points, as distinguished from his algebra of vectors, finds its especial application and utility is nearly coincident with that in which, when we use the methods of ordinary algebra, tetrahedral or anharmonic coordinates are more appropriate than rectilinear. In fact, Grassmann's algebra of points may be regarded as the application of the methods of multiple algebra to the notions connected with tetrahedral coordinates, just as his or Hamilton's algebra of vectors may be regarded as the application of the methods of multiple algebra to the notions connected with rectilinear coordinates. These methods, however, enrich the field to which they are applied with new notions. Thus the notion of the coordinates of a line in space, subsequently introduced by Plücker, was first given in the *Ausdehnungslehre* of 1844. It should also be observed that the utility of a multiple algebra when it takes the place of an ordinary algebra of four coordinates, is very much greater than when it takes the place of three coordinates, for the same reason that a multiple algebra taking the place of three coordinates is very much more useful than one taking the place of two. Grassmann's algebra of points will always command the admiration of geometers and analysts, and furnishes an instrument of marvellous power to the former, and in its general form, as applicable to space of any number of dimensions, to the latter. To the physicist an algebra of points is by no means so indispensable an instrument as an algebra of vectors.

Grassmann's algebra of vectors, which we have described as coincident with a part of Hamilton's system, is not really anything separate from his algebra of points, but constitutes a part of it, the vector arising when one point is subtracted from another. Yet it constitutes a whole, complete in itself, and we may separate it from the larger system to facilitate comparison with the methods of Hamilton.

We have, then, as geometrical algebras published in 1844, an algebra of vectors common to Hamilton and Grassmann, augmented on Hamilton's side by the quaternion, and on Grassmann's by his algebra of points. This statement should be made with the reservation that the *addition* both of vectors and of points had been given by earlier writers.

In both systems as finally developed we have the linear vector function, the theory of which is identical with that of strains and rotations. In Hamilton's system we have also the linear quaternion function, and in Grassmann's the linear function applied to the quantities of his algebra of points. This application gives those transformations in which projective properties are preserved, the doctrine of reciprocal figures or principle of duality, etc. (Grassmann's theory of the linear function is, indeed, broader than this, being coextensive with the theory of matrices; but we are here considering only the geometrical side of the theory.)

In his earliest writings on quaternions, Hamilton does not discuss the linear function. In his *Lectures on Quaternions* (1853), he treats of the inversion of the linear vector function, as also of the linear quaternion function, and shows how to find the latent roots of the vector function, with the corresponding axes for the case of real and unequal roots. He also gives a remarkable equation, *the symbolic cubic,* which the functional symbol must satisfy. This equation is a particular case of that which is given in Prof. Cayley's classical *Memoir on the Theory of Matrices* (1858), and which is called by Prof. Sylvester the Hamilton-Cayley equation. In his *Elements of Quaternions* (1866), Hamilton extends the symbolic equation to the quaternion function.

In Grassmann, although the linear function is mentioned in the first *Ausdehnungslehre,* we do not find so full a discussion of the subject until the second *Ausdehnungslehre* (1862), where he discusses the latent roots and axes, or what corresponds to axes in the general theory, the whole discussion relating to matrices of any order. The more difficult cases are included, as that of a strain in which all the roots are real, but there is only one axis or unchanged direction. On the formal side he shows how a linear function may be represented by a quotient or sum of quotients, and by a sum of products, *Lückenausdruck.*

More important, perhaps, than the question when this or that theorem was first published is the question where we first find those notions and notations which give the key to the algebra of linear functions, or the algebra of matrices, as it is now generally called. In vol. xxxi, p. 35, of *Nature,* Prof. Sylvester speaks of Cayley's "ever-memorable" *Memoir on Matrices* as constituting "a second birth of Algebra, its *avatar* in a new and glorified form," and refers to a passage in his *Lectures on Universal Algebra,* from which, I think, we are justified in inferring that this characterization of the memoir is largely due to the fact that it is there shown how matrices may be treated as extensive quantities, capable of addition as well as of multiplication. This idea, however, is older than the memoir of 1858. The *Lückenausdruck,* by which the matrix is expressed as a sum of a kind of products (*lückenhaltig,* or open), is described in a note at the end of the first *Ausdehnungslehre.* There we have the matrix given not only as a sum, but as a sum of products, introducing a multiplicative relation entirely different from the ordinary multiplication of matrices, and hardly less fruitful, but not lying nearly so near the surface as the relations to which Prof. Sylvester refers. The key to the theory of matrices is certainly given in the first *Ausdehnungslehre,* and if we call the birth of matricular analysis the second birth of algebra, we can give no later date to this event than the memorable year of 1844.

The immediate occasion of this communication is the following passage in the preface to the third edition of Prof. Tait's *Quaternions*:

"Hamilton not only published his theory complete, the year before the first (and extremely imperfect) sketch of the *Ausdehnungslehre* appeared; but had given ten years before, in his protracted study of Sets, the very processes of external and internal multiplication (corresponding to the Vector and Scalar parts of a product of two vectors) which have been put forward as specially the property of Grassmann."

For additional information we are referred to art. "Quaternions," *Encyc. Brit.,* where we read respecting the first *Ausdehnungslehre*:

"In particular two species of multiplication ('inner' and 'outer') of directed lines in one plane were given. The results of these two kinds of multiplication correspond respectively to the numerical and the directed parts of Hamilton's quaternion product. But Grassmann distinctly states in his preface that he had not had leisure to extend his method to angles in space. . . . But his claims, however great they may be, can in no way conflict with those of Hamilton, whose mode of multiplying *couples* (in which the 'inner' and 'outer' multiplication are essentially involved) was produced in 1833, and whose quaternion system was completed and published before Grassmann had elaborated for press even the rudimentary portions of his own system, in which the veritable difficulty of the whole subject, the application to angles in space, had not even been attacked."

I shall leave the reader to judge of the accuracy of the general terms used in these passages in comparing the first *Ausdehnungslehre* with Hamilton's system as published in 1843 or 1844. The specific statements respecting Hamilton and Grassmann require an answer.

It must be Hamilton's *Theory of Conjugate Functions or Algebraic Couples* (read to the Royal Irish Academy, 1833 and 1835, and published in vol. xvii of the *Transactions*) to which reference is made in the statements concerning his "protracted study of Sets" and "mode of multiplying *couples.*" But I cannot find anything like Grassmann's external or internal multiplication in this memoir, which is concerned, as the title pretty clearly indicates, with the theory of the complex quantities of ordinary algebra.

It is difficult to understand the statements respecting the *Ausdehnungslehre*, which seem to imply that Grassmann's two kinds of multiplication were subject to some kind of limitation to a plane. The external product is not limited in the first *Ausdehnungslehre* even to three dimensions. The internal, which is a comparatively simple matter, is mentioned in the first *Ausdehnungslehre* only in the preface, where it is defined, and placed beside the external product as relating to directed lines. There is not the least suggestion of any difference in the products in respect to the generality of their application to vectors.

The misunderstanding seems to have arisen from the following sentence in Grassmann's preface: "And in general, in the consideration of angles in space, difficulties present themselves, for the complete (*allseitig*) solution of which I have not yet had sufficient leisure." It is not surprising that Grassmann should have required more time for the development of some parts of his system, when we consider that Hamilton, on his discovery of quaternions, estimated the time which he should wish to devote to them at ten or fifteen years (see his letter to Prof. Tait in the *North British Review* for September 1866), and actually took several years to prepare for the press as many pages as Grassmann had printed in 1844. But any speculation as to the questions which Grassmann may have had principally in mind in the sentence quoted, and the particular nature of the difficulties which he found in them, however interesting from other points of view, seems a very precarious foundation for a comparison of the systems of Hamilton and Grassmann as published in the years 1843-44. Such a comparison should be based on the positive evidence of doctrines and methods actually published.

Such a comparison I have endeavoured to make, or rather to indicate the basis on which it may be made, so far as systems of geometrical algebra are concerned. As a contribution to analysis in general, I suppose that there is no question that Grassmann's system is of indefinitely greater extension, having no limitation to any particular number of dimensions.

IX.

QUATERNIONS AND THE ALGEBRA OF VECTORS.

[*Nature*, vol. XLVII. pp. 463, 464, Mar. 16, 1893.]

In a recent number of *Nature* [vol. xlvii, p. 151], Mr. McAulay puts certain questions to Mr. Heaviside and to me, relating to a subject of such importance as to justify an answer somewhat at length. I cannot of course speak for Mr. Heaviside, although I suppose that his views are not very different from mine on the most essential points, but even if he shall have already replied before this letter can appear, I shall be glad to add whatever of force may belong to independent testimony.

Mr. McAulay asks: "What is the *first* duty of the physical vector analyst *quâ* physical vector analyst?" The answer is not doubtful. It is to present the subject in such a form as to be most easily acquired, and most useful when acquired.

In regard to the slow progress of such methods towards recognition and use by physicists and others, which Mr. McAulay deplores, it does not seem possible to impute it to any want of uniformity of notation. I doubt whether there is any modern branch of mathematics which has been presented for so long a time with a greater uniformity of notation than quaternions.

What, then, is the cause of the fact which Mr. McAulay and all of us deplore? It is not far to seek. We need only a glance at the volumes in which Hamilton set forth his method. No wonder that physicists and others failed to perceive the possibilities of simplicity, perspicuity, and brevity which were contained in a system presented to them in ponderous volumes of 800 pages. Perhaps Hamilton may have intended these volumes as a sort of *thesaurus*, and we should look to his shorter papers for a compact account of his method. But if we turn to his earlier papers on Quaternions in the *Philosophical Magazine*, in which principally he introduced the subject to the notice of his contemporaries, we find them entitled "On Quaternions; or on a New System of Imaginaries in Algebra," and in them we find a great deal about imaginaries, and very little of a vector analysis. To show how slowly the system of vector analysis developed itself in the quaternionic *nidus*, we need only say that the symbols S, V, and ∇ do not appear until two or three years after the discovery of quaternions. In short, it seems to have been only a secondary object with Hamilton to express the geometrical relations of vectors,—secondary in time, and also secondary in this, that it was never allowed to give shape to his work.

But this relates to the past. In regard to the present *status*, I beg leave to quote what Mr. McAulay has said on another occasion (see *Phil. Mag.*, June 1892):—"Quaternions differ in an important respect from other branches of mathematics that are studied by mathematicians after they have in the course of years of hard labour laid the foundation of all their future work. In nearly all cases these branches are very properly so called. They each grow out of a definite spot of the main tree of mathematics, and derive their sustenance from the sap of the trunk as a whole. But not so with quaternions. To let these grow in the brain of a mathematician, he must start from the seed as with the rest of his mathematics regarded as a whole. He cannot graft them on his already flourishing tree, for they will die there. They are independent plants that require separate sowing and the consequent careful tending."

Can we wonder that mathematicians, physicists, astronomers, and geometers feel some doubt as to the value or necessity of something so separate from all other branches of learning? Can that be a natural treatment of the subject which has no relations to any other method, and, as one might suppose from reading some treatises, has only occurred to a single man? Or, at best, is it not discouraging to be told that in order to use the quaternionic method, one must give up the progress which he has already made in the pursuit of his favourite science, and go back to the beginning and start anew on a parallel course?

I believe, however, that if what I have quoted is true of vector methods, it is because there is something fundamentally wrong in the presentation of the subject. Of course, in some sense and to some extent it is and must be true. Whatever is special, accidental, and individual, will die, as it should; but that which is universal and essential should remain as an organic part of the whole intellectual acquisition. If that which is essential dies with the accidental, it must be because the accidental has been given the prominence which belongs to the essential. For myself, I should preach no such doctrine to those whom I wish to convert to the true faith.

In Italy, they say, all roads lead to Rome. In mechanics, kinematics, astronomy, physics, all study leads to the consideration of certain relations and operations. These are the capital notions; these should have the leading parts in any analysis suited to the subject.

If I wished to attract the student of any of these sciences to an algebra for vectors, I should tell him that the fundamental notions of this algebra were exactly those with which he was daily conversant. I should tell him that a vector algebra is so far from being any one man's production that half a century ago several were already working toward an algebra which should be primarily geometrical and not arithmetical, and that there is a remarkable similarity in the results to which these efforts led (see *Proc. A.A.A.S.* for 1886, pp. 37, ff.) [this vol. p. 91, ff.]. I should call his attention to the fact that Lagrange and Gauss used the notation $(\alpha\beta\gamma)$ to denote precisely the same as Hamilton by his $S(\alpha\beta\gamma)$, except that Lagrange limited the expression to unit vectors, and Gauss to vectors of which the length is the secant of the latitude, and I should show him that we have only to give up these limitations, and the expression (in connection with the notion of geometrical addition) is endowed with an immense wealth of transformations. I should call his attention to the fact that the notation $[r_1 r_2]$, universal in the theory of orbits, is identical with Hamilton's $V(\rho_1\rho_2)$, except that Hamilton takes the area as a vector, i.e., includes the notion of the direction of the normal to the plane of the triangle, and that with this simple modification (and with the notion of geometrical addition of surfaces as well as of lines) this expression becomes closely connected with the first-mentioned, and is not only endowed with a similar capability for transformation, but enriches the first with new capabilities. In fact, I should tell him that the notions which we use in vector analysis are those which he who reads between the lines will meet on every page of the great masters of analysis, or of those who have probed deepest the secrets of nature, the only difference being that the vector analyst, having regard to the weakness of the human intellect, does as the early painters who wrote beneath their pictures "This is a tree," "This is a horse."

I cannot attach quite so much importance as Mr. McAulay to uniformity of notation. That very uniformity, if it existed among those who use a vector analysis, would rather obscure than reveal their connection with the general course of modern thought in mathematics and physics. There are two ways in which we may measure the progress of any reform. The one consists in counting those who have adopted the *shibboleth* of the reformers; the other measure is the degree in which the community is imbued with the essential principles of the reform. I should apply the broader measure to the present case, and do not find it quite so bad as Mr. McAulay does.

Yet the question of notations, although not the vital question, is certainly important, and I assure Mr. McAulay that reluctance to make unnecessary innovations in notation has been a very powerful motive in restraining me from publication. Indeed my pamphlet on *Vector Analysis*, which has excited the animadversion of quaternionists, was never formally published, although rather widely distributed, so long as I had copies to distribute, among those who I thought might be interested in the subject. I may say, however, since I am called upon to defend my position, that I have found the notations of that pamphlet more flexible than those generally used. Mr. McAulay, at least, will understand what I mean by this, if I say that some of the relations which he has thought of sufficient importance to express by means of special devices (see *Proc. R.S.E.* for 1890-91), may be expressed at least as briefly in the notations which I have used, and without special devices. But I should not have been satisfied for the purposes of my pamphlet with any notation which should suggest even to the careless reader any connection with the notion of the quaternion. For I confess that one of my objects was to show that a system of vector analysis does not require any support from the notion of the quaternion, or, I may add, of the imaginary in algebra.

I should hardly dare to express myself with so much freedom, if I could not shelter myself behind an authority which will not be questioned.

I do not see that I have done anything very different from what the eminent mathematician upon whom Hamilton's mantle has fallen has been doing, it would seem, unconsciously. Contrast the system of quaternions, which he has described in his sketch of Hamilton's life and work in the *North British Review* for September, 1866, with the system which he urges upon the attention of physicists in the *Philosophical Magazine* in 1890. In 1866 we have a great deal about imaginaries, and nearly as much about the quaternion. In 1890 we have nothing about imaginaries, and little about the quaternion. Prof. Tait has spoken of the calculus of quaternions as throwing off in the course of years its early Cartesian trammels. I wonder that he does not see how well the progress in which he has led may be described as throwing off the yoke of the quaternion. A characteristic example is seen in the use of the symbol ∇. Hamilton applies this to a vector to form a quaternion, Tait to form a linear vector function. But while breathing a new life into the formulæ of quaternions, Prof. Tait stands stoutly by the letter.

Now I appreciate and admire the generous loyalty toward one whom he regards as his master, which has always led Prof. Tait to minimise the originality of his own work in regard to quaternions, and write as if everything was contained in the ideas which flashed into the mind of Hamilton at the classic Brougham Bridge. But not to speak of other claims of historical justice, we owe duties to our scholars as well as to our teachers, and the world is too large, and the current of modern thought is too broad, to be confined by the *ipse dixit* even of a Hamilton.

X.

QUATERNIONS AND VECTOR ANALYSIS.

[*Nature*, vol. XLVIII. pp. 364-367, Aug. 17, 1893.]

In a paper by Prof. C. G. Knott on "Recent Innovations in Vector Theory," of which an abstract has been given in *Nature* (vol. xlvii, pp. 590-593; see also a minor abstract on p. 287), the doctrine that the quaternion affords the only sufficient and proper basis for vector analysis is maintained by arguments based so largely on the faults and deficiencies which the author has found in my pamphlet, *Elements of Vector Analysis*, as to give to such faults an importance which they would not otherwise possess, and to make some reply from me necessary, if I would not discredit the cause of non-quaternionic vector analysis. Especially is this true in view of the warm commendation and endorsement of the paper, by Prof. Tait, which appeared in *Nature* somewhat earlier (p. 225).

The charge which most requires a reply is expressed most distinctly in the minor abstract, viz., "that in the development of his dyadic notation, Prof. Gibbs, being forced to bring the quaternion in, logically condemned his own position." This was incomprehensible to me until I received the original paper, where I found the charge specified as follows: "Although Gibbs gets over a good deal of ground without the explicit recognition of the complete product, which is the difference of his 'skew' and 'direct' products, yet even he recognises in plain language the versorial character of a vector, brings in the quaternion whose vector is the difference of a linear vector function and its conjugate, and does not hesitate to use the accursed thing itself in certain line, surface, and volume integrals" (*Proc. R.S.E.*, Session 1892-3, p. 236). These three specifications I shall consider in their inverse order, premising, however, that the *epitheta ornantia* are entirely my critic's.

The last charge is due entirely to an inadvertence. The integrals referred to are those given at the close of the major abstract in *Nature* (p. 593). My critic, in his original paper, states quite correctly that, according to my definitions and notations, they should represent dyadics. He multiplies them into a vector, introducing the vector under the integral sign, as is perfectly proper, provided, of course, that the vector is constant. But failing to observe this restriction, evidently through inadvertence, and finding that the resulting equations (thus interpreted) would not be true, he concludes that I must have meant something else by the original equations. Now, these equations will hold if interpreted in the quaternionic sense, as is, indeed, a necessary consequence of their holding in the dyadic sense, although the converse would not be true. My critic was thus led, in consequence of the inadvertence mentioned, to suppose that I had departed from my ordinary usage and my express definitions, and had intended the products in these integrals to be taken in the quaternionic sense. This is the sole ground for the last charge.

The second charge evidently relates to the notations Φ_S and $\Phi_\times$ (see *Nature*, vol. xlvii, p. 592). It is perfectly true that I have used a scalar and a vector connected with the linear vector operator, which, if combined, would form a quaternion. I have not thus combined them. Perhaps Prof. Knott will say that since I use both of them it matters little whether I combine them or not. If so I heartily agree with him.

The first charge is a little vague. I certainly admit that vectors may be used in connection with and to represent rotations I have no objection to calling them in such cases *versorial.* In that sense Lagrange and Poinsot, for example, used versorial vectors. But what has this to do with quaternions? Certainly Lagrange and Poinsot were not quaternionists.

The passage in the major abstract in *Nature* which most distinctly charges me with the use of the quaternion is that in which a certain expression which I use is said to represent the quaternion operator $q(\quad)q^{-1}$ (vol. xlvii, p. 592). It would be more accurate to say that my expression and the quaternionic expression represent the same operator. Does it follow that I have used a quaternion? Not at all. A quaternionic expression may represent a number. Does everyone who uses any expression for that number use quaternions? A quaternionic expression may represent a vector. Does everyone who uses any expression for that vector use quaternions? A quaternionic expression may represent a linear vector operator. If I use an expression for that linear vector operator do I therefore use quaternions? My critic is so anxious to prove that I use quaternions that he uses arguments which would prove that quaternions were in common use before Hamilton was born.

So much for the alleged use of the quaternion in my pamphlet. Let us now consider the faults and deficiencies which have been found therein and attributed to the want of the quaternion. The most serious criticism in this respect relates to certain integrating operators, which Prof. Tait unites with Prof. Knott in ridiculing. As definitions are wearisome, I will illustrate the use of the terms and notations which I have used by quoting a sentence addressed to the British Association a few years ago. The speaker was Lord Kelvin.

"Helmholtz first solved the problem—Given the spin in any case of liquid motion, to find the motion. His solution consists in finding the potentials of three ideal distributions of gravitational matter having densities respectively equal to $1/\pi$ of the rectangular components of the given spin; and, regarding for a moment these potentials as rectangular components of velocity in a case of liquid motion, taking the spin in this motion as the velocity in the required motion" (*Nature*, vol. xxxviii, p. 569).

In the terms and notations of my pamphlet the problem and solution may be thus expressed:

Given the curl in any case of liquid motion—to find the motion.

The required velocity is $1/4\pi$ of the curl of the potential of the given curl.

Or, more briefly—The required velocity is $\frac{1}{4\pi}$ of the Laplacian of the given curl.

Or in purely analytical form—Required ω in terms of $\nabla\times\omega$, when $\nabla.\omega=0$.

Solution: $\omega=1/4\pi\nabla\times\text{Pot}\,\nabla\times\omega=1/4\pi\,\text{Lap}\,\nabla\times\omega$.

(The Laplacian expresses the result of an operation like that by which magnetic force is calculated from electric currents distributed in space. This corresponds to the second form in which Helmholtz expressed his result.)

To show the incredible rashness of my critics, I will remark that these equations are among those of which it is said in the original paper (*Proc. R.S.E.*, Session 1892-93, p. 225), "Gibbs gives a good many equations—theorems I suppose they ape at being." I may add that others of the equations thus characterized are associated with names not less distinguished than that of Helmholtz. But that to which I wish especially to call attention is that the terms and notations in question express exactly the notions which physicists want to use.

But we are told (*Nature*, vol. xlvii, p. 287) that these integrating operators (Pot, Lap) are best expressed as inverse functions of ∇. To see how utterly inadequate the Nabla would have been to express the idea, we have only to imagine the exclamation points which the members of the British Association would have looked at each other if the distinguished speaker had said:

Helmholtz first solved the problem—Given the Nabla of the velocity in any case of liquid motion, to find the velocity. His solution was that the velocity was the Nabla of the inverse square of Nabla of the Nabla of the velocity. Or, that the velocity was the inverse Nabla of the Nabla of the velocity.

Or, if the problem and solution had been written thus: Required ω in terms of $\nabla\omega$ when $S\nabla\omega=0$.

Solution: $$\omega=\nabla\nabla^{-2}\nabla\omega=\nabla^{-1}\nabla\omega.$$

My critic has himself given more than one example of the unfitness of the inverse Nabla for the exact expression of thought. For example, when he says that I have taken "eight distinct steps to prove two equations, which are special cases of

$$\nabla^{-2}\nabla^{2}u=u,"$$

I do not quite know what he means. If he means that I have taken eight steps to prove Poisson's Equation (which certainly is not expressed by the equation cited, although it may perhaps be associated with it in some minds), I will only say that my proof is not very long, especially as I have aimed at greater rigor than is usually thought necessary. I cannot, however, compare my demonstration with that of quaternionic writers, as I have not been able (doubtless on account of insufficient search) to find any such.

To show how little foundation there is for the charge that the deficiencies of my system require to be pieced out by these integral operators, I need only say that if I wished to economise operators I might give up New, Lap, and Max, writing for them ∇ Pot, $\nabla\times$Pot, and $\nabla.$Pot, and if I wished further to economise in what costs so little, I could give up the potential also by using the notation $(\nabla.\nabla)^{-1}$ or ∇^{-2}. That is, I could have used this notation without greater sacrifice of precision than quaternionic writers seem to be willing to make. I much prefer, however, to avoid these inverse operators as essentially indefinite.

Nevertheless—although my critic has greatly obscured the subject by ridiculing operators, which I beg leave to maintain are not worthy of ridicule, and by thoughtlessly asserting that it was necessary for me to use them, whereas they are only necessary for me in the sense in which something of the kind is necessary for the quaternionist also, if he would use a notation irreproachable on the score of exactness—I desire to be perfectly candid. I do not wish to deny that the relations connected with these notations appear a little more simple in the quaternionic form. I had, indeed, this subject principally in mind when I said two years ago in *Nature* (vol. xliii, p. 512) [this vol. p. 158]: "There are a few formulæ in which there is a trifling gain in compactness in the use of the quaternion." Let us see exactly how much this advantage amounts to.

There is nothing which the most rigid quaternionist need object to in the notation for the potential, or indeed for the Newtonian. These represent respectively the operations by which the potential or the force of gravitation is calculated from the density of matter. A quaternionist would, however, apply the operator *New* not only to a scalar, as I have done, but to a vector also. The vector part of New ω (construed in the quaternionic sense) would be exactly what I have represented by Lap ω, and the scalar part, taken negatively, would be exactly what I have represented by Max ω. The quaternionist has here a slight economy in notations, which is of less importance, since all the operators—New, Lap, Max—may be expressed without ambiguity in terms of the potential, which is therefore the only one necessary for the exact expression of thought.

But what are the formulæ which it is necessary for one to remember who uses my notations? Evidently only those which contain the operator *Pot.* For all the others are derived from these by the simple substitutions

$$\text{New} = \nabla\,\text{Pot},$$
$$\text{Lap} = \nabla\times\text{Pot},$$
$$\text{Max} = \nabla.\,\text{Pot}.$$

Whether one is quaternionist or not, one must remember Poisson's Equation, which I write

$$\nabla.\nabla\,\text{Pot}\,\omega = -4\pi\omega,$$

and in quaternionic might be written

$$\nabla^2\,\text{Pot}\,\omega = 4\pi\omega.$$

If ω is a vector, in using my equations one has also to remember the general formulæ,

$$\nabla.\nabla\omega = \nabla\nabla.\omega - \nabla\times\nabla\times\omega$$

which as applied to the present case may be united with the preceding in the three-membered equation,

$$\nabla.\nabla\,\text{Pot}\,\omega = \nabla\nabla.\,\text{Pot}\,\omega - \nabla\times\nabla\times\text{Pot}\,\omega = -4\pi\omega.$$

This single equation is absolutely all that there is to burden the memory of the student, except that the symbols of differentiation (∇, $\nabla\times$, $\nabla.$) may be placed indifferently before or after the symbol for the potential, and that if we choose we may substitute as above *New* for ∇ Pot, etc. Of course this gives a good many equations, which on account of the importance of the subject (as they might almost be said to give the mathematics of the electro-magnetic field) I have written out more in detail than might seem necessary. I have also called the attention of the student to many things, which perhaps he might be left to himself to see. Prof. Knott says that the quaternionist obtains similar equations by the simplest transformations. He has failed to observe that the same is true in my *Vector Analysis*, when once I have proved Poisson's Equation. Perhaps he takes his model of brevity from Prof. Tait, who simplifies the subject, I believe, in his treatise on Quaternions, by taking this theorem for granted.

Nevertheless, since I am forced so often to disagree with Prof. Knott, I am glad to agree with him when I can. He says in his original paper (p. 226), "No finer argument in favour of the real quaternion vector analysis can be found than in the tangle and the jangle of sections 91 to 104 in the *Elements of Vector Analysis*." Now I am quite ready to plead guilty to the tangle. The sections mentioned, as is sufficiently evident to the reader, were written at two different times, sections 102-104 being an addition after a couple of years. The matter of these latter sections is not found in its natural place, and the result is well enough characterised as a *tangle*. It certainly does credit to the conscientious study which Prof. Knott has given to my pamphlet, that he has discovered that there is a violent dislocation of ideas just at this point. For such a fault of composition I have no sufficient excuse to offer, but I must protest against its being made the ground of any broad conclusions in regard to the fundamental importance of the quaternion.

Prof. Knott next proceeds to criticise—or at least to ridicule—my treatment of the linear vector function, with respect to which we read in the abstract:—"As developed in the pamphlet, the theory of the dyadic goes over much the same ground as is traversed in the last chapter of Kelland and Tait's *Introduction to Quaternions*. With the exception of a few of those lexicon products, for which Prof. Gibbs has such an affection, there is nothing of real value added to our knowledge of the linear vector function." It would not, I think, be difficult to show some inaccuracy in my critic's characterisation of the real content of this part of my pamphlet. But as algebra is a formal science, and as the whole discussion is concerning the best form of representing certain kinds of relations, the important question would seem to be whether there is anything of *formal* value in my treatment of the linear vector function.

Now Prof. Knott distinctly characterises in half a dozen words the difference in the spirit and method of my treatment of this subject from that which is traditional among quaternionists, when he says of what I have called dyadics—"these are not quantities, but operators" (*Nature*, vol. xlvii, p. 592). I do not think that I applied the word quantity to the dyadics, but Prof. Knott recognised that I treated them as quantities—not, of course, as the quantities of arithmetic, or of ordinary algebra, but as quantities in the broader sense, in which, for example, quaternions are called quantities. The fact that they may be operators does not prevent this. Just as in grammar verbs may be taken as substantives, viz., in the infinitive mood, so in algebra operators—especially such as are capable of quantitative variation—may be regarded as quantities when they are made the subject of algebraic comparison or operation. Now I would not say that it is necessary to treat every kind of operator as quantity, but I certainly think that one so important as the linear vector operator, and one which lends itself so well to such broader treatment, is worthy of it. Of course, when vectors are treated by the methods of ordinary algebra, linear vector operators will naturally be treated by the same methods, but in an algebra formed for the sake of expressing the relations between vectors, and in which vectors are treated as multiple quantities, it would seem an incongruity not to apply the methods of multiple algebra also to the linear vector operator.

The dyadic is practically the linear vector operator regarded as quantity. More exactly it is the multiple quantity of the ninth order which affords various operators according to the way in which it is applied. I will not venture to say what ought to be included in a treatise on quaternions, in which, of course, a good many subjects would have claims prior to the linear vector operator; but for the purposes of my pamphlet, in which the linear vector operator is one of the most important topics, I cannot but regard a treatment like that in Hamilton's *Lectures*, or *Elements*, as wholly inadequate *on the formal side*. To show what I mean, I have only to compare Hamilton's treatment of the quaternion and of the linear vector operator with respect to notations. Since quaternions have been identified with matrices, while the linear vector operator evidently belongs to that class of multiple quantities, it seems unreasonable to refuse to the one those notations which we grant to the other. Thus, if the quaternionist has e^q, $\log q$, $\sin q$, $\cos q$, why should not the vector analyst have e^Φ, $\log \Phi$, $\sin \Phi$, $\cos \Phi$, where Φ represents a linear vector operator? I suppose the latter are at least as useful to the physicist. I mention these notations first, because here the analogy is most evident. But there are other cases far more important, because more elementary, in which the analogy is not so near the surface, and therefore the difference in Hamilton's treatment of the two kinds of multiple quantity not so evident. We have, for example, the tensor of the quaternion, which has the important property represented by the equation: $\mathrm{T}(qr)=\mathrm{T}q\mathrm{T}r$.

There is a scalar quantity related to the linear vector operator, which I have represented by the notation $|\Phi|$ and called the *determinant* of Φ. It is in fact the determinant of the matrix by which Φ may be represented, just as the square of the tensor of q (sometimes called the *norm* of q) is the determinant of the matrix by which q may be represented. It may also be defined as the product of the latent roots of Φ, just as the square of the tensor of q might be defined as the product of the latent roots of q. Again, it has the property represented by the equation

$$|\Phi.\Psi|=|\Phi||\Psi|$$

which corresponds exactly with the preceding equation with both sides squared.

There is another scalar quantity connected with the quaternion and represented by the notation Sq. It has the important property expressed by the equation,

$$S(qrs)=S(rsq)=S(sqr),$$

and so for products of any number of quaternions, in which the cyclic order remains unchanged. In the theory of the linear vector operator there is an important quantity which I have represented by the notation Φ_S, and which has the property represented by the equation

$$(\Phi.\Psi.\Omega)_S=(\Psi.\Omega.\Phi)_S=(\Omega.\Phi.\Psi)_S,$$

where the number of the factors is as before immaterial. Φ_S may be defined as the sum of the latent roots of Φ, just as 2Sq may be defined as the sum of the latent roots of q.

The analogy of these notations may be further illustrated by comparing the equations

$$T(e^q)=e^{Sq}$$

and

$$|e^{\Phi}|=e^{\Phi_S}.$$

I do not see why it is not as reasonable for the vector analyst to have notations like $|\Phi|$ and Φ_S, as for the quaternionist to have the notations Tq and Sq.

This is of course an *argumentum ad quaternionisten.* I do not pretend that it gives the reason why I used these notations, for the identification of the quaternion with a matrix was, I think, unknown to me when I wrote my pamphlet. The real justification of the notations $|\Phi|$ and Φ_S is that they express functions of the linear vector operator *quâ* quantity, which physicists and others have continually occasion to use. And this justification applies to other notations which may not have their analogues in quaternions. Thus I have used $\Phi_\times$ to express a vector so important in the theory of the linear vector operator, that it can hardly be neglected in any treatment of the subject. It is described, for example, in treatises as different as Thomson and Tait's *Natural Philosophy* and Kelland and Tait's *Quaternions.* In the former treatise the components of the vector are, of course, given in terms of the elements of the linear vector operator, which is in accordance with the method of the treatise. In the latter treatise the vector is expressed by

$$V\alpha\alpha'+V\beta\beta'+V\gamma\gamma'.$$

As this supposes the linear vector operator to be given not by a single letter, but by several vectors, it must be regarded as entirely inadequate by any one who wishes to treat the subject in the spirit of multiple algebra, *i.e.* to use a single letter to represent the linear vector operator.

But my critic does not like the notations $|\Phi|$, Φ_S, $\Phi_\times$. His ridicule, indeed reaches high-water mark in the paragraphs in which he mentions them. Concerning another notation, $\Phi{}^{\times}_{\times}\Phi$ (defined in *Nature*, vol. xliii, p. 513) [this vol., p. 160], he exclaims, "Thus burden after burden, in the form of new notation, is added apparently for the sole purpose of exercising the faculty of memory." He would vastly prefer, it would appear, to write with Hamilton $m\phi'^{-1}$, "where m represents what the unit volume becomes under the influence of the linear operator." But this notation is only apparently compact, since the m requires explanation. Moreover, if a strain were given in what Hamilton calls the standard trinomial form, to write out the formula for the operator on surfaces in that standard form by the use of the expression $m\phi'^{-1}$ would require, it seems to me, ten (if not fifty) times the effort of memory and of ingenuity, which would be required for the same purpose with the use of $\frac{1}{2}\Phi{}^{\times}_{\times}\Phi$.

I may here remark that Prof. Tait's letter of endorsement of Prof. Knott's paper affords a striking illustration of the convenience and flexibility of a notation entirely analogous to $\Phi{}^{\times}_{\times}\Phi$, viz., $\Phi{:}\Phi$. He gives the form $S\nabla\nabla_1\, S\sigma\sigma_1$ to illustrate the advantage of quaternionic notations in point of brevity. If I understand his notation, this is what I should write $\nabla\sigma{:}\nabla\sigma$. (I take for granted that the suffixes indicate that ∇ applies as differential operator to σ, and ∇_1 to σ_1, σ and σ_1 being really identical in meaning, as also ∇ and ∇_1.) It will be observed that in my notation one dot unites in multiplication the two ∇'s, and the other the two σ's, and that I am able to leave each ∇ where it naturally belongs as differential operator. The quaternionist cannot do this, because the ∇ and σ cannot be left together without uniting to form a quaternion, which is not at all wanted. Moreover, I can write Φ for $\nabla\sigma$, and $\Phi{:}\Phi$ for $\nabla\sigma{:}\nabla\sigma$. The quaternionist also uses a ϕ, which is practically identical with my Φ (viz., the operator which expresses the relation between $d\sigma$ and $d\rho$), but I do not see how Prof. Knott, who I suppose dislikes $\Phi : \Phi$ as much as $\Phi{}^{\times}_{\times}\Phi$, would express $S\nabla\nabla_1\, S\sigma\sigma_1$ in terms of this ϕ.

It is characteristic of Prof. Knott's view of the subject, that in translating into quaternionic from a dyadic, or operator, as he calls it, he adds in each case an operand. In many cases it would be difficult to make the translation without this. But it is often a distinct advantage to be able to give the operator without the operand. For example, in translating into quaternionic my dyadic or operator $\Phi\times\rho$, he adds an operand, and exclaims, "The old thing!" Certainly, when this expression is applied to an operand, there is no advantage (and no disadvantage) in my notation as compared with the quaternionic. But if the quaternionist wished to express what I would write in the form $(\Phi\times\rho)^{-1}$, or $|\Phi\times\rho|$, or $(\Phi\times\rho)_S$, or $(\Phi\times\rho)_\times$, he would, I think, find the operand very much in the way.

XI.

ON DOUBLE REFRACTION AND THE DISPERSION OF COLORS IN PERFECTLY TRANSPARENT MEDIA.

[*American Journal of Science*, ser. 3, vol. XXIII, pp. 262–275, April, 1882.]

1. In calculating the velocity of a system of plane waves of homogeneous light, regarded as oscillating electrical fluxes, in transparent and sensibly homogeneous bodies, whether singly or doubly refracting, we may assume that such a body is a very fine-grained structure, so that it can be divided into parts having their dimensions very small in comparison with the wave-length, each of which may be regarded as entirely similar to every other, while in the interior of each there are wide differences in electrical as in other physical properties. Hence, the average electrical displacement in such parts of the body may be expressed as a function of the time and the coordinates of position by the ordinary equations of wave-motion, while the real displacement at any point will in general differ greatly from that represented by such equations.

It is the object of this paper to investigate the velocity of light in perfectly transparent media which have not the property of circular polarization in a manner which shall take account of this difference between the real displacements and those represented by the ordinary equations of wave-motion. We shall find that this difference will account for the dispersion of colors, without affecting the validity of the laws of Huyghens and Fresnel for double refraction with respect to light of any one color.

In this investigation, it is assumed that the electrical displacements are *solenoidal*, or, in other words, that they are such as not to produce any change in electrical density. The disturbance in the medium is treated as consisting entirely of such electrical displacements and fluxes, and not complicated by any distinctively magnetic phenomena. It might therefore be more accurate to call the theory (as here developed) *electrical* rather than *electromagnetic*. The latter term is nevertheless retained in accordance with general usage, and with that of the author of the theory.

Since the velocity which we are seeking is equal to the wave-length divided by the period of oscillation, the problem reduces to finding the ratio of these quantities, and may be simplified in some respects by supposing that we have to do with a system of stationary waves. That the relation of the wave-length and the period is the same for stationary as for progressive waves is evident from the consideration that a system of stationary waves may be formed by two systems of progressive waves having opposite directions.

2. Let x, y, z be the rectangular coordinates of any point in the medium, which with the system of waves we may regard as indefinitely extended, and let $\xi+\xi'$, $\eta+\eta'$, $\zeta+\zeta'$ be the components of electrical displacement at that point at the time t; ξ, η, ζ being the average values of the components of electrical displacement at that time in a wave-plane passing through the point. Then $\xi, \eta, \zeta, \xi', \eta', \zeta'$ are perfectly defined quantities, of which ξ, η, ζ are connected with x, y, z, and t by the ordinary equations of wave-motion, while each of the quantities ξ', η', ζ' has always zero for its average value in any wave-plane. We may call ξ, η, ζ the components of the *regular* part of the displacement, and ξ', η', ζ' the components of the *irregular* part of the displacement. In like manner, the differential coefficients of these quantities with respect to the time, $\dot{\xi}$, $\dot{\eta}$, $\dot{\zeta}$, $\dot{\xi}'$, $\dot{\eta}'$, $\dot{\zeta}'$, may be called respectively the components of the regular part of the flux, and the components of the irregular part of the flux.

Let the whole space be divided into elements of volume Dv, very small in all dimensions in comparison with a wave-length, but enclosing portions of the medium which may be treated as entirely similar to one another, and therefore not infinitely small. Thus a crystal may be divided into elementary parallelopipeds, all the vertices of which are similarly situated with respect to the internal structure of the crystal. Amorphous solids and liquids may not be capable of division into equally small portions of which physical similarity can be predicated with the same rigor. Yet we may suppose them capable of a division substantially satisfying the requirements.

From these definitions it follows that at any given instant the average value of each of the quantities ξ', η', ζ' in an element Dv is zero. For the average value in one such element must be sensibly the same as in any other situated on the same wave-plane. If this average were not zero, the average for the wave-plane would not be zero. Moreover, at any given instant, the values of ξ, η, ζ may be regarded as constant throughout any element Dv, and as representing the average values of the components of displacement in that element. The same will be true of the quantities $\dot{\xi}'$, $\dot{\eta}'$, $\dot{\zeta}'$ and $\dot{\xi}$, $\dot{\eta}$, $\dot{\zeta}$.

3. Since we have excluded the case of media which have the property of circular polarization, we shall not impair the generality of our results if we suppose that we have to do with linearly polarized light, i.e., that the regular part of the displacement is everywhere parallel to the same fixed line, all cases not already excluded being

reducible to this. Then, with the origin of coordinates and the zero of time suitably chosen, the regular part of the displacement may be represented by the equations

$$\left.\begin{aligned} \xi &= \alpha \cos 2\pi \frac{u}{l} \cos 2\pi \frac{t}{p}, \\ \eta &= \beta \cos 2\pi \frac{u}{l} \cos 2\pi \frac{t}{p}, \\ \zeta &= \gamma \cos 2\pi \frac{u}{l} \cos 2\pi \frac{t}{p}, \end{aligned}\right\} \tag{1}$$

where l denotes the wave-length, p the period of vibration, α, β, γ the maximum amplitudes of the displacements ξ, η, ζ, and u the distance of the point considered from the wave-plane which passes through the origin. Since u is a linear function of x, y, and z, we may regard these equations as giving the values of ξ, η, ζ, for a given system of waves, in terms of x, y, z, and t.

4. The components of the irregular displacement, ξ', η', ζ', at any given point, will evidently be simple harmonic functions of the time, having the same period as the regular part of the displacement. That they will also have the same phase is not quite so evident, and would not be the case in a medium in which there were any absorption or dispersion of light. It will however appear from the following considerations that in perfectly transparent media the irregular oscillations are synchronous with the regular. For if they are not synchronous, we may resolve the irregular oscillations into two parts, of which one shall be synchronous with the regular oscillations, and the other shall have a difference of phase of one-fourth of a complete oscillation. Now if the medium is one in which there is no absorption or dispersion of light, we may assume that the same electrical configurations may also be passed through in the inverse order, which would be represented analytically by writing $-t$ for t in the equations which give ξ, η, ζ, ξ', η', ζ', as functions of x, y, z, and t. But this change would not affect the regular oscillations, nor the synchronous part of the irregular oscillations, which depends on the cosine of the time, while the non-synchronous part of the irregular oscillations, which depends on the sine of the time, would simply have its direction reversed. Hence, by taking first one-half the sum, and secondly one-half the difference, of the original motion and that obtained by substitution of $-t$ for t, we may separate the non-synchronous part of the irregular oscillations from the rest of the motion. Therefore, the supposed non-synchronous part of the irregular displacement, if capable of existence, is at least wholly independent of the wave-motion and need not be considered by us.

We may go farther in the determination of the quantities ξ', η', ζ'. For in view of the very fine-grained structure of the medium, it will easily appear that the manner in which the general or average flux in any element Dv (represented by ξ, η, ζ) distributes itself among the molecules and intermolecular spaces must be entirely determined by the amount and direction of that flux and its period of oscillation. Hence, and on account of the superposable character of the motions which we are considering, we may conclude that the values of ξ', η', ζ' at any given point in the medium are capable of expression as linear functions of ξ, η, ζ in a manner which shall be independent of the time and of the orientation of the wave-planes and the distance of a nodal plane from the point considered, so long as the period of oscillation remains the same. But a change in the period may presumably affect the relation between ξ', η', ζ' and ξ, η, ζ to a certain extent. And the relation between ξ', η', ζ' and ξ, η, ζ will vary rapidly as we pass from one point to another within the element Dv.

5. In the motion which we are considering there occur alternately instants of no velocity and instants of no displacement. The statical energy of the medium at an instant of no velocity must be equal to its kinetic energy at an instant of no displacement. Let us examine each of these quantities, and consider the equation which expresses their equality.

6. Since in every part of an element Dv the irregular as well as the regular part of the displacement is entirely determined (for light of a given period) by the values of ξ, η, ζ, the statical energy of the element must be a quadratic function of ξ, η, ζ, say

$$(\mathrm{A}\xi^2+\mathrm{B}\eta^2+\mathrm{C}\zeta^2+\mathrm{E}\eta\zeta+\mathrm{F}\zeta\xi+\mathrm{G}\xi\eta)\mathrm{D}v,$$

where A, B, etc. depend only on the nature of the medium and the period of oscillation. At an instant of no velocity, when

$$\sin 2\pi\frac{t}{p}=0, \quad \text{and} \quad \cos^2 2\pi\frac{t}{p}=1,$$

the above expression will reduce by equations (1) to

$$(\mathrm{A}\alpha^2+\mathrm{B}\beta^2+\mathrm{C}\gamma^2+\mathrm{E}\beta\gamma+\mathrm{F}\gamma\alpha+\mathrm{G}\alpha\beta)\cos^2 2\pi\frac{u}{l}\,\mathrm{D}v.$$

Since the average value of $\cos^2 2\pi\frac{u}{l}$ in an indefinitely extended space is $\frac{1}{2}$, we have for the statical energy in a unit of volume

$$\mathrm{S}=\tfrac{1}{2}(\mathrm{A}\alpha^2+\mathrm{B}\beta^2+\mathrm{C}\gamma^2+\mathrm{E}\beta\gamma+\mathrm{F}\gamma\alpha+\mathrm{G}\alpha\beta). \qquad (2)$$

7. The kinetic energy of the whole medium is represented by the double volume-integral*

$$\tfrac{1}{2}\Sigma\iint\frac{(\dot\xi+\dot\xi')_1(\dot\xi+\dot\xi')_2}{r}\,dv_1\,dv_2,$$

* The fluxes are supposed to be measured by the electromagnetic system of units. It is to be observed that the difference of opinion which has prevailed with respect to the estimation of the energy of electrical currents does not extend to such as are *solenoidal*, which may be regarded as composed of closed circuits.

where dv_1, dv_2 are two infinitesimal elements of volume, $(\dot{\xi}+\dot{\xi}')_1$, $(\dot{\xi}+\dot{\xi}')_2$ the corresponding components of flux, r the distance between the elements, and Σ denotes a summation with respect to the coordinate axes. Separating the integrations, we may write for the same quantity

$$\tfrac{1}{2}\Sigma\int(\dot{\xi}+\dot{\xi}')_1\left[\int\frac{(\dot{\xi}+\dot{\xi}')_2}{r}\,dv_2\right]dv_1.$$

It is evident that the integral within the brackets is derived from $\dot{\xi}+\dot{\xi}'$ by the same process by which the potential of any mass is derived from its density. If we use the symbol *Pot* to express this relation, we may write for the kinetic energy

$$\tfrac{1}{2}\Sigma\int(\dot{\xi}+\dot{\xi}')\,\mathrm{Pot}\,(\dot{\xi}+\dot{\xi}')dv.$$

The operation denoted by this symbol is evidently distributive, so that $\mathrm{Pot}\,(\dot{\xi}+\dot{\xi}')=\mathrm{Pot}\,\dot{\xi}+\mathrm{Pot}\,\dot{\xi}'$. The expression for the kinetic energy may therefore be expanded into

$$\tfrac{1}{2}\Sigma\int\dot{\xi}\,\mathrm{Pot}\,\dot{\xi}\,dv+\tfrac{1}{2}\Sigma\int\dot{\xi}\,\mathrm{Pot}\,\dot{\xi}'\,dv+\tfrac{1}{2}\Sigma\int\dot{\xi}'\,\mathrm{Pot}\,\dot{\xi}\,dv+\tfrac{1}{2}\Sigma\int\dot{\xi}'\,\mathrm{Pot}\,\dot{\xi}'\,dv.$$

But $\dot{\xi}'$, and therefore $\mathrm{Pot}\,\dot{\xi}'$, has in every wave-plane the average value zero. Also $\dot{\xi}$, and therefore $\mathrm{Pot}\,\dot{\xi}$, has in every wave-plane a constant value. Therefore the second and third integrals in the above expression will vanish, leaving for the kinetic energy

$$\tfrac{1}{2}\Sigma\int\dot{\xi}\,\mathrm{Pot}\,\dot{\xi}\,dv+\tfrac{1}{2}\Sigma\int\dot{\xi}'\,\mathrm{Pot}\,\dot{\xi}'\,dv, \tag{3}$$

which is to be calculated for a time of no displacement, when

$$\dot{\xi}=\pm\frac{2\pi\alpha}{p}\cos 2\pi\frac{u}{l},\quad \dot{\eta}=\pm\frac{2\pi\beta}{p}\cos 2\pi\frac{u}{l},\quad \dot{\zeta}=\pm\frac{2\pi\gamma}{p}\cos 2\pi\frac{u}{l}. \tag{4}$$

The form of the expression (3) indicates that the kinetic energy consists of two parts, one of which is determined by the regular part of the flux, and the other by the irregular part of the flux.

8. The value of $\mathrm{Pot}\,\dot{\xi}$ may be easily found by integration, but perhaps more readily by Poisson's well-known theorem, that if q is any function of position in space (as the density of a certain mass),

$$\frac{d^2\,\mathrm{Pot}\,q}{dx^2}+\frac{d^2\,\mathrm{Pot}\,q}{dy^2}+\frac{d^2\,\mathrm{Pot}\,q}{dz^2}=-4\pi q, \tag{5}$$

where the direction of the coordinate axes is immaterial, provided that they are rectangular. In applying this to $\mathrm{Pot}\,\dot{\xi}$, we may place two of the axes in a wave-plane. This will give

$$\frac{d^2\,\mathrm{Pot}\,\dot{\xi}}{du^2}=-4\pi\dot{\xi}. \tag{6}$$

In a nodal plane, $\mathrm{Pot}\,\dot{\xi}=0$, since $\dot{\xi}$ has equal positive and negative values in elements of volume symmetrically distributed with respect to any point in such a plane. In a wave-crest (or plane in which $\dot{\xi}$ has a maximum value), Pot $\dot{\xi}$ will also have a maximum value, which we may call K. For intermediate points we may determine its value from the consideration that the total disturbance may be resolved into two systems of waves, one having a wave-crest, and the other a nodal plane passing through the point for which the potential is sought. The maximum amplitudes of these component systems will be to the maximum amplitude of the original system as $\cos 2\pi\frac{u}{l}$ and $\sin 2\pi\frac{u}{l}$ to unity. But the second of the component systems will contribute nothing to the value of the potential. We thus obtain

$$\text{Pot}\,\dot{\xi} = \text{K}\cos 2\pi\frac{u}{l},$$

$$\frac{d^2\,\text{Pot}\,\dot{\xi}}{du^2} = -\frac{4\pi^2}{l^2}\text{K}\cos 2\pi\frac{u}{l} = -\frac{4\pi^2}{l^2}\text{Pot}\,\dot{\xi}.$$

Comparing this with equation (6), we have

$$-\frac{4\pi^2}{l^2}\text{Pot}\,\dot{\xi} = -4\pi\dot{\xi},$$

$$\text{Pot}\,\dot{\xi} = \frac{l^2}{\pi}\dot{\xi}. \tag{7}$$

Hence, and by equations (4),

$$\tfrac{1}{2}\Sigma\int\dot{\xi}\,\text{Pot}\,\dot{\xi}\,dv = \frac{l^2}{2\pi}\Sigma\int\dot{\xi}^2\,dv = \frac{2\pi l^2}{p^2}(\alpha^2+\beta^2+\gamma^2)\int\cos^2 2\pi\frac{u}{l}\,dv.$$

The kinetic energy of the regular part of the flux is therefore, for each unit of volume,

$$\text{T} = \frac{\pi l^2}{p^2}(\alpha^2+\beta^2+\gamma^2). \tag{8}$$

9. With respect to the kinetic energy of the irregular part of the flux, it is to be observed that, since $\dot{\xi}'$, $\dot{\eta}'$, $\dot{\zeta}'$ have their average values zero in spaces which are very small in comparison with a wave-length, the integrations implied in the notations Pot $\dot{\xi}'$, Pot $\dot{\eta}'$, Pot $\dot{\zeta}'$ may be confined to a sphere of a radius which is small in comparison with a wave-length. Since within such a sphere $\dot{\xi}'$, $\dot{\eta}'$, $\dot{\zeta}'$ are sensibly determined by the values of $\dot{\xi}$, $\dot{\eta}$, $\dot{\zeta}$ at the center of the sphere, which is the point for which the value of the potentials are sought, Pot $\dot{\xi}'$, Pot $\dot{\eta}'$, Pot $\dot{\zeta}'$ must be functions—evidently linear functions—of $\dot{\xi}$, $\dot{\eta}$, $\dot{\zeta}$; and $\dot{\xi}'$ Pot $\dot{\xi}'$, $\dot{\eta}'$ Pot $\dot{\eta}'$, $\dot{\zeta}'$ Pot $\dot{\zeta}'$ must be quadratic functions of the same quantities. But these functions will vary with the position of the point considered with reference to the adjacent molecules.

Now the expression for the kinetic energy of the irregular part of the flux,

$$\tfrac{1}{2}\Sigma\int\dot{\xi}'\,\text{Pot}\,\dot{\xi}'\,dv,$$

indicates that we may regard the infinitesimal element dv as having the energy (due to this part of the flux)

$$\tfrac{1}{2}\Sigma\, \dot{\xi}' \operatorname{Pot} \dot{\xi}'\, dv.$$

Let us consider the energy due to the irregular flux which will belong to the above defined element Dv, which is not infinitely small, but which has the advantage of being one of physically similar elements which make up the whole medium. The energy of this element is found by adding the energies of all the infinitesimal elements of which it is composed. Since these are quadratic functions of the quantities $\dot{\xi}, \dot{\eta}, \dot{\zeta}$, which are sensibly constant throughout the element Dv, the sum will be a quadratic function of $\dot{\xi}, \dot{\eta}, \dot{\zeta}$, say

$$(\mathrm{A}'\dot{\xi}^2+\mathrm{B}'\dot{\eta}^2+\mathrm{C}'\dot{\zeta}^2+\mathrm{E}'\dot{\eta}\dot{\zeta}+\mathrm{F}'\dot{\zeta}\dot{\xi}+\mathrm{G}'\dot{\xi}\dot{\eta})\mathrm{D}v,$$

which will therefore represent the energy of the element Dv due to the irregular flux. The coefficients A′, B′, etc., are determined by the nature of the medium and the period of oscillation. They will be constant throughout the medium, since one element Dv does not differ from another.

This expression reduces by equations (4) to

$$\frac{4\pi^2}{p^2}(\mathrm{A}'\alpha^2+\mathrm{B}'\beta^2+\mathrm{C}'\gamma^2+\mathrm{E}'\beta\gamma+\mathrm{F}'\gamma\alpha+\mathrm{G}'\alpha\beta)\cos^2 2\pi\frac{u}{l}\,\mathrm{D}v.$$

The kinetic energy of the irregular flux in a unit of volume is therefore

$$\mathrm{T}'=\frac{2\pi^2}{p^2}(\mathrm{A}'\alpha^2+\mathrm{B}'\beta^2+\mathrm{C}'\gamma^2+\mathrm{E}'\beta\gamma+\mathrm{F}'\gamma\alpha+\mathrm{G}'\alpha\beta). \tag{9}$$

10. Equating the statical and kinetic energies, we have

$$\tfrac{1}{2}(\mathrm{A}\alpha^2+\mathrm{B}\beta^2+\mathrm{C}\gamma^2+\mathrm{E}\beta\gamma+\mathrm{F}\gamma\alpha+\mathrm{G}\alpha\beta)$$
$$=\frac{\pi l^2}{p^2}(\alpha^2+\beta^2+\gamma^2)+\frac{2\pi^2}{p^2}(\mathrm{A}'\alpha^2+\mathrm{B}'\beta^2+\mathrm{C}'\gamma^2+\mathrm{E}'\beta\gamma+\mathrm{F}'\gamma\alpha+\mathrm{G}'\alpha\beta). \tag{10}$$

The velocity (V) of the corresponding system of progressive waves is given by the equation

$$\mathrm{V}^2=\frac{l^2}{p^2}=\frac{1}{2\pi}\,\frac{\mathrm{A}\alpha^2+\mathrm{B}\beta^2+\mathrm{C}\gamma^2+\mathrm{E}\beta\gamma+\mathrm{F}\gamma\alpha+\mathrm{G}\alpha\beta}{\alpha^2+\beta^2+\gamma^2}$$
$$-\frac{2\pi}{p^2}\,\frac{\mathrm{A}'\alpha^2+\mathrm{B}'\beta^2+\mathrm{C}'\gamma^2+\mathrm{E}'\beta\gamma+\mathrm{F}'\gamma\alpha+\mathrm{G}'\alpha\beta}{\alpha^2+\beta^2+\gamma^2}. \tag{11}$$

If we set

$$a=\frac{1}{2\pi}\mathrm{A}-\frac{2\pi}{p^2}\mathrm{A}', \quad b=\frac{1}{2\pi}\mathrm{B}-\frac{2\pi}{p^2}\mathrm{B}', \quad \text{etc.,} \tag{12}$$

and

$$\rho^2=\alpha^2+\beta^2+\gamma^2,$$

the equation reduces to

$$\mathrm{V}^2=\frac{a\alpha^2+b\beta^2+c\gamma^2+e\beta\gamma+f\gamma\alpha+g\alpha\beta}{\rho^2}. \tag{13}$$

For a given medium and light of a given period, the coefficients a, b, etc., are constant.

This relation between the velocity of the waves and the direction of oscillation is capable of a very simple geometrical expression. Let r be the radius vector of the ellipsoid

$$ax^2+by^2+cz^2+eyz+fzx+gxy=1. \tag{14}$$

Then
$$\frac{1}{r^2}=\frac{ax^2+by^2+cz^2+eyz+fzx+gxy}{r^2}.$$

If this radius is drawn parallel to the electrical oscillations, we shall have

$$\frac{x}{r}=\frac{\alpha}{\rho}, \quad \frac{y}{r}=\frac{\beta}{\rho}, \quad \frac{z}{r}=\frac{\gamma}{\rho},$$

and
$$V^2=\frac{1}{r^2}. \tag{15}$$

That is, the wave-velocity for any particular direction of oscillation is represented in the ellipsoid by the reciprocal of the radius vector which is parallel to that direction.

11. This relation between the wave-length, the period, and the direction of vibration, must hold true not only of such vibrations as actually occur, but also of such as we may imagine to occur under the influence of constraints determining the direction of vibration in the wave-plane. The directions of the natural or unconstrained vibrations in any wave-plane may be determined by the general mechanical principle that if the type of a natural vibration is infinitesimally altered by the application of a constraint, the value of the period will be stationary.* Hence, in a system of stationary waves such as we have been considering, if the direction of an unconstrained vibration is infinitesimally varied in its wave-plane by a constraint while the wave-length remains constant, the period will be stationary. Therefore, if the direction of the unconstrained vibration is infinitesimally varied by constraint, and the period remains rigorously constant, the wave-length will be stationary. Hence, if we make a central section of the above described ellipsoid parallel to any wave-plane, the directions of natural vibration for that wave-plane will be parallel to the radii vectores of stationary value in that section, viz., to the axes of the ellipse, when the section is elliptical, or to all radii, when the section is circular.

12. For light of a single period, our hypothesis has led to a perfectly definite result, our equations expressing the fundamental laws of double refraction as enunciated by Fresnel. But if we ask how the velocity of light varies with the period, that is, if we seek

* See Rayleigh's *Theory of Sound*, vol. i, p. 84.

to derive from the same equations the laws of the dispersion of colors, we shall not be able to obtain an equally definite result, since the quantities A, B, etc., and A′, B′, etc., are unknown functions of the period. If, however, we make the assumption, which is hardly likely to be strictly accurate, but which may quite conceivably be not far removed from the truth, that the manner in which the general or average flux in any small part of the medium distributes itself among the molecules and intermolecular spaces is independent of the period, the quantities A, B, etc., and A′, B′, etc., will be constant, and we obtain a very simple relation between V and p, which appears to agree tolerably well with the results of experiment.

If we set
$$H=\frac{A\alpha^2+B\beta^2+C\gamma^2+E\beta\gamma+F\gamma\alpha+G\alpha\beta}{\rho^2}, \tag{16}$$

and
$$H'=\frac{A'\alpha^2+B'\beta^2+C'\gamma^2+E'\beta\gamma+F'\gamma\alpha+G'\alpha\beta}{\rho^2}, \tag{17}$$

our general equation (11) becomes

$$V^2=\frac{H}{2\pi}-\frac{2\pi H'}{p^2}, \tag{18}$$

where H and H′ will be constant for any given direction of oscillation, when A, B, etc., and A′, B′, etc., are constant. If we wish to introduce into the equation the absolute index of refraction (n) and the wave-length in vacuo (λ) in place of V and p, we may divide both sides of the equation by the square of the constant (k) representing the velocity of light in vacuo. Then, since

$$\frac{V}{k}=\frac{1}{n}, \quad \text{and} \quad kp=\lambda,$$

our equation reduces to

$$\frac{1}{n^2}=\frac{H}{2\pi k^2}-\frac{2\pi H'}{\lambda^2}. \tag{19}$$

It is well known that the relation between n and λ may be tolerably well but by no means perfectly represented by an equation of this form.

13. If we now give up the presumably inaccurate supposition that A, B, etc., and A′, B′, etc., are constant, equation (19) will still subsist, but H and H′ will not be constant for a given direction of oscillation, but will be functions of p, or, what amounts to the same, of λ. Although we cannot therefore use the equation to derive *a priori* the relation between n and λ, we may use it to derive the values of H and H′ from the empirically determined relation between n and λ. To do this, we must make use again of the general principle that an

infinitesimal variation in the type of a vibration, due to a constraint, will not affect the period. If we first consider a certain system of stationary waves, then a system in which the wave-length is greater by an infinitesimal dl (the direction of oscillation remaining the same), the period will be increased by an infinitesimal dp, and the manner in which the flux distributes itself among the molecules and intermolecular spaces will presumably be infinitesimally changed. But if we suppose that in the second system of waves there is applied a constraint compelling the flux to distribute itself in the same way among the molecules and intermolecular spaces as in the first system (so that ξ', η', ζ' shall be the same functions as before of ξ, η, ζ,—a supposition perfectly compatible with the fact that the values of ξ, η, ζ are changed), this constraint, according to the principle cited, will not affect the period of oscillation. Our equations will apply to such a constrained type of oscillation, and A, B, etc., and A′, B′, etc., and therefore H and H′, will have the same values in the last described system of waves as in the first system, although the wave-length and the period have been varied. Therefore, in differentiating equation (18), which is essentially an equation between l and p, or its equivalent (19), we may treat H and H′ as constant. This gives

$$-\frac{2}{n^3}\frac{dn}{d\lambda}=\frac{4\pi \mathrm{H}'}{\lambda^3}.$$

We thus obtain the values of H′ and H

$$\mathrm{H}'=-\frac{\lambda^3}{2\pi n^3}\frac{dn}{d\lambda}, \qquad \mathrm{H}=\frac{2\pi k^2}{n^2}-\frac{2\pi k^3\lambda}{n^3}\frac{dn}{d\lambda}. \tag{20}$$

By determining the values of H and H′ for different directions of oscillation, we may determine the values of A, B, etc., and A′, B′, etc.

By means of these equations, the ratios of the statical energy (S), the kinetic energy due to the regular part of the flux (T), and the kinetic energy due to the irregular part of the flux (T′), are easily obtained in a form which admits of experimental determination. Equations (8) and (9) give

$$\mathrm{T}=\frac{\pi\rho^2 l^2}{p^2}, \qquad \mathrm{T}'=\frac{2\pi^2\mathrm{H}'\rho^2}{p^2}.$$

Therefore, by (20),

$$\frac{\mathrm{T}'}{\mathrm{T}}=\frac{2\pi\mathrm{H}'}{l^2}=\frac{2\pi\mathrm{H}'n^2}{\lambda^2}=-\frac{\lambda}{n}\frac{dn}{d\lambda}=-\frac{d\log n}{d\log\lambda}. \tag{21}$$

$$\frac{\mathrm{S}}{\mathrm{T}}=\frac{\mathrm{T}+\mathrm{T}'}{\mathrm{T}}=1+\frac{\mathrm{T}'}{\mathrm{T}}=\frac{d\log\lambda-d\log n}{d\log\lambda}=\frac{d\log l}{d\log\lambda}. \tag{22}$$

$$\frac{\mathrm{T}'}{\mathrm{S}}=-\frac{d\log n}{d\log l}. \tag{23}$$

Since S, T, and T′ are essentially positive quantities, their ratios must be positive. Equation (21) therefore requires that the index of refraction shall increase as the period or wave-length in vacuo diminishes. Experiment has shown no exceptions to this rule, except such as are manifestly attributable to the absorption of light.

14. It remains to consider the relations between the optical properties of a medium and the planes or axes of symmetry which it may possess. If we consider the statical energy per unit of volume (S) and the period as constant, we may regard equation (2) as the equation of an ellipsoid, the radii vectores of which represent in direction and magnitude the amplitudes of systems of waves having the same statical energy. In like manner, if we consider the kinetic energy of the irregular part of the flux per unit of volume (T′) and the period as constant, we may regard equation (9) as the equation of an ellipsoid, the radii vectores of which represent in direction and magnitude the amplitudes of systems of waves having the same kinetic energy due to the irregular part of the flux. These ellipsoids, which we may distinguish as the ellipsoids (A, B, etc.) and (A′, B′, etc.), as well as the ellipsoid before described, which we may call the ellipsoid (a, b, etc.), must be independent in their form and their orientation of the directions of the axes of coordinates, being determined entirely by the nature of the medium and the period of oscillation. They must therefore possess the same kind of symmetry as the internal structure of the medium.

If the medium is symmetrical about a certain axis, each ellipsoid must have an axis parallel to that. If the medium is symmetrical with respect to a certain plane, each ellipsoid must have an axis at right angles to that plane. If the medium after a revolution of less than 180° about a certain axis is then equivalent to the medium in its first position, or symmetrical with it with respect to a plane at right angles to that axis, each ellipsoid must have an axis of revolution parallel to that axis. These relations must be the same for light of all colors, and also for all temperatures of the medium.

15. From these principles we may infer the optical characteristics of the different crystallographic systems.

In crystals of the isometric system, as in amorphous bodies, the three ellipsoids reduce to spheres. Such media are optically isotropic at least so far as any properties are concerned which come within the scope of this paper.

In crystals of the tetragonal or hexagonal systems, the three ellipsoids will have axes of rotation parallel to the principal crystallographic axis. Since the ellipsoid (a, b, etc.) has but one circular section, there will be but one optic axis, which will have a fixed direction.

In crystals of the orthorhombic system, the three ellipsoids will have their axes parallel to the rectangular crystallographic axes. If we take these directions for the axes of coordinates, E, F, G, E′, F′, G′, e, f, g will vanish and equation (13) will reduce to

$$V^2 = \frac{a\alpha^2 + b\beta^2 + c\gamma^2}{\rho^2}.$$

If the coordinate axes are so placed that

$$a > b > c,$$

the optic axes will lie in the X-Z plane, making equal angles ϕ with the axis of Z, which may be determined by the equation

$$\tan^2\phi = \frac{a-b}{b-c} = \frac{p^2(A-B) - 4\pi^2(A'-B')}{p^2(B-C) - 4\pi^2(B'-C')}.$$

To get a rough idea of the manner in which ϕ varies with the period, we may regard A, B, C, A′, B′, C′ as constant in this equation.

But since the lengths of the axes of the ellipsoid (a, b, etc.) vary with the period, it may easily happen that the order of the axes with respect to magnitude is not the same for all colors. In that case, the optic axes for certain colors will lie in one of the principal planes, and for other colors in another. For the color at which the change takes place, the two optic axes will coincide. The differential coefficient $\frac{d\phi}{dp}$ becomes infinitely great as the optic axes approach coincidence.

In crystals of the monoclinic system, each of the three ellipsoids will have an axis perpendicular to the plane of symmetry. We may choose this direction for the axis of X. Then F, G, F′, G′, f, g, will vanish and equation (13) will reduce to

$$V^2 = \frac{a\alpha^2 + b\beta^2 + c\gamma^2 + e\beta\gamma}{\rho^2}.$$

The angle θ made by one of the axes of the ellipsoid (a, b, etc.) in the plane of symmetry with the axis of Y and measured toward the axis of Z, is determined by the equation

$$\tan 2\theta = \frac{e}{c-b} = \frac{p^2E - 4\pi^2E'}{p^2(C-B) - 4\pi^2(C'-B')}.$$

To get a rough idea of the *dispersion* of the axes of the ellipsoid (a, b, etc.) in the plane of symmetry, we may regard B, C, E, B′, C′, E′, as constant in this equation, and suppose the axis of Y so placed as to make E vanish.

It is evident that in this system the plane of the optic axes will be fixed, or will rotate about one of the lines which bisect the angles made by the optic axes, according as the mean axis of the ellipsoid

(a, b, etc.) is perpendicular to the plane of symmetry or lies in that plane. In the first case the *dispersion* of the two optic axes will be unequal. The same crystal, however, with light of different colors, or at different temperatures, may afford an example of each case.

In crystals of the triclinic system, since the ellipsoids (A, B, etc.) and (A′, B′, etc.) are determined by considerations of a different nature, and there are no relations of symmetry to cause a coincidence in the directions of their axes, there will not in general be any such coincidence. Therefore the three axes of the ellipsoid (a, b, etc.), that is, the two lines which bisect the angles of the optic axes and their common normal, will vary in position with the color of the light.

16. It appears from this foregoing discussion that by the electromagnetic theory of light we may not only account for the dispersion of colors (including the dispersion of the lines which bisect the angles of the optic axes in doubly refracting media), but may also obtain Fresnel's laws of double refraction for every kind of homogeneous light *without neglect of the quantities which determine the dispersion of colors.*

But a closer approximation than that of this paper will be necessary to explain the phenomena of circularly polarizing media, which depend on very minute differences of wave-velocity, represented perhaps by a few units in the sixth significant figure of the index of refraction. That the degree of approximation which will give the laws of circular and elliptic polarization will not add any terms to the equations of this paper, except such as vanish for media which do not exhibit this phenomenon, will be shown in another number of this Journal.

XII.

ON DOUBLE REFRACTION IN PERFECTLY TRANSPARENT MEDIA WHICH EXHIBIT THE PHENOMENA OF CIRCULAR POLARIZATION.

[*American Journal of Science*, ser. 3, vol. XXIII, pp. 460-476, June, 1882.]

1. IN the April number of this Journal,* the velocity of propagation of a system of plane waves of light, regarded as oscillating electrical fluxes, was discussed with such a degree of approximation as would account for the dispersion of colors and give Fresnel's laws of double refraction. It is the object of this paper to supplement that discussion by carrying the approximation so much further as is necessary in order to embrace the phenomena of circularly polarizing media.

2. If we imagine all the velocities in any progressive system of plane waves to be reversed at a given instant without affecting the displacements, and the system of wave-motion thus obtained to be superposed upon the original system, we obtain a system of stationary waves having the same wave-length and period of oscillation as the original progressive system. If we then reduce the magnitude of the displacements in the uniform ratio of two to one, they will be identical, at an instant of maximum displacement, with those of the original system at the same instant.

Following the same method as in the paper cited, let us especially consider the system of stationary waves, and divide the whole displacement into the *regular* part, represented by ξ, η, ζ, and the *irregular* part, represented by ξ', η', ζ', in accordance with the definitions of § 2 of that paper.

3. The *regular* part of the displacement is subject to the equations of wave-motion, which may be written (in the most general case of plane stationary waves)

$$\left.\begin{aligned}\xi&=\left(\alpha_1\cos 2\pi\frac{u}{l}+\alpha_2\sin 2\pi\frac{u}{l}\right)\cos 2\pi\frac{t}{p},\\ \eta&=\left(\beta_1\cos 2\pi\frac{u}{l}+\beta_2\sin 2\pi\frac{u}{l}\right)\cos 2\pi\frac{t}{p},\\ \zeta&=\left(\gamma_1\cos 2\pi\frac{u}{l}+\gamma_2\sin 2\pi\frac{u}{l}\right)\cos 2\pi\frac{t}{p},\end{aligned}\right\}\qquad(1)$$

* See page 182 of this volume.

where l denotes the wave-length, p the period of oscillation, u the distance of the point considered from the wave-plane passing through the origin, α_1, β_1, γ_1 the amplitudes of the displacements ξ, η, ζ in the wave-plane passing through the origin, and α_2, β_2, γ_2 their amplitudes in a wave-plane one-quarter of a wave-length distant and on the side toward which u increases. If we also write L, M, N for the direction-cosines of the wave-normal drawn in the direction in which u increases, we shall have the following necessary relations:

$$L^2+M^2+N^2=1, \tag{2}$$

$$u=Lx+My+Nz, \tag{3}$$

$$L\alpha_1+M\beta_1+N\gamma_1=0, \quad L\alpha_2+M\beta_2+N\gamma_2=0. \tag{4}$$

4. That the *irregular* part of the displacement (ξ', η', ζ') at any given point is a simple harmonic function of the time, having the same period and phase as the regular part of the displacement (ξ, η, ζ), may be proved by the single principle of superposition of motions, and is therefore to be regarded as exact in a discussion of this kind. But the further conclusion of the preceding paper (§ 4), "that the values of ξ', η', ζ' at any given point in the medium are capable of expression as linear functions of ξ, η, ζ in a manner which shall be independent of the time and of the orientation of the wave-planes and the distance of a nodal plane from the point considered, so long as the period of oscillation remains the same," is evidently only approximative, although a very close approximation. A very much closer approximation may be obtained, if we regard ξ', η', ζ', at any given point of the medium and for light of a given period, as linear functions of ξ, η, ζ and the nine differential coefficients

$$\frac{d\xi}{dx}, \ \frac{d\eta}{dx}, \ \frac{d\zeta}{dx}, \ \frac{d\xi}{dy}, \ \text{etc.}$$

We shall write ξ, η, ζ *and diff. coeff.* to denote these twelve quantities.

From this it follows immediately that with the same degree of approximation $\dot{\xi}'$, $\dot{\eta}'$, $\dot{\zeta}'$ may be regarded, for a given point of the medium and light of a given period, as linear functions of $\dot{\xi}$, $\dot{\eta}$, $\dot{\zeta}$ and the differential coefficients of $\dot{\xi}$, $\dot{\eta}$, $\dot{\zeta}$ with respect to the coordinates. For these twelve quantities we shall write $\dot{\xi}$, $\dot{\eta}$, $\dot{\zeta}$ *and diff. coeff.*

5. Let us now proceed to equate the statical energy of the medium at an instant of no velocity with its kinetic energy at an instant of no displacement. It will be convenient to estimate each of these quantities for a unit of volume.

6. The statical energy of an infinitesimal element of volume may be represented by $\sigma\, dv$, where σ is a quadratic function of the components of displacement $\xi+\xi'$, $\eta+\eta'$, $\zeta+\zeta'$. Since for that element of volume ξ', η', ζ' may be regarded as linear functions of ξ, η, ζ *and diff. coeff.*,

we may regard σ as a quadratic function of ξ, η, ζ *and diff. coeff.*, or as a linear function of the seventy-eight squares and products of these quantities. But the seventy-eight coefficients by which this function is expressed will vary with the position of the element of volume with respect to the surrounding molecules.

In estimating the statical energy for any considerable space by the integral

$$\int \sigma \, dv,$$

it will be allowable to substitute for the seventy-eight coefficients contained implicitly in σ their average values throughout the medium. That is, if we write s for a quadratic function of ξ, η, ζ, *and diff. coeff.* in which the seventy-eight coefficients are the space-averages of those in σ, the statical energy of any considerable space may be estimated by the integral

$$\int s \, dv.$$

(This will appear most distinctly if we suppose the integration to be first effected for a thin slice of the medium bounded by two wave-planes.) The seventy-eight coefficients of this function s are determined solely by the nature of the medium and the period of oscillation.

We may divide s into three parts, of which the first ($s_{\prime}$) contains the squares and products of ξ, η, ζ, the second ($s_{\prime\prime}$) contains the products of ξ, η, ζ with the differential coefficients, and the third ($s_{\prime\prime\prime}$) contains the squares and products of the differential coefficients. It is evident that the average statical energy of the whole medium per unit of volume is the space-average of s, and that it will consist of three parts, which are the space-averages of $s_{\prime}$, $s_{\prime\prime}$, and $s_{\prime\prime\prime}$, respectively. These parts we may call $S_{\prime}$, $S_{\prime\prime}$, and $S_{\prime\prime\prime}$. Only the first of these was considered in the preceding paper.

Now the considerations which justify us in neglecting, for an approximate estimate, the terms of s which contain the differential coefficients of ξ, η, ζ with respect to the coordinates, will apply with especial force to the terms which contain the squares and products of these differential coefficients. Therefore, to carry the approximation one step beyond that of the preceding paper, it will only be necessary to take account of $s_{\prime}$ and $s_{\prime\prime}$ and of $S_{\prime}$ and $S_{\prime\prime}$.

7. We may set

$$s_{\prime} = A\xi^2 + B\eta^2 + C\zeta^2 + E\eta\zeta + F\zeta\xi + G\xi\eta, \tag{5}$$

where, for a given medium and light of a given period, A, B, C, E, F, G are constant.

Since the average values of

$$\sin^2 2\pi\frac{u}{l}, \quad \cos^2 2\pi\frac{u}{l}, \quad \sin 2\pi\frac{u}{l}\cos 2\pi\frac{u}{l}$$

are respectively $\frac{1}{2}$, $\frac{1}{2}$, and 0, and since at the time to be considered

$$\cos^2 2\pi\frac{t}{p}=1,$$

it will appear from inspection of equations (1) that

$$\begin{aligned}S_{,}=&\tfrac{1}{2}(A\alpha_1^2+B\beta_1^2+C\gamma_1^2+E\beta_1\gamma_1+F\gamma_1\alpha_1+G\alpha_1\beta_1)\\&+\tfrac{1}{2}(A\alpha_2^2+B\beta_2^2+C\gamma_2^2+E\beta_2\gamma_2+F\gamma_2\alpha_2+G\alpha_2\beta_2).\end{aligned}\qquad(6)$$

This is the first part of the statical energy of the whole medium per unit of volume.

8. The second part of the statical energy of the whole medium per unit of volume ($S_{,,}$) is the space-average of $s_{,,}$, which is a linear function of the twenty-seven products of ξ, η, ζ with their differential coefficients with respect to the coordinates. Now since

$$\xi\frac{d\xi}{dx}=\tfrac{1}{2}\frac{d(\xi^2)}{dx},\quad \eta\frac{d\eta}{dx}=\tfrac{1}{2}\frac{d(\eta^2)}{dx},\quad \text{etc.,}$$

the space-average of such products will be zero, and they will contribute nothing to the value of $S_{,,}$. There will be nine of these products, in which the same component of displacement appears twice. The remaining eighteen products may be divided into pairs according to the letters which they contain, as

$$\eta\frac{d\zeta}{dx}\ \text{and}\ \zeta\frac{d\eta}{dx}.$$

A linear function of the eighteen products may also be regarded as a linear function of the sums and differences of the products in such pairs. But since

$$\eta\frac{d\zeta}{dx}+\zeta\frac{d\eta}{dx}=\frac{d(\eta\zeta)}{dx},$$

the terms of $s_{,,}$ containing such sums will contribute nothing to the value of $S_{,,}$. We have left a linear function of the nine differences

$$\eta\frac{d\zeta}{dx}-\zeta\frac{d\eta}{dx},\quad \zeta\frac{d\xi}{dx}-\xi\frac{d\zeta}{dx},\quad \xi\frac{d\eta}{dx}-\eta\frac{d\xi}{dx},\quad \text{etc.}$$

(the unwritten expressions being obtained by substituting in the denominators dy and dz for dx), which constitutes the part of $s_{,,}$ that we have to consider. $S_{,,}$ is therefore a linear function of the space-averages of these nine quantities. But by (3)

$$\eta\frac{d\zeta}{dx}-\zeta\frac{d\eta}{dx}=L\left(\eta\frac{d\zeta}{du}-\zeta\frac{d\eta}{du}\right),$$

and the space-average of this, at a moment of maximum displacement, is by (1)

$$\frac{2\pi L}{l}(\beta_1\gamma_2-\gamma_1\beta_2).$$

By such reductions it appears that $lS_{\prime\prime}$ is a linear function of the nine products of L, M, N with

$$\beta_1\gamma_2-\gamma_1\beta_2,\quad \gamma_1\alpha_2-\alpha_1\gamma_2,\quad \alpha_1\beta_2-\beta_1\alpha_2.$$

Now if we set

$$\Theta=L(\beta_1\gamma_2-\gamma_1\beta_2)+M(\gamma_1\alpha_2-\alpha_1\gamma_2)+N(\alpha_1\beta_2-\beta_1\alpha_2), \tag{7}$$

we have by (4) and (2)

$$L\Theta=\beta_1\gamma_2-\gamma_1\beta_2,\quad M\Theta=\gamma_1\alpha_2-\alpha_1\gamma_2,\quad N\Theta=\alpha_1\beta_2-\beta_1\alpha_2. \tag{8}$$

Therefore $lS_{\prime\prime}$ is a linear function of the nine products of L, M, N with $L\Theta$, $M\Theta$, $N\Theta$. That is, $lS_{\prime\prime}$ is the product of Θ and a quadratic function of L, M and N. We may therefore write

$$S_{\prime\prime}=\frac{\Phi}{l}\Theta=\frac{\Phi}{l}[L(\beta_1\gamma_2-\gamma_1\beta_2)+M(\gamma_1\alpha_2-\alpha_1\gamma_2)+N(\alpha_1\beta_2-\beta_1\alpha_2)], \tag{9}$$

where Φ is a quadratic function of L, M and N, dependent, however, on the nature of the medium and the period of oscillation.

9. It will be useful to consider more closely the geometrical significance of the quantity Θ. For this purpose it will be convenient to have a definite understanding with respect to the relative position of the coordinate axes.

We shall suppose that the axes of X, Y, and Z are related in the same way as lines drawn to the right, forward and upward, so that a rotation from X to Y appears clockwise to one looking in the direction of Z.

Now if from any same point, as the origin of coordinates, we lay off lines representing in direction and magnitude the displacements in all the different wave-planes, we obtain an ellipse, which we may call the *displacement-ellipse.** Of this, one radius vector (ρ_1) will have the components α_1, β_1, γ_1, and another (ρ_2) the components α_2, β_2, γ_2. These will belong to conjugate diameters, each being parallel to the tangent at the extremity of the other. The area of the ellipse will therefore be equal to the parallelogram of which ρ_1 and ρ_2 are two sides, multiplied by π. Now it is evident that $\beta_1\gamma_2-\gamma_1\beta_2$, $\gamma_1\alpha_2-\alpha_1\gamma_2$, $\alpha_1\beta_2-\alpha_1\beta_2$ are numerically equal to the projections of this parallelogram on the planes of the coordinate axes, and are each positive or negative according as a revolution from ρ_1 to ρ_2 appears clockwise or counter-clockwise to one looking in the direction of the proper coordinate axis. Hence, Θ will be numerically equal to the parallelogram, that is, to the area of the displacement-ellipse divided by π, and will be positive or negative

* This ellipse, which represents the simultaneous displacements in different parts of the field, will also represent the successive displacements at any same point in the corresponding system of progressive waves.

according as a revolution from ρ_1 to ρ_2 appears clockwise or counter-clockwise to one looking in the direction of the wave-normal. Since ρ_1 and ρ_2 are determined by displacements in planes one-quarter of a wave-length distant from each other, and the plane to which the latter relates lies on the side toward which the wave-normal is drawn, it follows that Θ is positive or negative according as the combination of displacements has the character of a right-handed or a left-handed screw.

10. The kinetic energy of the medium, which is to be estimated for an instant of no displacement, may be shown as in § 7 of the former paper (page 185 of this volume) to consist of two parts, of which one relates to the regular flux $(\dot{\xi}, \dot{\eta}, \dot{\zeta})$, and the other to the irregular flux $(\dot{\xi}', \dot{\eta}', \dot{\zeta}')$. The first, in the notation of that paper, is represented by

$$\tfrac{1}{2}\int(\dot{\xi}\,\mathrm{Pot}\,\dot{\xi}+\dot{\eta}\,\mathrm{Pot}\,\dot{\eta}+\dot{\zeta}\,\mathrm{Pot}\,\dot{\zeta})dv,$$

which reduces to

$$\frac{l^2}{2\pi}\int(\dot{\xi}^2+\dot{\eta}^2+\dot{\zeta}^2)\,dv.$$

By substitution of the values given by equations (1), we obtain for the kinetic energy due to the regular flux in a unit of volume

$$\mathrm{T}=\frac{\pi l^2}{p^2}(\alpha_1{}^2+\beta_1{}^2+\gamma_1{}^2+\alpha_2{}^2+\beta_2{}^2+\gamma_2{}^2). \tag{10}$$

11. The kinetic energy of the irregular part of the flux is represented by the volume-integral

$$\int\tfrac{1}{2}(\dot{\xi}'\,\mathrm{Pot}\,\dot{\xi}'+\dot{\eta}'\,\mathrm{Pot}\,\dot{\eta}'+\dot{\zeta}'\,\mathrm{Pot}\,\dot{\zeta}')\,dv.$$

Now, since $\dot{\xi}'$ $\dot{\eta}'$, $\dot{\zeta}'$ are everywhere linear functions of $\dot{\xi}$, $\dot{\eta}$, $\dot{\zeta}$ *and diff. coeff.* (see § 4), and since the integrations implied in the notation *Pot* may be confined to a sphere of which the radius is small in comparison with a wave length,* and since within such a sphere $\dot{\xi}$, $\dot{\eta}$, $\dot{\zeta}$ *and diff. coeff.* are sufficiently determined (in a linear form), by the values of the same twelve quantities at the center of the sphere, it follows that Pot $\dot{\xi}'$, Pot $\dot{\eta}'$, Pot $\dot{\zeta}'$ must be linear functions of the values of $\dot{\xi}$, η, $\dot{\zeta}$ *and diff. coeff.* at the point for which the potential is sought. Hence,

$$\tfrac{1}{2}(\dot{\xi}'\,\mathrm{Pot}\,\dot{\xi}'+\dot{\eta}'\,\mathrm{Pot}\,\dot{\eta}'+\dot{\zeta}'\,\mathrm{Pot}\,\dot{\zeta}')$$

will be a quadratic function of $\dot{\xi}$, $\dot{\eta}$, $\dot{\zeta}$ *and diff. coeff.* But the seventy-eight coefficients by which this function is expressed will vary with the position of the point considered with respect to the surrounding molecules.

---

* See § 9 of the former paper, on page 187 of this volume.

Yet, as in the case of the statical energy, we may substitute the average values of these coefficients for the coefficients themselves in the integral by which we obtain the energy of any considerable space. The kinetic energy due to the irregular part of the flux is thus reduced to a quadratic function of $\dot{\xi}$, $\dot{\eta}$, $\dot{\zeta}$ *and diff. coeff.* which has constant coefficients for a given medium and light of a given period.

The function may be divided into three parts, of which the first contains the squares and products of $\dot{\xi}$, $\dot{\eta}$, $\dot{\zeta}$, the second the products of $\dot{\xi}$, $\dot{\eta}$, $\dot{\zeta}$ with their differential coefficients, and the third, which may be neglected, the squares and products of the differential coefficients.

We may proceed with the reduction precisely as in the case of the statical energy, except that the differentiations with respect to the time will introduce the constant factor $\frac{4\pi^2}{p^2}$. This will give for the first part of the kinetic energy of the irregular flux per unit of volume

$$\begin{aligned}T'_{,}=&\frac{2\pi^2}{p^2}(A'\alpha_1^2+B'\beta_1^2+C'\gamma_1^2+E'\beta_1\gamma_1+F'\gamma_1\alpha_1+G'\alpha_1\beta_1)\\&+\frac{2\pi^2}{p^2}(A'\alpha_2^2+B'\beta_2^2+C'\gamma_2^2+E'\beta_2\gamma_2+F'\gamma_2\alpha_2+G'\alpha_2\beta_2),\end{aligned}\tag{11}$$

and for the second part of the same

$$\begin{aligned}T'_{,,}&=\frac{4\pi^2\Phi'}{p^2l}\Theta\\&=\frac{4\pi^2\Phi'}{p^2l}[L(\beta_1\gamma_2-\gamma_1\beta_2)+M(\gamma_1\alpha_2-\alpha_1\gamma_2)+N(\alpha_1\beta_2-\beta_1\alpha_2)],\end{aligned}\tag{12}$$

where A′, B′, C′, E′, F′, G′ are constant, and Φ' a quadratic function of L, M, and N, for a given medium and light of a given period.

12. Equating the statical and kinetic energies, we have

$$S_{,}+S_{,,}=T+T'_{,}+T'_{,,},$$

that is, by equations (6), (9), (10), (11), and (12),

$$\begin{aligned}&\tfrac{1}{2}(A\alpha_1^2+B\beta_1^2+C\gamma_1^2+E\beta_1\gamma_1+F\gamma_1\alpha_1+G\alpha_1\beta_1)\\&+\tfrac{1}{2}(A\alpha_2^2+B\beta_2^2+C\gamma_2^2+E\beta_2\gamma_2+F\gamma_2\alpha_2+G\alpha_2\beta_2)\\&+\frac{\Phi}{l}[L(\beta_1\gamma_2-\gamma_1\beta_2)+M(\gamma_1\alpha_2-\alpha_1\gamma_2)+N(\alpha_1\beta_2-\beta_1\alpha_2)]\\&=\frac{\pi l^2}{p^2}(\alpha_1^2+\beta_1^2+\gamma_1^2+\alpha_2^2+\beta_2^2+\gamma_2^2)\\&+\frac{2\pi^2}{p^2}(A'\alpha_1^2+B'\beta_1^2+C'\gamma_1^2+E'\beta_1\gamma_1+F'\gamma_1\alpha_1+G'\alpha_1\beta_1)\\&+\frac{2\pi^2}{p^2}(A'\alpha_2^2+B'\beta_2^2+C'\gamma_2^2+E'\beta_2\gamma_2+F'\gamma_2\alpha_2+G'\alpha_2\beta_2)\\&+\frac{4\pi^2\Phi'}{p^2l}[L(\beta_1\gamma_2-\gamma_1\beta_2)+M(\gamma_1\alpha_2-\alpha_1\gamma_2)+N(\alpha_1\beta_2-\beta_1\alpha_2)].\end{aligned}\tag{13}$$

If we set
$$a=\frac{A}{2\pi}-\frac{2\pi A'}{p^2}, \quad b=\frac{B}{2\pi}-\frac{2\pi B'}{p^2}, \quad \text{etc.,} \tag{14}$$
and
$$\phi=\frac{\Phi}{2\pi p}-\frac{2\pi\Phi'}{p^3}, \tag{15}$$
the equation reduces to
$$\begin{aligned} &a\alpha_1^2+b\beta_1^2+c\gamma_1^2+e\beta_1\gamma_1+f\gamma_1\alpha_1+g\alpha_1\beta_1 \\ &+a\alpha_2^2+b\beta_2^2+c\gamma_2^2+e\beta_2\gamma_2+f\gamma_2\alpha_2+g\alpha_2\beta_2 \\ &+\frac{2p\phi}{l}[L(\beta_1\gamma_2-\gamma_1\beta_2)+M(\gamma_1\alpha_2-\alpha_1\gamma_2)+N(\alpha_1\beta_2-\beta_1\alpha_2)] \\ &=\frac{l^2}{p^2}(\alpha_1^2+\beta_1^2+\gamma_1^2+\alpha_2^2+\beta_2^2+\gamma_2^2), \end{aligned} \tag{16}$$
where a, b, c, e, f, g are constant, and ϕ a quadratic function of L, M, N, for a given medium and light of a given period.

13. Now this equation, which expresses a relation between the constants of the equations of wave-motion (1), will apply, with those equations, not only to such vibrations as actually take place, but also to such as we may imagine to take place under the influence of constraints determining the type of vibration. The free or unconstrained vibrations, with which alone we are concerned, are characterized by this, that infinitesimal variations (by constraint) of the type of vibration, that is, of the ratios of the quantities α_1, β_1, γ_1, α_2, β_2, γ_2, will not affect the period by any quantity of the same order of magnitude.* These variations must however be consistent with equations (4), which require that
$$L\,d\alpha_1+M\,d\beta_1+N\,d\gamma_1=0, \qquad L\,d\alpha_2+M\,d\beta_2+N\,d\gamma_2=0. \tag{17}$$
Hence, to obtain the conditions which characterize free vibration, we may differentiate equation (16) with respect to $\alpha_1, \beta_1, \gamma_1, \alpha_2, \beta_2, \gamma_2$, regarding all other letters as constant, and give to $d\alpha_1$, $d\beta_1$, $d\gamma_1$, $d\alpha_2$, $d\beta_2$, $d\gamma_2$, such values as are consistent with equations (17). Now $d\alpha_1, d\beta_1, d\gamma_1$, are independent of $d\alpha_2, d\beta_2, d\gamma_2$, and for either three variations, values proportional either to $\alpha_1, \beta_1, \gamma_1$, or to $\alpha_2, \beta_2, \gamma_2$, are possible. If, then, we differentiate equation (16) with respect to α_1, β_1, γ_1, and substitute first α_1, β_1, γ_1, and then α_2, β_2, γ_2, for $d\alpha_1$, $d\beta_1$, $d\gamma_1$, and also differentiate with respect to α_2, β_2, γ_2, with similar substitutions, we shall obtain all the independent equations which this principle will yield.

If we differentiate with respect to α_1, β_1, γ_1, and write α_1, β_1, γ_1 for $d\alpha_1$, $d\beta_1$, $d\gamma_1$, we obtain
$$\begin{aligned} &a\alpha_1^2+b\beta_1^2+c\gamma_1^2+e\beta_1\gamma_1+f\gamma_1\alpha_1+g\alpha_1\beta_1 \\ &+\frac{p\phi}{l}[L(\beta_1\gamma_2-\gamma_1\beta_2)+M(\gamma_1\alpha_2-\alpha_1\gamma_2)+N(\alpha_1\beta_2-\beta_1\alpha_2)] \\ &=\frac{l^2}{p^2}(\alpha_1^2+\beta_1^2+\gamma_1^2). \end{aligned} \tag{18}$$

* Compare § 11 of the former paper, page 189 of this volume.

If we differentiate with respect to $\alpha_1, \beta_1, \gamma_1$, and write $\alpha_2, \beta_2, \gamma_2$ for $d\alpha_1, d\beta_1, d\gamma_1$, we obtain

$$2a\alpha_1\alpha_2+2b\beta_1\beta_2+2c\gamma_1\gamma_2+e(\beta_1\gamma_2+\gamma_1\beta_2)+f(\gamma_1\alpha_2+\alpha_1\gamma_2)$$
$$+g(\alpha_1\beta_2+\beta_1\alpha_2)=\frac{2l^2}{p^2}(\alpha_1\alpha_2+\beta_1\beta_2+\gamma_1\gamma_2). \qquad (19)$$

If we differentiate with respect to $\alpha_2, \beta_2, \gamma_2$, and write $\alpha_2, \beta_2, \gamma_2$ for $d\alpha_2, d\beta_2, d\gamma_2$, we obtain

$$a\alpha_2^2+b\beta_2^2+c\gamma_2^2+e\beta_2\gamma_2+f\gamma_2\alpha_2+g\alpha_2\beta_2$$
$$+\frac{p\phi}{l}[\mathrm{L}(\beta_1\gamma_2-\gamma_1\beta_2)+\mathrm{M}(\gamma_1\alpha_2-\alpha_1\gamma_2)+\mathrm{N}(\alpha_1\beta_2-\beta_1\alpha_2)]$$
$$=\frac{l^2}{p^2}(\alpha_2^2+\beta_2^2+\gamma_2^2). \qquad (20)$$

The equation derived by differentiating with respect to $\alpha_2, \beta_2, \gamma_2$, and writing $\alpha_1, \beta_1, \gamma_1$ for $d\alpha_2, d\beta_2, d\gamma_2$, is identical with (19). We should also observe that equations (18) and (20) by addition give equation (16), which therefore will not need to be considered in addition to the last three equations.

14. The geometrical signification of our equations may now be simplified by a suitable choice of the position of the origin of coordinates, which is as yet wholly arbitrary.

We shall hereafter suppose that the origin is placed in a plane of maximum or minimum displacement,* if such there are. In the case of circular polarization, in which the displacements are everywhere equal, its position is immaterial. The lines ρ_1 and ρ_2, of which $\alpha_1, \beta_1, \gamma_1$ and $\alpha_2, \beta_2, \gamma_2$ are respectively the components, will now be the semi-axes of the displacement-ellipse, and therefore at right angles. (See § 9.) The case of circular polarization will not constitute any exception. Hence,

$$\alpha_1\alpha_2+\beta_1\beta_2+\gamma_1\gamma_2=0, \qquad (21)$$

and by § 9,

$$\Theta=\mathrm{L}(\beta_1\gamma_2-\gamma_1\beta_2)+\mathrm{M}(\gamma_1\alpha_2-\alpha_1\gamma_2)+\mathrm{N}(\alpha_1\beta_2-\beta_1\alpha_2)=\pm\rho_1\rho_2, \qquad (22)$$

where we are to read + or − in the last member according as the system of displacements has the character of a right-handed or a left-handed screw.

15. Equation (19) is now reduced to the form

$$2a\alpha_1\alpha_2+2b\beta_1\beta_2+2c\gamma_1\gamma_2+e(\beta_1\gamma_2+\gamma_1\beta_2)$$
$$+f(\gamma_1\alpha_2+\alpha_1\gamma_2)+g(\alpha_1\beta_2+\beta_1\alpha_2)=0, \qquad (23)$$

* The reader will perceive that an earlier limitation of the position of the origin by a supposition of this nature, involving a limitation of the values of $\alpha_1, \beta_1, \gamma_1, \alpha_2, \beta_2, \gamma_2$, would have been embarrassing in the operations of the last paragraph.

which has a very simple geometrical signification. If we consider the ellipsoid

$$ax^2+by^2+cz^2+eyz+fzx+gxy, \tag{24}$$

and especially its central section by a plane parallel to the planes of the wave-system which we are considering, it will easily appear that the equation

$$2ax_1x_2+2by_1y_2+2cz_1z_2+e(y_1z_2+z_1y_2)$$
$$+f(z_1x_2+x_1z_2)+g(x_1y_2+y_1x_2)=0$$

will hold of any two points x_1, y_1, z_1 and x_2, y_2, z_2 which belong to conjugate diameters of this central section. Therefore equation (23) expresses that the displacements α_1, β_1, γ_1 and α_2, β_2, γ_2 are parallel to conjugate diameters of the central section of the ellipsoid (24) by a wave-plane. But since the displacements α_1, β_1, γ_1 and α_2, β_2, γ_2 are also at right angles to each other, it follows that they are parallel to the axes of the central section of the ellipsoid (24) by a wave-plane. That is:—The axes of the displacement-ellipse coincide in direction with those of a central section of the ellipsoid (24) by a wave-plane.

16. If we write U_1, U_2 for the reciprocals of the semi-axes of the central section of the ellipsoid (24) by a wave-plane, U_1 being the reciprocal of the one to which the displacement α_1, β_1, γ_1 is parallel, we have

$$a\alpha_1^2+b\beta_1^2+c\gamma_1^2+e\beta_1\gamma_1+f\gamma_1\alpha_1+g\alpha_1\beta_1=U_1^2(\alpha_1^2+\beta_1^2+\gamma_1^2), \tag{25}$$

as is at once evident if we substitute the coordinates of an extremity of the axis for the proportional quantities α_1, β_1, γ_1. So also

$$a\alpha_2^2+b\beta_2^2+c\gamma_2^2+e\beta_2\gamma_2+f\gamma_2\alpha_2+g\alpha_2\beta_2=U_2^2(\alpha_2^2+\beta_2^2+\gamma_2^2). \tag{26}$$

If we write V for the velocity of propagation of the system of progressive waves corresponding to the system of stationary waves which we have been considering, we shall have

$$V=\frac{l}{p}. \tag{27}$$

By equations (22), (25), and (26), equations (18) and (20) are reduced to the form

$$U_1^2\rho_1^2\pm\frac{\phi}{V}\rho_1\rho_2=V^2\rho_1^2, \qquad U_2^2\rho_2^2\pm\frac{\phi}{V}\rho_1\rho_2=V^2\rho_2^2, \tag{28}$$

where we are to read + or − according as the disturbance has the character of a right-handed or a left-handed screw. In a progressive system of waves, when the combination of displacements has the character of a right-handed screw, the rotations will be such as appear clockwise to the observer, who looks in the direction opposite to that of the propagation of light. We shall call such a ray *right-handed*.

We may here observe that in case $\phi=0$ the solution of these equations is very simple. We have necessarily either $\rho_2=0$ and $V^2=U_1^2$, or $\rho_1=0$ and $V^2=U_2^2$. In this case, the light is linearly polarized, and the directions of oscillation and the velocities of propagation are given by Fresnel's law. Experiment has shown that this is the usual case. We wish, however, to investigate the case in which ϕ does not vanish. Since the term containing ϕ arises from the consideration of those quantities which it was allowable to neglect in the first approximation, we may assume that ϕ is always very small in comparison with V^3, U_1^3, or U_2^3.

17. Equations (28) may be written

$$V^2-U_1^2=\pm\frac{\phi}{V}\frac{\rho_2}{\rho_1}, \quad V^2-U_2^2=\pm\frac{\phi}{V}\frac{\rho_1}{\rho_2}. \tag{29}$$

By multiplication we obtain

$$V^2(V^2-U_1^2)(V^2-U_2^2)=\phi^2. \tag{30}$$

Since ϕ is a very small quantity, it is evident from inspection of this equation that it will admit three values of V^2, of which one will be a very little greater than the greater of the two quantities U_1^2 and U_2^2, another will be a very little less than the less of the same two quantities, and the third will be a very small quantity. It is evident that the values of V^2 with which we have to do are those which differ but little from U_1^2 and U_2^2.*

For the numerical computation of V, when U_1, U_2, and ϕ are known numerically, we may divide the equation by V^2, and then solve it as if the second member were known. This will give

$$V^2=\frac{U_1^2+U_2^2}{2}\pm\sqrt{\frac{\phi^2}{V^2}+\frac{(U_1^2-U_2^2)^2}{4}}. \tag{31}$$

By substituting U_1U_2 for V^2 in the second member, we may obtain a close approximation to the two values of V^2. Each of the values obtained may be improved by substitution of that value for V^2 in the second member of the equation.

For either value of V^2, we may easily find the ratio of ρ_1 to ρ_2, that is, the ratio of the axes of the displacement-ellipse, from one of equations (29), or from the equation

$$\frac{\rho_2^2}{\rho_1^2}=\frac{V^2-U_1^2}{V^2-U_2^2} \tag{32}$$

obtained by combining the two.

---

* We should not attribute any physical significance to the third value of V^2. For this value would imply a wave-length very small in comparison with the length of ordinary waves of light, and with respect to which our fundamental assumption that the wave-length is very great in comparison with the distances of contiguous molecules would be entirely false. Our analysis, therefore, furnishes no reason for supposing that any such velocities are possible for the propagation of electrical disturbances.

In equations (29), we are to read + or − in the second members, according as the ray is right-handed or left-handed. (See § 16.) It follows that if the value of ϕ is positive, the greater velocity will belong to a right-handed ray, and the smaller to a left-handed, but if the value of ϕ is negative, the opposite is the case. Except when $\phi=0$, and the polarization is linear, there will be one right-handed and one left-handed ray for any given wave-normal and period.

18. When $U_1=U_2$, equations (29) give

$$\rho_1=\rho_2, \quad V^2=U^2\pm\frac{\phi}{V},$$

where U represents the common value of U_1 and U_2. The polarization is therefore circular. The converse is also evident from equations (29), viz., that a ray can be circularly polarized only when the direction of its wave-normal is such that $U_1=U_2$. Such a direction, which is determined by a circular section of the ellipsoid (24) precisely as an optic axis of a crystal which conforms to Fresnel's law of double refraction, may be called an optic axis, although its physical properties are not the same as in the more ordinary case.* If we write V_R and V_L, respectively, for the wave-velocities of the right-handed and left-handed rays, we have

$$V_R^2=U^2+\frac{\phi}{V_R}, \quad V_L^2=U^2-\frac{\phi}{V_L}; \tag{33}$$

whence
$$V_R^2-V_L^2=\phi\left(\frac{1}{V_R}+\frac{1}{V_L}\right)=\phi\,\frac{V_R+V_L}{V_R V_L},$$

and
$$V_R-V_L=\frac{\phi}{V_R V_L}. \tag{34}$$

The phenomenon best observed with respect to an optic axis is the rotation of the plane of linearly polarized light. If we denote by θ the amount of this rotation per unit of the distance traversed by the wave-plane, regarding it as positive when it appears clockwise to the

* Our experimental knowledge of circularly or elliptically polarizing media is confined to such as are optically either isotropic or uniaxial. The general theory of such media, embracing the case of two optic axes, has however been discussed by Professor von Lang ("Theorie der Circularpolarization," *Sitz.-Ber. Wiener Akad.*, vol. lxxv, p. 719). The general results of the present paper, although derived from physical hypotheses of an entirely different nature, are quite similar to those of the memoir cited. They would become identical, the writer believes, by the substitution of a constant for $\frac{p\phi}{l}$ or $\frac{\phi}{V}$ in the equations of this paper. (See especially equations (18), (20), (28).)

That a complete discussion of the subject on any theory must include the case of biaxial media having the property of circular or elliptical polarization, is evident from the consideration that it must at least be possible to produce examples of such media artificially. An isotropic or uniaxial crystal may be made biaxial by pressure. If it has the property of circular and elliptic polarization, that property cannot be wholly destroyed by the application of small pressures.

observer, who looks in the direction opposite to that of the propagation of the light,* we have

$$\theta=\frac{\pi}{p}\left(\frac{1}{V_L}-\frac{1}{V_R}\right). \tag{35}$$

By the preceding equation, this reduces to

$$\theta=\frac{\pi\phi}{pV_R{}^2V_L{}^2}. \tag{36}$$

Without any appreciable error, we may substitute U^4 for $V_R{}^2V_L{}^2$, which will give†

$$\theta=\frac{\pi\phi}{pU^4}. \tag{37}$$

19. Since these equations involve unknown functions of the period they will not serve for an exact determination of the relation between θ and the period. For a rough approximation, however, we may assume that the manner in which the general displacement in any small part of the medium distributes itself among the molecules and intermolecular spaces is independent of the period, being determined entirely by the values of ξ, η, ζ, and their differential coefficients with respect to the coordinates.‡ For a fixed direction of the wave-normal, Φ and Φ' will then be constant. Now equations (15) and (36) give

$$\theta=\frac{\Phi}{2p^2V_R{}^2V_L{}^2}-\frac{2\pi^2\Phi'}{p^4V_R{}^2V_L{}^2}. \tag{38}$$

To express this result in terms of the quantities directly observed, we may use the equations

$$p=\frac{\lambda}{k},\quad V_R=\frac{k}{n_R},\quad V_L=\frac{k}{n_L},\quad U=\frac{k}{n},$$

where k denotes the velocity of light *in vacuo*, λ the wave-length *in vacuo* of the light employed, n_R, n_L the absolute indices of refraction of the two rays, and n the index for the optic axis as derived from the ellipsoid (24) by Fresnel's law. We thus obtain

$$\theta=\frac{\Phi n_R{}^2n_L{}^2}{2k^2\lambda^2}-\frac{2\pi^2\Phi' n_R{}^2n_L{}^2}{\lambda^4}. \tag{39}$$

* When the rotation of the plane of polarization appears clockwise to the observer, it has the character of a *left-handed* screw. But the circularly polarized ray to which V_R relates, the rotation of which also appears clockwise to the observer, has the character of a *right-handed* screw.

† The degree of accuracy of this substitution may be shown as follows. By (33)

$$V_R(V_R{}^2-U^2)=V_L(U^2-V_L{}^2),$$

whence

$$V_R{}^3+V_L{}^3=(V_R+V_L)U^2,$$

$$V_R{}^2-V_RV_L+V_L{}^2=U^2,$$

$$V_RV_L=U^2-(V_R-V_L)^2.$$

‡ Compare § 12 of the former paper, on page 189 of this volume.

In the case of uniaxial crystals, the direction of the optic axis is fixed. We may therefore write

$$\theta = n_R{}^2 n_L{}^2 \left(\frac{K}{\lambda^2} + \frac{K'}{\lambda^4}\right), \tag{40}$$

regarding K and K′ as constants. If we had used equation (37), we should have had the factor n^4 instead of $n_R{}^2 n_L{}^2$. Since this factor varies but slowly with λ, it may be neglected, if its omission is compensated in the values of K and K′. The formula being only approximative, such a simplification will not necessarily render it less accurate.

20. But without any such assumption as that contained in the last paragraph, we may easily obtain formulæ for the experimental determination of Φ and Φ' for the optic axis of a uniaxial crystal. Considerations analogous to those of § 13 of the former paper (page 190 of this volume), show that in differentiating equation (39) we may regard Φ and Φ' as constant, although they may actually vary with λ. This equation may be written

$$\frac{\theta\lambda^2}{n^4} = \frac{\Phi}{2k^2} - \frac{2\pi^2\Phi'}{\lambda^2}. \tag{41}$$

Therefore,

$$\frac{d\left(\frac{\theta\lambda^2}{n^4}\right)}{d\left(\frac{1}{\lambda^2}\right)} = -2\pi^2\Phi'. \tag{42}$$

When Φ' has been determined by this equation, Φ may be found from the preceding.

21. If we wish to represent ϕ geometrically, like U_1 and U_2, we may construct the surfaces

$$Ax^2 + By^2 + Cz^2 + Eyz + Fzx + Gxy = \pm 1, \tag{43}$$

the coefficients A, B, etc., being the same by which ϕ is expressed in terms of L^2, M^2, etc. The numerical value of ϕ, for any direction of the wave-normal, will thus be represented by the square of the reciprocal of the radius vector of the surface drawn in the same direction. The positive or negative character of ϕ must be separately indicated. There are here two cases to be distinguished. If the sign of ϕ is the same in all directions, the surface will be an ellipsoid, and we have only to know whether all the values of ϕ are to be taken positively or all negatively. But if ϕ is positive for some directions and negative for others, the surface will consist of two conjugate hyperboloids, to one of which the positive, and to the other the negative values belong.

22. The manner in which the ellipsoid (24) may be partially determined by the relations of symmetry which the medium may possess, has been sufficiently discussed in the former paper.

With respect to the quantity ϕ, and the surfaces which determine it, the following principle is of fundamental importance. If one body is identical in its internal structure with the image by reflection of another, the values of ϕ in corresponding lines in the two bodies will be numerically equal but have opposite signs.*

It follows that if a body is identical in internal structure with its own image by reflection, the value of ϕ (if not zero for all directions) must be positive for some directions and negative for others. Moreover, the above described surface by which ϕ is represented must consist of two conjugate hyperboloids, of which one is identical in form with the image by reflection of the other. This requires that the hyperboloids shall be right cylinders with conjugate rectangular hyperbolas for bases. A crystal characterized by such properties will belong to the tetragonal system. Since $\phi=0$ for the optic axis, it would be difficult to distinguish a case of this kind from an ordinary uniaxial crystal, unless the ellipsoid (24) should approach very closely to a sphere.†

It is only in the very limited case described in the last paragraph that a medium which is identical in its internal structure with its image by reflection can have the property of circular or elliptic polarization. To media which are unlike their images by reflection, and have the property of circular polarization, we may apply the following general principles.

If the medium has any axis of symmetry, the ellipsoid or hyperboloids which represent the values of ϕ will have an axis in the same direction. If the medium after a revolution of less than 180° about any axis is equivalent to the medium in its first position, the ellipsoid or hyperboloids will have an axis of revolution in that direction.

23. The laws of the propagation of light in plane waves, which

---

* The necessity of the opposite signs will perhaps appear most readily from the consideration that the direction of rotation of the plane of polarization must be opposite in the two bodies.

† There is no difficulty in conceiving of the constitution of a body which would have the properties described above. Thus, we may imagine a body with molecules of a spiral form, of which one-half are right-handed and one-half left-handed, and we may suppose that the motion of electricity is opposed by a less resistance within them than without. If the axes of the right-handed molecules are parallel to the axis of X, and those of the left-handed molecules to the axis of Y, their effects would counterbalance one another when the wave-normal is parallel to the axis of Z. But when the wave-normal (of a beam of linearly polarized light) is parallel to the axis of X, the left-handed molecules would produce a left-handed (negative) rotation of the plane of polarization, the right-handed molecules having no effect; and when the wave-normal is parallel to the axis of Y, the reverse would be the case.

have thus been derived from the single hypothesis that the disturbance by which light is transmitted consists of solenoidal electrical fluxes, and which apply to light of different colors and to the most general case of perfectly transparent and sensibly homogeneous media not subject to magnetic action,* are essentially those which are generally received as embodying the results of experiment. In no particular, so far as the writer is aware, do they conflict with the results of experiment, or require the aid of auxiliary and forced hypotheses to bring them into harmony therewith.

In this respect, the electromagnetic theory of light stands in marked contrast with that theory in which the properties of an elastic solid are attributed to the ether,—a contrast which was very distinct in Maxwell's derivation of Fresnel's laws from electrical principles, but becomes more striking as we follow the subject farther into its details, and take account of the want of absolute homogeneity in the medium, so as to embrace the phenomena of the dispersion of colors and circular and elliptical polarization.

---

* The rotation of the plane of polarization which is produced by magnetic action has been discussed by Maxwell (*Treatise on Electricity and Magnetism*, vol. ii, chap. xxi), and by Rowland (*Amer. Journ. Math.*, vol. iii, p. 107).

XIII.

ON THE GENERAL EQUATIONS OF MONOCHROMATIC LIGHT IN MEDIA OF EVERY DEGREE OF TRANSPARENCY.

[*American Journal of Science*, ser 3, vol. XXV, pp. 107-118, February, 1883.]

1. THE last April and June numbers of this Journal* contain an investigation of the velocity of plane waves of light, in which they are regarded as consisting of solenoidal electrical fluxes in an indefinitely extended medium of uniform and very fine-grained structure. It was also supposed that the medium was perfectly transparent, although without discussion of the physical properties on which transparency depends, and that the electrical motions were not complicated by any distinctively magnetic phenomena.

In the present paper † the subject will be treated with more generality, so as to obtain the general equations of monochromatic light for media of every degree of transparency, whether sensibly homogeneous or otherwise, which have a very fine-grained molecular structure as measured by a wave-length of light. There will be no restriction with respect to magnetic influence, except that an oscillating magnetization of the medium will be excluded. ‡

In order to conform as much as possible to the ordinary view of

---

* See pages 182–194 and 195–210 of this volume.

† This paper contains, with some additional developments, the substance of a communication to the National Academy of Sciences in November, 1882.

‡ Where a body capable of magnetization is subjected to the influence of light (as when light is reflected from the surface of iron), there are two simple hypotheses which present themselves with respect to the magnetic state of the body. One is that the magnetic forces due to the light are not of sufficient duration to allow the molecular changes which constitute magnetization to take place to any sensible extent. The other is that the magnetization has a constant ratio to the magnetic force without regard to its duration. We might easily make a more general hypothesis which would embrace both of those mentioned as extreme cases, and which would be irreproachable from a theoretical stand-point; but it would complicate our equations to a degree which would not be compensated by their greater generality, since no phenomena depending on such magnetization have been observed, so far as the writer is aware, or are likely to be, except in a very limited class of cases.

For the purposes of this paper, therefore, it has seemed better to exclude media capable of magnetization, except so far as the first mentioned hypothesis may be applicable. But it does not appear that this requires us to exclude cases in which the medium is subject to the influence of a permanent magnetic force, such as produces the phenomenon of the magnetic rotation of the plane of polarization.

electrical phenomena,* we shall not introduce at first the hypothesis of Maxwell that electrical fluxes are solenoidal.† Our results, however, will be such as to require us to admit the substantial truth of this hypothesis, if we regard the processes involved in the transmission of light as electrical.

With regard to the undetermined questions of electrodynamic induction, we shall adopt provisionally that hypothesis which appears the most simple, yet proceed in such a manner that it will be evident exactly how our results must be altered, if we prefer any other hypothesis.

Electrical quantities will be treated as measured in electromagnetic units.

2. We must distinguish, as before, between the *actual* electrical displacements, which are too complicated to follow in detail with analysis, and which in their minutiæ elude experimental demonstration, and the displacements as *averaged* for spaces which are large enough to smooth out their minor irregularities, but not so large as to obliterate to any sensible extent those more regular features of the electrical motion, which form the subject of optical experiment. These spaces must therefore be large as measured by the least distances between molecules, but small as measured by a wave-length of light. We shall also have occasion to consider similar averages for other quantities, as electromotive force, the electrostatic potential, etc. It will be convenient to suppose that the space for which the average is taken is the same in all parts of the field,‡ say a sphere of uniform radius having its center at the point considered.

Whatever may be the quantities considered, such averages will be represented by the notation

$$[\qquad]_{\text{Ave}}.$$

* It has, perhaps, retarded the acceptance of the electromagnetic theory of light that it was presented in connection with a theory of electrical action, which is probably more difficult to prove or disprove, and certainly presents more difficulties of comprehension, than the connection of optical and electrical phenomena, and which, as resting largely on *a priori* considerations, must naturally appear very differently to different minds. Moreover, the mathematical method by which the subject was treated, while it will remain a striking monument of its author's originality of thought, and profoundly modify the development of mathematical physics, must nevertheless, by its wide departure from ordinary methods, have tended to repel such as might not make it a matter of serious study.

† A flux is said to be *solenoidal* when it satisfies the conditions which characterize the motion of an incompressible fluid,—in other words, if u, v, w are the rectangular components of the flux, when

$$\frac{du}{dx}+\frac{dv}{dy}+\frac{dw}{dz}=0,$$

and the normal component of the flux is the same on both sides of any surfaces of discontinuity which may exist.

‡ This is rather to fix our ideas, than on account of any mathematical necessity. For the space for which the average is taken may in general be considerably varied without sensibly affecting the value of the average.

If, then, ξ, η, ζ denote the components of the actual displacement at the point considered,

$$[\xi]_{\text{Ave}}, \qquad [\eta]_{\text{Ave}}, \qquad [\zeta]_{\text{Ave}}$$

will represent the average values of these components in the small sphere about that point. These average values we shall treat as functions of the coordinates of the center of the sphere and of the time, and may call them, for brevity, the *average values* of ξ, η, ζ. But however they may be designated, it is essential to remember that it is a space-average for a certain very small space, and never a time-average, that is intended.

The object of this paper will be accomplished when we have expressed (explicitly or implicitly) the relations which subsist between the values of $[\xi]_{\text{Ave}}$, $[\eta]_{\text{Ave}}$, $[\zeta]_{\text{Ave}}$, at different times and in different parts of the field,—in other words, when we have found the conditions which these quantities must satisfy as functions of the time and the coordinates.

3. Let us suppose that luminous vibrations of any one period* are somewhere excited, and that the disturbance is propagated through the medium. The motions which are excited in any part of the medium, and the forces by which they are kept up, will be expressed by harmonic functions of the time, having the same period,† as may be proved by the single principle of the superposition of motions quite independently of any theory of the constitution of the medium, or of the nature of the motions, as electrical or otherwise. This is equally true of the actual motions, and of the averages which we are to consider. We may therefore set

$$\left.\begin{array}{l}[\xi]_{\text{Ave}} = a_1 \cos \dfrac{2\pi}{p}t + a_2 \sin \dfrac{2\pi}{p}t, \\ \qquad\text{etc.,}\end{array}\right\} \qquad (1)$$

* There is no real loss of generality in making the light monochromatic, since in every case it may be divided into parts, which are separately propagated, and each of which is monochromatic to any required degree of approximation.

† It is of course possible that the expressions for the forces and displacements should have constant terms. But these will disappear, if the displacements are measured from the state of equilibrium about which the system vibrates, and we leave out of account in measuring the forces (and the electrostatic potential) that which would belong to the system in the state of equilibrium. To prevent misapprehension, it should be added that the term *electrical displacement* is *not* used in the restricted sense of *dielectric displacement* or *polarization*. The variation of the electrical displacement, as the term is used in this paper, constitutes what Maxwell calls the total motion of electricity or true current, and what he divides into two parts, which he distinguishes as the current of conduction and the variation of the electrical displacement. Such a division of the total motion of electricity is not necessary for the purposes of this paper, and the term displacement is used with reference to the total motion of electricity in a manner entirely analogous to that in which the term is ordinarily used in the theory of wave-motion.

where t denotes the time, p the period, and a_1, a_2, functions of the coordinates. It follows that

$$\left.\begin{array}{c}[\ddot{\xi}]_{\text{Ave}} = -\frac{4\pi^2}{p^2}[\xi]_{\text{Ave}}, \\ \text{etc.}\end{array}\right\} \qquad (2)$$

4. Now, on the electrical theory, these motions are excited by electrical forces, which are of two kinds, distinguished as electrostatic and electrodynamic. The electrostatic force is determined by the electrostatic potential. If we write q for the actual value of the potential, and $[q]_{\text{Ave}}$ for its value as averaged in the manner specified above, the components of the actual electrostatic force will be

$$-\frac{dq}{dx}, \quad -\frac{dq}{dy}, \quad -\frac{dq}{dz};$$

and for the average values of these components in the small spaces described above we may write

$$-\frac{d[q]_{\text{Ave}}}{dx}, \quad -\frac{d[q]_{\text{Ave}}}{dy}, \quad -\frac{d[q]_{\text{Ave}}}{dz},$$

for it will make no difference whether we take the average before or after differentiation.

5. The electrodynamic force is determined by the acceleration of electrical flux in all parts of the field, but physicists are not entirely agreed in regard to the laws by which it is determined. This difference of opinion is however of less importance, since it will not affect the result if electrical fluxes are always solenoidal. According to the most simple law, the components of the force are given by the volume-integrals

$$-\iiint\frac{\ddot{\xi}}{r}dv, \quad -\iiint\frac{\ddot{\eta}}{r}dv, \quad -\iiint\frac{\ddot{\zeta}}{r}dv,$$

where dv represents an element of volume, and r the distance of this element from the point for which the value of the electromotive force is to be determined. In other words, the components of the force at any point are determined from the components of acceleration in all parts of the field by the same process by which (in the theories of gravitation, etc.) the value of the potential at any point is determined from the density of matter in all parts of space, except that the sign is to be reversed. Adopting this law, provisionally at least, we may express it by saying that the components of electrodynamic force are equal to the potentials taken negatively of the components of acceleration of electrical flux. And we may write, for brevity,

$$-\text{Pot}\,\ddot{\xi}, \quad -\text{Pot}\,\ddot{\eta}, \quad -\text{Pot}\,\ddot{\zeta},$$

for the components of force, using the symbol *Pot* to denote the operation by which the potential of a mass is derived from its density. For the average values of these components in the small spaces defined above, we may write

$$-\text{Pot}\,[\ddot{\xi}]_{\text{Ave}}, \qquad -\text{Pot}\,[\ddot{\eta}]_{\text{Ave}}, \qquad -\text{Pot}\,[\ddot{\zeta}]_{\text{Ave}},$$

since it will make no difference whether we take the average before or after the operation of taking the potential.

6. If we write X, Y, Z for the components of the total electromotive force (electrostatic and electrodynamic), we have

$$\left.\begin{aligned}&[X]_{\text{Ave}} = -\text{Pot}\,[\ddot{\xi}]_{\text{Ave}} - \frac{d[q]_{\text{Ave}}}{dx},\\ &\text{etc.,}\end{aligned}\right\} \tag{3}$$

or by (2)

$$\left.\begin{aligned}&[X]_{\text{Ave}} = \frac{4\pi^2}{p^2}\,\text{Pot}\,[\xi]_{\text{Ave}} - \frac{d[q]_{\text{Ave}}}{dx},\\ &\text{etc.}\end{aligned}\right\} \tag{4}$$

It will be convenient to represent these relations by a vector notation. If we represent the displacement by **U**, and the electromotive force by **E**, the three equations of (3) will be represented by the single vector equation

$$[\mathbf{E}]_{\text{Ave}} = -\text{Pot}\,[\ddot{\mathbf{U}}]_{\text{Ave}} - \nabla[q]_{\text{Ave}}, \tag{5}$$

and the three equations of (4) by the single vector equation

$$[\mathbf{E}]_{\text{Ave}} = \frac{4\pi^2}{p^2}\,\text{Pot}\,[\mathbf{U}]_{\text{Ave}} - \nabla[q]_{\text{Ave}}, \tag{6}$$

where, in accordance with quaternionic usage, $\nabla[q]_{\text{Ave}}$ represents the vector which has for components the derivatives of $[q]_{\text{Ave}}$ with respect to rectangular coordinates. The symbol *Pot* in such a vector equation signifies that the operation which is denoted by this symbol in a scalar equation is to be performed upon each of the components of the vector.

7. We may here observe that if we are not satisfied with the law adopted for the determination of electrodynamic force we have only to substitute for $-Pot$ in these vector equations, and in those which follow, the symbol for the operation, whatever it may be, by which we calculate the electrodynamic force from the acceleration.* For the operation must be of such a character that if the acceleration consist of any number of parts, the force due to the whole acceleration will be the resultant of the forces due to the separate parts. It will evidently make no difference whether we take an average before or after such an operation.

* The same would not be true of the corresponding scalar equations, (3) and (4). For one component of the force might depend upon all the components of acceleration. Such is in fact the case with the law of electromotive force proposed by Weber.

8. Let us now examine the relation which subsists between the values of $[\mathbf{E}]_{\text{Ave}}$ and $[\mathbf{U}]_{\text{Ave}}$ for the same point, that is, between the average electromotive force and the average displacement in a small sphere with its center at the point considered. We have already seen that the forces and the displacements are harmonic functions of the time having a common period.

A little consideration will show that if the average electromotive force in the sphere is given as a function of the time, the displacements in the sphere, both average and actual, must be entirely determined. Especially will this be evident, if we consider that since we have made the radius of the sphere very small in comparison with a wave-length, the average force must have sensibly the same value throughout the sphere (that is, if we vary the position of the center of the sphere for which the average is taken by a distance not greater than the radius, the value of the average will not be sensibly affected), and that the difference of the actual and average force at any point is entirely determined by the motions in the immediate vicinity of that point. If, then, certain oscillatory motions may be kept up in the sphere under the influence of electrostatic and electrodynamic forces due to the motion in the whole field, and if we suppose the motions in and very near that sphere to be unchanged, but the motions in the remoter parts of the field to be altered, only not so as to affect the average resultant of electromotive force in the sphere, the actual resultant of electromotive force will also be unchanged throughout the sphere, and therefore the motions in the sphere will still be such as correspond to the forces.

Now the average displacement is a harmonic function of the time having a period which we suppose given. It is therefore entirely determined for the whole time the vibrations continue by the values of the six quantities

$$[\xi]_{\text{Ave}},\quad [\eta]_{\text{Ave}},\quad [\zeta]_{\text{Ave}},\quad [\dot{\xi}]_{\text{Ave}},\quad [\dot{\eta}]_{\text{Ave}},\quad [\dot{\zeta}]_{\text{Ave}}$$

at any one instant. For the same reason the average electromotive force is entirely determined for the whole time by the values of the six quantities

$$[X]_{\text{Ave}},\quad [Y]_{\text{Ave}},\quad [Z]_{\text{Ave}},\quad [\dot{X}]_{\text{Ave}},\quad [\dot{Y}]_{\text{Ave}},\quad [\dot{Z}]_{\text{Ave}}$$

for the same instant. The first six quantities will therefore be functions of the second, and the principle of the superposition of motions requires that they shall be homogeneous functions of the first degree. And the second six quantities will be homogeneous functions of the first degree of the first six. The coefficients by which these functions are expressed will depend upon the nature of the medium in the vicinity of the point considered. They will also depend upon the period of vibration, that is, upon the color of the light.*

We may therefore write in vector notation

$$[\mathbf{E}]_{\mathrm{Ave}} = \Phi[\mathbf{U}]_{\mathrm{Ave}} + \Psi[\dot{\mathbf{U}}]_{\mathrm{Ave}} \tag{7}$$

where Φ and Ψ denote linear functions.†

The optical properties of media are determined by the form of these functions. But all forms of linear functions would not be consistent with the principle of the conservation of energy.

In media which are more or less opaque, and which therefore absorb energy, Ψ must be of such a form that the function always makes an acute angle (or none) with the independent variable. In perfectly transparent media, Ψ must vanish, unless the function is at right angles to the independent variable. So far as is known, the last occurs only when the medium is subject to magnetic influence. In perfectly transparent media, the principle of the conservation of energy requires that Φ should be self-conjugate, i.e., that for three directions at right angles to one another, the function and independent variable should coincide in direction.

In all isotropic media not subject to magnetic influence, it is probable that Φ and Ψ reduce to numerical coefficients, as is certainly the case with Φ for transparent isotropic media.

9. Comparing the two values of $[\mathbf{E}]_{\mathrm{Ave}}$, we have

$$\frac{4\pi^2}{p^2}\,\mathrm{Pot}\,[\mathbf{U}]_{\mathrm{Ave}} - \nabla[q]_{\mathrm{Ave}} = \Phi[\mathbf{U}]_{\mathrm{Ave}} + \Psi[\dot{\mathbf{U}}]_{\mathrm{Ave}}. \tag{8}$$

This equation, in connection with that by which we express the solenoidal character of the displacements, if we regard them as necessarily solenoidal, or in connection with that which expresses the relation between the electrostatic potential and the displacements, if we reject the solenoidal hypothesis, may be regarded as the general equation of the vibrations of monochromatic light, considered as oscillating electrical fluxes. For the symbol *Pot*, however, we must substitute the symbol representing the operation by which electromotive force is calculated from acceleration of flux, with the negative sign, if we are not satisfied with the law provisionally adopted.

---

* The relations between the displacements in one of the small spaces considered and the average electromotive force is mathematically analogous to the relation between the displacements in a system of a high degree of complexity and certain forces exerted from without, which are harmonic functions of the time and under the influence of which the system vibrates. The ratio of the displacements to the forces will in general vary with the period, and may vary very rapidly.

An example in which these functions vary very rapidly with the period is afforded by the phenomena of selective absorption and abnormal dispersion.

† A vector is said to be a linear function of another, when the three components of the first are homogeneous functions of the first degree of the three components of the second.

It is important to observe that the existence of molecular vibrations of ponderable matter, due to the passage of light through the medium, will not affect the reasoning by which this equation has been established, provided that the nature and intensity of these vibrations in any small part of the medium (as measured by a wave-length) are entirely determined by the electrical forces and motions in that part of the medium. But the equation would not hold in case of molecular vibrations due to magnetic force. Such vibrations would constitute an oscillating magnetization of the medium, which has already been excluded from the discussion.

The supposition which has sometimes been made,* that electricity possesses a certain mass or inertia, would not at all affect the validity of the equation.

10. The equation may be reduced to a form in some respects more simple by the use of the so-called imaginary quantities. We shall write ι for $\surd(-1)$. If we differentiate with respect to the time, and substitute $-\frac{4\pi^2}{p^2}[\mathbf{U}]_{\text{Ave}}$ for $[\ddot{\mathbf{U}}]_{\text{Ave}}$, we obtain

$$\frac{4\pi^2}{p^2}\text{Pot}\,[\dot{\mathbf{U}}]_{\text{Ave}}-\nabla[\dot{q}]_{\text{Ave}}=\Phi[\dot{\mathbf{U}}]_{\text{Ave}}-\frac{4\pi^2}{p^2}\Psi[\mathbf{U}]_{\text{Ave}}.$$

If we multiply this equation by ι, either alone or in connection with any real factor, and add it to the preceding, we shall obtain an equation which will be equivalent to the two of which it is formed. Multiplying by $-\frac{p\iota}{2\pi}$ and adding, we have

$$\frac{4\pi^2}{p^2}\text{Pot}\left([\mathbf{U}]_{\text{Ave}}-\iota\frac{p}{2\pi}[\dot{\mathbf{U}}]_{\text{Ave}}\right)-\nabla\left([q]_{\text{Ave}}-\iota\frac{p}{2\pi}[\dot{q}]_{\text{Ave}}\right)$$
$$=\left(\Phi+\iota\frac{2\pi}{p}\Psi\right)\left([\mathbf{U}]_{\text{Ave}}-\iota\frac{p}{2\pi}[\dot{\mathbf{U}}]_{\text{Ave}}\right).$$

If we set

$$\mathbf{W}=[\mathbf{U}]_{\text{Ave}}-\iota\frac{p}{2\pi}[\dot{\mathbf{U}}]_{\text{Ave}}, \tag{9}$$

$$Q=[q]_{\text{Ave}}-\iota\frac{p}{2\pi}[\dot{q}]_{\text{Ave}}, \tag{10}$$

$$\Theta=\Phi+\iota\frac{2\pi}{p}\Psi, \tag{11}$$

our equation reduces to

$$\frac{4\pi^2}{p^2}\text{Pot}\,\mathbf{W}-\nabla Q=\Theta\mathbf{W}. \tag{12}$$

In this equation Θ denotes a complex linear vector function, i.e., a vector function of which the X-, Y-, and Z-components are expressed in terms of the X-, Y-, and Z-components of the independent variable by means of coefficients of the form $a+\iota b$. $\mathbf{W}$ is a bivector of which

* See Weber, *Abhandl. d. K. Sächs. Gesellsch. d. Wiss.*, vol. vi, pp. 593-597; Lorberg, *Crelle's Journal*, vol. lxi, p. 55.

the real part represents the averaged displacement $[\mathbf{U}]_{\text{Ave}}$, and the coefficient of ι the rate of increase of the same multiplied by a constant factor. This bivector therefore represents the average state of a small part of the field both with respect to position and velocity. We may also say that the coefficient of ι in $\mathbf{W}$ represents the value of the averaged displacement $[\mathbf{U}]_{\text{Ave}}$ at a time one-quarter of a vibration earlier than the time principally considered.

11. It may serve to fix our ideas to see how $\mathbf{W}$ is expressed as a function of the time. We may evidently set

$$[\mathbf{U}]_{\text{Ave}} = \mathbf{A}_1 \cos \frac{2\pi}{p} t + \mathbf{A}_2 \sin \frac{2\pi}{p} t$$

where $\mathbf{A}_1$ and $\mathbf{A}_2$ are vectors representing the amplitudes of the two parts into which the vibration is resolved. Then

$$\frac{p}{2\pi} [\dot{\mathbf{U}}]_{\text{Ave}} = -\mathbf{A}_1 \sin \frac{2\pi}{p} t + \mathbf{A}_2 \cos \frac{2\pi}{p} t,$$

and

$$[\mathbf{U}]_{\text{Ave}} - \iota \frac{p}{2\pi} [\dot{\mathbf{U}}]_{\text{Ave}} = (\mathbf{A}_1 - \iota\, \mathbf{A}_2) \left(\cos \frac{2\pi}{p} t + \iota \sin \frac{2\pi}{p} t \right);$$

that is, if we set $\mathbf{A} = \mathbf{A}_1 - \iota\, \mathbf{A}_2$,

$$\mathbf{W} = \mathbf{A} e^{\frac{2\pi \iota t}{p}}. \tag{13}$$

In like manner we may obtain

$$Q = g e^{\frac{2\pi \iota t}{p}}, \tag{14}$$

where g is a biscalar, or complex quantity of ordinary algebra. Substituting these values in (12), and cancelling the common factor containing the time, we have

$$\frac{4\pi^2}{p^2} \operatorname{Pot} \mathbf{A} - \nabla g = \Theta \mathbf{A}. \tag{15}$$

Our equation is thus reduced to one between $\mathbf{A}$ and g, and may easily be reduced to one in $\mathbf{A}$ alone.* Now $\mathbf{A}$ represents six numerical quantities (viz., the three components of $\mathbf{A}_1$, and the three of $\mathbf{A}_2$), which may be called the six components of amplitude. The equation, therefore, substantially represents the relations between the six components of amplitude in different parts of the field.† The equation is, however, not really different from (12), since $\mathbf{A}$ and g are only particular values of $\mathbf{W}$ and Q.

* The terms ∇Q, ∇q are allowed to remain in these equations, because the best manner of eliminating them will depend somewhat upon our admission or rejection of the solenoidal hypothesis.

† The representation of the six components of amplitude by a single letter should not be regarded as an analytical artifice. It only leaves undivided in our notation that which is undivided in the nature of things. The separation of the six components of amplitude is artificial, in that it introduces arbitrary elements into the discussion, viz. the directions of the axes of the coordinates, and the zero of time.

12. From the general equation given above (8, 12, or 15), in connection with the solenoidal hypothesis, we may easily derive the laws of the propagation of plane waves in the interior of a sensibly homogeneous medium, and the laws of reflection and refraction at surfaces between such media. This has been done by Maxwell,* Lorentz,† and others,‡ with fundamental equations more or less similar.

The method, however, by which the fundamental equation has been established in this paper seems free from certain objections which have been brought against the ordinary form of the theory. As ordinarily treated, the phenomena are made to depend entirely on the inductive capacity and the conductivity of the medium, in a manner which may be expressed by the equation

$$[\mathbf{U}]_{\text{Ave}} = \left(\frac{\mathrm{K}}{4\pi} - \frac{p^2\mathrm{C}}{4\pi^2}\frac{d}{dt}\right)\left(\frac{4\pi^2}{p^2}\operatorname{Pot}[\mathbf{U}]_{\text{Ave}} - \nabla[q]_{\text{Ave}}\right), \tag{16}$$

which will be equivalent to (12), if

$$\mathbf{W} = \left(\frac{\mathrm{K}}{4\pi} - \iota\frac{p\mathrm{C}}{2\pi}\right)\left(\frac{4\pi^2}{p^2}\operatorname{Pot}\mathbf{W} - \nabla\mathrm{Q}\right), \tag{17}$$

where K and C denote in the most general case the linear vector functions, but in isotropic bodies the numerical coefficients, which represent inductive capacity and conductivity. By a simple transformation {see (9) and (10)}, this equation becomes

$$\Theta^{-1} = \frac{\mathrm{K}}{4\pi} - \iota\frac{p\mathrm{C}}{2\pi}, \tag{18}$$

where Θ^{-1} represents the function inverse to Θ.

Now, while experiment appears to verify the existence of such a law as is expressed by equation (12), it does not show that Θ has the precise form indicated by equation (16). In other words, experiment does not satisfactorily verify the relations expressed by (16) and (17), if K and C are understood to be the operators (or, in isotropic bodies, the numbers) which represent inductive capacity and conductivity in the ordinary sense of the terms.

The discrepancy is most easily shown in the most simple case, when the medium is isotropic and perfectly transparent, and Θ reduces to a numerical quantity. The square of the velocity of plane waves is then equal to $\frac{\Theta}{4\pi}$, and equation (18) would make it independent of the

---

* *Phil. Trans.*, vol. clv (1865), p. 459, or *Treatise on Electricity and Magnetism*, chap. xx.

† Schlömilch's *Zeitschrift*, vol. xxii, pp. 1-30 and 205-219; xxiii, pp. 197-210.

‡ See Fitzgerald, *Phil. Trans.*, vol. clxxi, p. 691; J. J. Thomson, *Phil. Mag.*, (5), vol. ix, p. 284; Rayleigh, *Phil. Mag.* (5), vol. xii, p. 81.

That the electromagnetic theory of light gives the conditions relative to the boundary of different media, which are required by the phenomena of reflection and refraction, was first shown by Helmholtz. See *Crelle's Journal*, vol. lxxii (1870), p. 57.

period; that is, would give no dispersion of colors. The case is essentially the same in transparent bodies which are not isotropic.*

The case is worse with metals, which are characterized electrically by great conductivity, and optically by great opacity. In their papers cited above, Lorentz and Rayleigh have observed that the experiments of Jamin on the reflection of light from metallic surfaces would often require, as ordinarily interpreted on the electromagnetic theory, a negative value for the inductive capacity of the metal. This would imply that the electrical equilibrium in the metal is unstable. The objection, therefore, is essentially the same as that which Lord Rayleigh had previously made to Cauchy's theory of metallic reflection, viz., that the apparent mechanical explanation of the phenomena is illusory, since the numerical values given by experiment as interpreted on Cauchy's theory would involve an unstable equilibrium of the ether in the metal.†

13. All this points to the same conclusion—that the ordinary view of the phenomena is inadequate. The object of this paper will be accomplished, if it has been made clear how a point of view more in accordance with what we know of the molecular constitution of bodies will give that part of the ordinary theory which is verified by experiment, without including that part which is in opposition to observed facts.‡

---

* See note to the first paper of Lorentz, cited above, Schlömilch, vol. xxii, p. 23.

† See *Phil. Mag.* (4), vol. xliii (1872), p. 321.

‡ The consideration of the processes which we may suppose to take place in the smallest parts of a body through which light is transmitted, farther than is necessary to establish the general equation given above, is foreign to the design of this paper. Yet a word may be added with respect to the difficulties signalized in the ordinary form of the theory. The comparatively simple case of a perfectly transparent body has been examined more in detail in one of the papers already cited, where there is given an explanation of the dispersion of colors from the point of view of this paper. It is there shown that the effect of the non-homogeneity of the body in its smallest parts is to add a term to the expression for the kinetic energy of electrical waves, which for an isotropic body may be roughly described as similar to that which would be required if the electricity had a certain mass or inertia. (See especially §§ 7, 9 and 12, [this volume pages 185 ff.]) The same must be true of media of any degree of opacity. Now the difficulty with the optical properties of the metals is that the real part of Θ (or Θ^{-1}) is in some cases negative. This implies that at a moment of greatest displacement the electromotive force is in the direction opposite to the displacement, instead of having the same direction, as in transparent isotropic bodies. Now a certain part of the electromotive force must be required to oppose the apparent inertia, and another part to oppose the electrical elasticity of the medium. These parts of the force must have opposite directions. In transparent bodies the latter part is by far the greater. But it need not surprise us that the former should be the greater in some metals.

It has been remarked by Lorentz that the difficulty with respect to metals would be in a measure relieved if we should suppose electricity to have the property of inertia. (See § 11 of his third paper, Schlömilch's *Zeitschrift*, vol. xxiii, p. 208.) But a supposition of this kind, taken literally, would involve a dispersion of colors in vacuo, and still be inadequate, as Lorentz remarks, to explain the phenomena observed in metals.

While the writer has aimed at a greater degree of rigor than is usual in the establishment of the fundamental equation of monochromatic light, it is not claimed that this equation is absolutely exact. The contrary is evident from the fact that the equation does not embrace the phenomena which characterize such circularly polarizing bodies as quartz. This, however, only implies the neglect of extremely small quantities—very small, for example, as compared with those which determine the dispersion of colors. In one of the papers already cited,* the case of a perfectly transparent body is treated with a higher degree of approximation, so as to embrace the phenomena in question.

* See page 195 of this volume.

XIV.

A COMPARISON OF THE ELASTIC AND THE ELECTRICAL THEORIES OF LIGHT WITH RESPECT TO THE LAW OF DOUBLE REFRACTION AND THE DISPERSION OF COLORS.

[*American Journal of Science*, ser. 3, vol. xxxv, pp. 467–475, June, 1888.]

It is claimed for the electrical * theory of light that it is free from serious difficulties, which beset the explanation of the phenomena of light by the dynamics of elastic solids. Just what these difficulties are, and why they do not occur in the explanation of the same phenomena by the dynamics of electricity, has not perhaps been shown with all the simplicity and generality which might be desired. Such a treatment of the subject is however the more necessary on account of the ever-increasing bulk of the literature on either side, and the confusing multiplicity of the elastic theories. It is the object of this paper to supply this want, so far as respects the propagation of plane waves in transparent and sensibly homogeneous media. The simplicity of this part of the subject renders it appropriate for the first test of any optical theory, while the precision of which the experimental determinations are capable, renders the test extremely rigorous.

It is moreover, as the writer believes, an appropriate time for the discussion proposed, since on one hand the experimental verification of Fresnel's Law has recently been carried to a degree of precision far exceeding anything which we have had before,† and on the other, the

* The term *electrical* seems the most simple and appropriate to describe that theory of light which makes it consist in electrical motions. The cases in which any distinctively magnetic action is involved in the phenomena of light are so exceptional, that it is difficult to see any sufficient reason why the general theory should be called *electromagnetic*, unless we are to call all phenomena electromagnetic which depend on the motions of electricity.

† In the recent experiments of Professor Hastings relating to the index of refraction of the extraordinary ray in Iceland spar for the spectral line D_2 and a wave-normal inclined at about 31° to the optic axis, the difference between the observed and the calculated values was only two or three units in the sixth decimal place (in the seventh significant figure), which was about the probable error of the determinations. See *Am. Jour. Sci.* ser. 3, vol. xxxv, p. 60.

discovery of a remarkable theorem relating to the vibrations of a strained solid * has given a new impulse to the study of the elastic theory of light.

Let us first consider the facts to which a correct theory must conform.

It is generally admitted that the phenomena of light consist in motions (of the type which we call wave-motions) of something which exists both in space void of ponderable matter, and in the spaces between the molecules of bodies, perhaps also in the molecules themselves. The kinematics of these motions is pretty well understood; the question at issue is whether it agrees with the dynamics of elastic solids or with the dynamics of electricity.

In the case of a simple harmonic wave-motion, which alone we need consider, the wave-velocity (V) is the quotient of the wave-length (l) by the period of vibration (p). These quantities can be determined with extreme accuracy. In media which are sensibly homogeneous but not isotropic the wave-velocity V, for any constant value of the period, is a quadratic function of the direction cosines of a certain line, viz., the normal to the so-called "plane of polarization." The physical characteristics of this line have been a matter of dispute. Fresnel considered it to be the direction of displacement. Others have maintained that it is the common perpendicular to the wave-normal and the displacement. Others again would define it as that component of the displacement which is perpendicular to the wave-normal. This of course would differ from Fresnel's view only in case the displacements are not perpendicular to the wave-normal, and would in that case be a necessary modification of his view. Although this dispute has been one of the most celebrated in physics, it seems to be at length substantially settled, most directly by experiments upon the scattering of light by small particles, which seems to show decisively that in isotropic media at least the displacements are normal to the "plane of polarization," and also, with hardly less cogency, by the difficulty of accounting for the intensities of reflected and refracted light on any other

* Sir Wm. Thomson has shown that if an elastic incompressible solid in which the potential energy of any homogeneous strain is proportional to the sum of the squares of the reciprocals of the principal elongations *minus* three is subjected to any homogeneous strain by forces applied to its surface, the transmission of plane waves of distortion, superposed on this homogeneous strain, will follow exactly Fresnel's law (including the direction of displacement), the three principal velocities being proportional to the reciprocals of the principal elongations. It must be a surprise to mathematicians and physicists to learn that a theorem of such simplicity and beauty has been waiting to be discovered in a field which has been so carefully gleaned. See page 116 of the current volume (xxv) of the *Philosophical Magazine*.

supposition.* It should be added that all diversity of opinion on this subject has been confined to those whose theories are based on the dynamics of elastic bodies. Defenders of the electrical theory have always placed the electrical displacement at right angles to the "plane of polarization." It will, however, be better to assume this direction of the displacement as probable rather than as absolutely certain, not so much because many are likely to entertain serious doubts on the subject, as in order not to exclude views which have at least a historical interest.

The wave-velocity, then, for any constant period, is a quadratic function of the cosines of a certain direction, which is probably that of the displacement, but in any case determined by the displacement and the wave-normal. The coefficients of this quadratic function are functions of the period of vibration. It is important to notice that these coefficients vary separately, and often quite differently, with the period, and that the case does not at all resemble that of a quadratic function of the direction-cosines multiplied by a quantity depending on the period.

In discussing the dynamics of the subject we may gain something in simplicity by considering a system of stationary waves, such as results from two similar systems of progressive waves moving in opposite directions. In such a system the energy is alternately entirely kinetic and entirely potential. Since the total energy is constant, we may set the average kinetic energy per unit of volume at the moment when there is no potential energy, equal to the average potential energy per unit of volume when there is no kinetic energy.† We may call this the equation of energies. It will contain the quantities l and p, and thus furnish an expression for the velocity of either system of progressive waves. We have to see whether the elastic or the electric theory gives the expression most conformed to the facts.

Let us first apply the elastic theory to the case of the so-called

* "At the same time, if the above reasoning be valid, the question as to the direction of the vibrations in polarized light is decided in accordance with the view of Fresnel. . . . I confess I cannot see any room for doubt as to the result it leads to. . . . I only mean that *if* light, as is generally supposed, consists of transversal vibrations similar to those which take place in an elastic solid, the vibration must be normal to the plane of polarization." Lord Rayleigh "On the Light from the Sky, its Polarization and Color;" *Phil. Mag.* (4), xli (1871), p. 109.

"Green's dynamics of polarization by reflexion, and Stokes' dynamics of the diffraction of polarized light, and Stokes' and Rayleigh's dynamics of the blue sky, all agree in, as it seems to me, irrefragably, demonstrating Fresnel's original conclusion, that in plane polarized light the line of vibration is perpendicular to the plane of polarization." Sir Wm. Thomson, *loc. citat.*

† The terms *kinetic energy* and *potential energy* will be used in this paper to denote these average values.

vacuum. If we write h for the amplitude measured in the middle between two nodal planes, the velocities of displacement will be as $\frac{h}{p}$, and the kinetic energy will be represented by $A\frac{h^2}{p^2}$, where A is a constant depending on the density of the medium. The potential energy, which consists in distortion of the medium, may be represented by $B\frac{h^2}{l^2}$, where B is a constant depending on the rigidity of the medium. The equation of energies, on the elastic theory, is therefore

$$A\frac{h^2}{p^2}=B\frac{h^2}{l^2} \tag{1}$$

which gives

$$V^2=\frac{l^2}{p^2}=\frac{B}{A}. \tag{2}$$

In the electrical theory, the kinetic energy is not determined by the simple formula of ordinary dynamics from the square of the velocity of each element, but is found by integrating the product of the velocities of each pair of elements divided by the distance between them. Very elementary considerations suffice to show that a quantity thus determined when estimated per unit of volume will vary as the square of the wave-length. We may therefore set $Fl^2\frac{h^2}{p^2}$ for the kinetic energy, F being a constant. The potential energy does not consist in distortion of the medium, but depends upon an elastic resistance to the separation of the electricities, which constitutes the electrical displacement, and is proportioned to the square of this displacement. The average value of the potential energy per unit of volume will therefore be represented in the electrical theory by Gh^2, where G is a constant, and the equation of energies will be

$$Fl^2\frac{h^2}{p^2}=Gh^2 \tag{3}$$

which gives

$$V^2=\frac{l^2}{p^2}=\frac{G}{F}. \tag{4}$$

Both theories give a constant velocity, as is required. But it is instructive to notice the profound difference in the equations of energy from which this result is derived. In the elastic theory the square of the wave-length appears in the potential energy as a divisor; in the electrical theory it appears in the kinetic energy as a factor.

Let us now consider how these equations will be modified by the presence of ponderable matter, in the most general case of transparent and sensibly homogeneous bodies. This subject is rendered much more simple by the fact that the distances between the ponderable molecules are very small compared with a wave-length. Or, what amounts to the same thing, but may present a more distinct picture to the imagination, the wave-length may be regarded as enormously great in comparison with the distances between neighboring molecules. Whatever view we take of the motions which constitute light, we can hardly suppose them (disturbed as they are by the presence of the ponderable molecules) to be in strictness represented by the equations of wave-motion. Yet in a certain sense a wave-motion may and does exist. If, namely, instead of the actual displacement at any point, we consider the average displacement in a space large enough to contain an immense number of molecules, and yet small as measured by a wave-length, such average displacements may be represented by the equations of wave-motion; and it is only in this sense that any theory of wave-motion can apply to the phenomena of light in transparent bodies. When we speak of displacements, amplitudes, velocities (of displacement), etc., it must therefore be understood in this way.

The actual kinetic energy, on either theory, will evidently be greater than that due to the motion thus averaged or smoothed, and to a degree presumably depending on the direction of the displacement. But since displacement in any direction may be regarded as compounded of displacements in three fixed directions, the additional energy will be a quadratic function of the components of velocity of displacement, or, in other words, a quadratic function of the direction-cosines of the displacement multiplied by the square of the amplitude and divided by the square of the period.* This additional energy may be understood as including any part of the kinetic energy of the wave-motion which may belong to the ponderable particles. The term to be added to the kinetic energy on the electric theory may therefore be written $f_D \frac{h^2}{p^2}$, where f_D is a quadratic function of the direction-cosines of the displacement. The elastic theory requires a term of precisely the same character, but since the term to which it is to be added is of the same general form, the two may be incorporated in a single term of the form $A_D \frac{h^2}{p^2}$, where A_D is a quadratic function of the direction-cosines of the displacement. We must, however, notice that both A_D and f_D are not entirely independent of the period. For the manner in which the flux of the luminiferous medium is distributed among the ponderable molecules will naturally depend somewhat upon the period. The same is true of the degree to which the molecules may be thrown into vibration. But A_D and f_D will be independent of the wave-length (except so far as this is

---

* For proof *in extenso* of this proposition, when the motions are supposed electrical, the reader is referred to page 187 of this volume.

connected with the period), because the wave-length is enormously great compared with the size of the molecules and the distances between them.

The potential energy on the elastic theory must be increased by a term of the form $b_D h^2$, where b_D is a quadratic function of the direction-cosines of the displacement. For the ponderable particles must oppose a certain elastic resistance to the displacement of the ether, which in æolotropic bodies will presumably be different in different directions. The potential energy on the electric theory will be represented by a single term of the same form, say $G_D h^2$, where a quadratic function of the direction-cosines of the displacement, G_D, takes the place of the constant G, which was sufficient when the ponderable particles were absent. Both G_D and b_D will vary to some extent with the period, like A_D and f_D, and for the same reason.

In regard to that potential energy, which on the elastic theory is independent of the direct action of the ponderable molecules, it has been supposed that in æolotropic bodies the effect of the molecules is such as to produce an æolotropic state in the ether, so that the energy of a distortion varies with its orientation. This part of the potential energy will then be represented by $B_{ND}\frac{h^2}{l^2}$, where B_{ND} is a function of the directions of the wave-normal and the displacement. It may easily be shown that it is a quadratic function both of the direction-cosines of the wave-normal and of those of the displacement. Also, that if the ether in the body when undisturbed is not in a state of stress due to forces at the surface of the body, or if its stress is uniform in all directions, like a hydrostatic pressure, the function B_{ND} must be symmetrical with respect to the two sets of direction-cosines.

The equation of energies for the elastic theory is therefore

$$A_D\frac{h^2}{p^2}=B_{ND}\frac{h^2}{l^2}+b_D h^2, \tag{5}$$

which gives

$$V^2=\frac{l^2}{p^2}=\frac{B_{ND}}{A_D-b_D p^2}. \tag{6}$$

The equation of energies for the electrical theory is

$$Fl^2\frac{h^2}{p^2}+f_D\frac{h^2}{p^2}=G_D h^2, \tag{7}$$

which gives

$$V^2=\frac{l^2}{p^2}=\frac{G_D}{F}-\frac{f_D}{Fp^2}. \tag{8}$$

It is evident at once that the electrical theory gives exactly the form that we want. For any constant period the square of the wave-velocity is a quadratic function of the direction-cosines of the displacement. When the period varies, this function varies, the different coefficients in the function varying separately, because G_D and f_D will not in general be similar functions.* If we consider a constant direction of displacement while the period varies, G_D and f_D will only vary so far as the type of the motion varies, i.e., so far as the manner in which the flux distributes itself among the ponderable molecules and intermolecular spaces, and the extent to which the molecules take part in the motion are changed. There are cases in which these vary rapidly with the period, viz., cases of selective absorption and abnormal dispersion. But we may fairly expect that there will be many cases in which the character of the motion in these respects will not vary much with the period. $\frac{G_D}{F}$ and $\frac{f_D}{F}$ will then be sensibly constant and we have an approximate expression for the general law of dispersion, which agrees remarkably well with experiment.†

If we now return to the equation of energies obtained from the elastic theory, we see at once that it does not suggest any such relation as experiment has indicated, either between the wave-velocity and the direction of displacement, or between the wave-velocity and the period. It remains to be seen whether it can be brought to agree with experiment by any hypothesis not too violent.

In order that V^2 may be a quadratic function of any set of direction-cosines, it is necessary that A_D and b_D shall be independent of the direction of the displacement, in other words, in the case of a crystal like Iceland spar, that the direct action of the ponderable molecules upon the ether, shall affect both the kinetic and the potential energy in the same way, whether the displacement take place in the direction of the optic axis or at right angles to it. This is contrary to everything which we should expect. If, nevertheless, we make this supposition, it remains to consider B_{ND}. This must be a quadratic function of a certain direction, which is almost certainly that of the displacement. If the medium is free from external stress (other than hydrostatic), B_{ND}, as we have seen, is symmetrical with respect to the wave-normal and the direction of displacement, and a quadratic function of the direction-cosines of each. The only single direction of which it can be a function is the common perpendicular to these two directions. If the wave-normal and the displacement are perpendicular, the direction-cosines

* But G_D, f_D, and V^2, considered as functions of the direction of displacement, are all subject to any law of symmetry which may belong to the structure of the body considered. The resulting optical characteristics of the different crystallographic systems are given on pages 192-194.

† This will appear most distinctly if we consider that V divided by the velocity of light *in vacuo* gives the reciprocal of the index of refraction, and p multiplied by the same quantity gives the wave-length *in vacuo*.

of the common perpendicular to both will be linear functions of the direction-cosines of each, and a quadratic function of the direction-cosines of the common perpendicular will be a quadratic function of the direction-cosines of each. We may thus reconcile the theory with the law of double refraction, in a certain sense, by supposing that A_D and b_D are independent of the direction of displacement, and that B_{ND} and therefore V^2 is a quadratic function of the direction-cosines of the common perpendicular to the wave-normal and the displacement. But this supposition, besides its intrinsic improbability so far as A_D and b_D are concerned, involves a direction of the displacement which is certainly or almost certainly wrong.

We are thus driven to suppose that the undisturbed medium is in a state of stress, which, moreover, is not a simple hydraulic stress. In this case, by attributing certain definite physical properties to the medium, we may make the function B_{ND} become independent of the direction of the wave-normal, and reduce to a quadratic function of the direction-cosines of the displacement.* This entirely satisfies Fresnel's Law, including the direction of displacement, if we can suppose A_D and b_D independent of the direction of displacement. But this supposition, in any case difficult for aeolotropic bodies, seems quite irreconcilable with that of a permanent (not hydrostatic) stress.

For this stress can only be kept up by the action of the ponderable molecules, and by a sort of action which hinders the passage of the ether past the molecules. Now the phenomena of reflection and refraction would be very different from what they are, if the optical homogeneity of a crystal did not extend up very close to the surface. This implies that the stress is produced by the ponderable particles in a very thin lamina at the surface of the crystal, much less in thickness, it would seem probable, than a wave-length of yellow light. And this again implies that the power of the ponderable particles to pin down the ether, as it were, to a particular position is very great, and that the term in the energy relating to the motion of the ether relative to the ponderable particles is very important. This is the term containing the factor b_D, which it is difficult to suppose independent of the direction of displacement because the dimensions and arrangement of the particles are different in different directions. But our present hypothesis has brought in a new reason for supposing b_D to depend on the direction of displacement, viz., on account of the stress of the medium. A general displacement of the medium midway between two nodal planes, when it is restrained at innumerable points by the ponderable particles, will

* See note on page 224.

produce special distortions due to these particles. The nature of these distortions is wholly determined by the direction of displacement, and it is hard to conceive of any reason why the energy of these distortions should not vary with the direction of displacement, like the energy of the general distortion of the wave-motion, which is partly determined by the displacement and partly by the wave-normal.*

But the difficulties of the elastic theory do not end with the law of double refraction, although they are there more conspicuous on account of the definite and simple law by which they can be judged. It does not easily appear how the equation of energies can be made to give anything like the proper law of the dispersion of colors. Since for given directions of the wave-normal and displacement, or in an isotropic body, B_{ND} is constant, and also A_D and b_D, except so far as the type of the vibration varies, the formula requires that the square of the index of refraction (which is inversely as V^2) should be equal to a constant diminished by a term proportional to the square of the period, except so far as this law is modified by a variation of the type of vibration. But experiment shows nothing like this law. Now the variation in the type of vibration is sometimes very important,—it plays the leading rôle in the phenomena of selective absorption and abnormal dispersion,—but this is certainly not always the case. It seems hardly possible to suppose that the type of vibration is always so variable as entirely to mask the law which is indicated by the formula when A_D and b_D (with B_{ND}) are regarded as constant. This is especially evident when we consider that the effect on the wave-velocity of a small variation in the type of vibration will be a small quantity of the second order.†

The phenomena of dispersion, therefore, corroborate the conclusion which seemed to follow inevitably from the law of double refraction alone.

---

* The reader may perhaps ask how the above reasoning is to be reconciled with the fact that the law of double refraction has been so often deduced from the elastic theory. The troublesome terms are b_D and the variable part of A_D, which express the direct action of the ponderable molecules on the ether. So far as the (quite limited) reading and recollection of the present writer extend, those who have sought to derive the law of double refraction from the theory of elastic solids have generally either neglected this direct action—a neglect to which Professor Stokes calls attention more than once in his celebrated "Report on Double Refraction" (*Brit. Assoc.*, 1862, pp. 264, 268)—or taking account of this action they have made shipwreck upon a law different from Fresnel's and contradicted by experiment.

† See pages 190, 191 of this volume, or Lord Rayleigh's *Theory of Sound*, vol. i, p. 84.

XV.

A COMPARISON OF THE ELECTRIC THEORY OF LIGHT AND SIR WILLIAM THOMSON'S THEORY OF A QUASI-LABILE ETHER.

[*American Journal of Science*, ser. 3, vol. XXXVII, pp. 139-144, February, 1889.]

A REMARKABLE paper by Sir William Thomson, in the November number of the *Philosophical Magazine*, has opened a new vista in the possibilities of the theory of an elastic ether. Since the general theory of elasticity gives three waves characterized by different directions of displacement for a single wave-plane, while the phenomena of optics show but two, the first point in accommodating any theory to observation, is to get rid (absolutely or sensibly) of the third wave. For this end, it has been common to make the ether incompressible, or, as it is sometimes expressed, to make the velocity of the third wave infinite. The velocity of the wave of compression becomes in fact infinite as the compressibility vanishes. Of course it has not escaped the notice of physicists that we may also get rid of the third wave by making its velocity zero, as may be done by giving certain values to the constants which express the elastic properties of the medium, but such values have appeared impossible, as involving an unstable state of the medium. The condition of incompressibility, absolute or approximate, has therefore appeared necessary.* This question of instability has now, however, been subjected to a more searching examination, with the result that the instability does not really exist "*provided we either suppose the medium to extend all through boundless space, or give it a fixed containing vessel as its boundary.*" This renders possible a very simple theory of light, which has been shown to give Fresnel's laws for the intensities of reflected and refracted light and for double refraction, so far as concerns the phenomena which can be directly observed. The displacement in an aeolotropic medium is in the same plane passing through the wave-normal as was supposed by Fresnel,

* It was under this impression that the paper entitled "A Comparison of the Elastic and the Electric Theories of Light with respect to the Law of Double Refraction and the Dispersion of Colors," [this volume pp. 223-231], was written. The conclusions of that paper, except so far as respects the dispersion of colors, will not apply to the new theory.

but its position in that plane is different, being perpendicular to the ray instead of to the wave-normal.*

It is the object of this paper to compare this new theory with the electric theory of light. In the limiting cases, that is, when we regard the velocity of the missing wave in the elastic theory as zero, and in the electric theory as infinite, we shall find a remarkable correspondence between the two theories, the motions of monochromatic light within isotropic or aeolotropic media of any degree of transparency or opacity, and at the boundary between two such media, being represented by equations absolutely identical, except that the symbols which denote displacement in one theory denote force in the other, and *vice versâ*.† In order to exhibit this correspondence completely and clearly, it is necessary that the fundamental principles of the two theories should be treated with the same generality, and, so far as possible, by the same method. The immediate consequences of the new theory will therefore be deduced with the same generality and essentially by the same method which has been used with reference to the electric theory in a former volume of this Journal [page 211 of this volume].

The elastic properties of the ether, according to the new theory, *in its limiting case*, may be very simply expressed by means of a vector operator, for which we shall use Maxwell's designation. The *curl* of a vector is defined to be another vector so derived from the first that if u, v, w be the rectangular components of the first, and u', v', w', those of its curl,

$$u'=\frac{dw}{dy}-\frac{dv}{dz},\quad v'=\frac{du}{dz}-\frac{dw}{dx},\quad w'=\frac{dv}{dx}-\frac{du}{dy},\tag{1}$$

where x, y, z are rectangular coordinates. With this understanding, if the displacement of the ether is represented by the vector $\mathfrak{E}$, the force exerted upon any element by the surrounding ether will be

$$-\mathrm{B}\ \mathrm{curl}\ \mathrm{curl}\ \mathfrak{E}\ dx\ dy\ dz,\tag{2}$$

where B is a scalar (the so-called *rigidity* of the ether) having the same constant value throughout all space, whether ponderable matter is present or not.

Where there is no ponderable matter, this force must be equated to the reaction of the inertia of the ether. This gives, with omission of the common factor $dx\ dy\ dz$,

$$\mathrm{A}\ddot{\mathfrak{E}}=-\mathrm{B}\ \mathrm{curl}\ \mathrm{curl}\ \mathfrak{E},\tag{3}$$

where A denotes the density of the ether.

* Sir William Thomson, *loc. citat.* R. T. Glazebrook, *Phil. Mag.*, December, 1888.

† In giving us a new interpretation of the equations of the electric theory, the author of the new theory has in fact enriched the mathematical theory of physics with something which may be compared to the celebrated *principle of duality* in geometry.

The presence of ponderable matter disturbs the motions of the ether, and renders them too complicated for us to follow in detail. Nor is this necessary, for the quantities which occur in the equations of optics represent average values, taken over spaces large enough to smooth out the irregularities due to the ponderable particles, although very small as measured by a wave-length.* Now the general principles of harmonic motion† show that to maintain in any element of volume the motion represented by

$$\mathfrak{E} = \mathfrak{A} e^{2\pi\iota \frac{t}{p}}, \tag{4}$$

$\mathfrak{A}$ being a complex vector constant, will require a force from outside represented by a complex linear vector function of $\mathfrak{E}$, that is, the three components of the force will be complex linear functions of the three components of $\mathfrak{E}$. We shall represent this force by

$$\mathrm{B}\Psi\ddot{\mathfrak{E}}\, dx\, dy\, dz, \tag{5}$$

where Ψ represents a complex linear vector function.‡

If we now equate the force required to maintain the motion in any element to that exerted upon the element by the surrounding ether, we have the equation

$$\Psi\ddot{\mathfrak{E}} = -\operatorname{curl} \operatorname{curl} \mathfrak{E}, \tag{6}$$

which expresses the general law for the motion of monochromatic light within any sensibly homogeneous medium, and may be regarded as implicitly including the conditions relating to the boundary of two such media, which are necessary for determining the intensities of reflected and refracted light.

For let u, v, w be the components of $\mathfrak{E}$,
u', v', w' " " curl $\mathfrak{E}$,
u'', v'', w'' " " curl curl $\mathfrak{E}$,

so that

$$u' = \frac{dw}{dy} - \frac{dv}{dz}, \quad v' = \frac{du}{dz} - \frac{dw}{dx}, \quad w' = \frac{dv}{dx} - \frac{du}{dy},$$

$$u'' = \frac{dw'}{dy} - \frac{dv'}{dz}, \quad v'' = \frac{du'}{dz} - \frac{dw'}{dx}, \quad w'' = \frac{dv'}{dx} - \frac{du'}{dy};$$

and let the interface be perpendicular to the axis of Z. It is evident

* This is in no respect different from what is always tacitly understood in the theory of sound, where the displacements, velocities, densities considered are always such average values. But in the theory of light, it is desirable to have the fact clearly in mind on account of the two interpenetrating media (imponderable and ponderable), the laws of light not being in all respects the same as they would be for a single homogeneous medium.

† See Lord Rayleigh's *Theory of Sound*, vol. i, chapters iv, v.

‡ It amounts essentially to the same thing, whether we regard the force as a linear vector function of $\mathfrak{E}$ or of $\ddot{\mathfrak{E}}$, since these differ only by the constant factor $-\frac{4\pi^2}{p^2}$. But there are some advantages in expressing the force as a function of $\ddot{\mathfrak{E}}$, because the greater part of the force, in the most important cases, is required to overcome the inertia of the ether, and is thus more immediately connected with $\ddot{\mathfrak{E}}$.

that if u' or v' is discontinuous at the interface, the value of u'' or v'' becomes in a sense infinite, i.e., curl curl $\mathfrak{E}$, and therefore by (6) $\Psi\ddot{\mathfrak{E}}$, will be infinite. Now both $\mathfrak{E}$ and Ψ are discontinuous at the interface, but infinite values for $\Psi\ddot{\mathfrak{E}}$ are not admissible. Therefore u' and v' are continuous. Again, if u or v is discontinuous, u' or v' will become infinite, and therefore u'' or v''. Therefore u and v are continuous. These conditions may be expressed in the most general manner by saying that the components of $\mathfrak{E}$ and curl $\mathfrak{E}$ parallel to the interface are continuous. This gives four complex scalar conditions, or in all eight scalar conditions, for the motion at the interface, which are sufficient to determine the amplitude and phase of the two reflected and the two refracted rays in the most general case. It is easy, however, to deduce from these four complex conditions, two others, which are interesting and sometimes convenient. It is evident from the definitions of w' and w'' that if u, v, u', and v' are continuous at the interface w' and w'' will also be continuous. Now $-w''$ is equal to the component of $\Psi\ddot{\mathfrak{E}}$ normal to the interface. The following quantities are therefore continuous at the interface:

$$\left.\begin{array}{ll}\text{the components parallel to the interface of} & \mathfrak{E},\\ \text{the component normal to the interface of} & \Psi\ddot{\mathfrak{E}},\\ \text{all components of} & \text{curl } \mathfrak{E}.\end{array}\right\} \qquad (7)$$

To compare these results with those derived from the electrical theory, we may take the general equation of monochromatic light on the electrical hypothesis from a paper in a former volume of this Journal. This equation, which with an unessential difference of notation may be written *

$$-\operatorname{Pot}\ddot{\mathfrak{F}} - \nabla Q = 4\pi\Phi\mathfrak{F}, \qquad (8)$$

was established by a method and considerations similar to those which have been used to establish equation (6), except that the ordinary law of electrodynamic induction had the place of the new law of elasticity. $\mathfrak{F}$ is a complex vector representing the electrical displacement as a harmonic function of the time; Φ is a complex linear vector operator, such that $4\pi\Phi\mathfrak{F}$ represents the electromotive force necessary to keep up the vibration $\mathfrak{F}$. Q is a complex scalar representing the electrostatic potential, ∇Q the vector of which the three components are

$$\frac{dQ}{dx}, \quad \frac{dQ}{dy}, \quad \frac{dQ}{dz}.$$

Pot denotes the operation by which in the theory of gravitation the potential is calculated from the density of matter.† When it is

* See page 218 of this volume, equation (12).

† The symbol $-\operatorname{Pot}$ is therefore equivalent to $4\pi\nabla^{-2}$, as used by Sir William Thomson (with a happy economy of symbols) at the last meeting of British Association to express the same law of electrodynamic induction, except that the symbol is here used as a vector operator. See *Nature*, vol. xxxviii, p. 571, *sub init.*

applied as here to a vector, the three components of the result are to be calculated separately from the three components of the operand. $-\nabla Q$ is therefore the electrostatic force, and $-\text{Pot}\,\ddot{\mathfrak{F}}$ the electrodynamic force. In establishing the equation, it was not assumed that the electrical motions are *solenoidal*, or such as to satisfy the so-called "equation of continuity." We may now, however, make this assumption, since it is the extreme case of the electric theory which we are to compare with the extreme case of the elastic.

It results from the definitions of *curl* and ∇ that curl $\nabla Q=0$. We may therefore eliminate Q from equation (8) by taking the curl. This gives

$$-\text{curl Pot}\,\ddot{\mathfrak{F}}=4\pi\,\text{curl}\,\Phi\mathfrak{F}. \tag{9}$$

Since curl curl and $\frac{1}{4\pi}$ Pot are inverse operators for solenoidal vectors, we may get rid of the symbol Pot by taking the curl again. We thus get

$$-\ddot{\mathfrak{F}}=\text{curl curl}\,\Phi\mathfrak{F}. \tag{10}$$

The conditions for the motion at the boundary between different media are easily obtained from the following considerations. Pot $\ddot{\mathfrak{F}}$ and Q are evidently continuous at the interface. Therefore the components parallel to the interface of ∇Q, and by (8) of $\Phi\mathfrak{F}$, will be continuous. Again, curl Pot $\ddot{\mathfrak{F}}$ is continuous at the interface, as appears from the consideration that curl Pot $\ddot{\mathfrak{F}}$ is the magnetic force due to the electrical motions $\ddot{\mathfrak{F}}$. Therefore, by (9), curl $\Phi\mathfrak{F}$ is continuous. The solenoidal condition requires that the component of $\mathfrak{F}$ normal to the interface shall be continuous.

The following quantities are therefore continuous at the interface:

$$\left.\begin{array}{ll}\text{the components parallel to the interface of} & \Phi\mathfrak{F},\\ \text{the component normal to the interface of} & \mathfrak{F},\\ \text{all components of} & \text{curl}\,\Phi\mathfrak{F}.\end{array}\right\} \tag{11}$$

Of these conditions, the two relating to the normal components of $\mathfrak{F}$ and curl $\Phi\mathfrak{F}$ are easily shown to result from the other four conditions, as in the analogous case in the elastic theory.

If we now compare in the two theories the differential equations of the motion of monochromatic light for the interior of a sensibly homogeneous medium, (6) and (10), and the special conditions for the boundary between two such media as represented by the continuity of the quantities (7) and (11), we find that these equations and conditions become identical, if

$$\mathfrak{F}=\Psi\mathfrak{E}, \tag{12}$$

$$\mathfrak{E}=\Phi\mathfrak{F}, \tag{13}$$

$$\Psi=\Phi^{-1}. \tag{14}$$

In other words, the displacements in either theory are subject to the same general and surface conditions as the forces required to maintain the vibrations in an element of volume in the other theory.

To fix our ideas in regard to the signification of Ψ and Φ, we may consider the case of isotropic media, in which these operators reduce to ordinary algebraic quantities, simple or complex. Now the *curl* of any vector necessarily satisfies the solenoidal condition (the so-called "equation of continuity"), therefore by (6) $\Psi\mathfrak{E}$ and $\mathfrak{E}$ will be solenoidal. So also will $\mathfrak{F}$ and $\Phi\mathfrak{F}$ in the electrical theory. Now for solenoidal vectors

$$-\text{curl curl} = \frac{d^2}{dx^2} + \frac{d^2}{dy^2} + \frac{d^2}{dz^2}, \tag{15}$$

so that the equations (6) and (10) reduce to

$$\Psi\ddot{\mathfrak{E}} = \left(\frac{d^2}{dx^2} + \frac{d^2}{dy^2} + \frac{d^2}{dz^2}\right)\mathfrak{E}, \tag{16}$$

$$\ddot{\mathfrak{F}} = \left(\frac{d^2}{dx^2} + \frac{d^2}{dy^2} + \frac{d^2}{dz^2}\right)\Phi\mathfrak{F}. \tag{17}$$

For a simple train of waves, the displacement, in either theory, may be represented by a constant multiplied by

$$e^{\iota(gt+ax+by+cz)} \tag{18}$$

Our equations then reduce again to

$$g^2\Psi\mathfrak{E} = (a^2+b^2+c^2)\mathfrak{E}, \tag{19}$$

$$g^2\mathfrak{F} = (a^2+b^2+c^2)\Phi\mathfrak{F}. \tag{20}$$

Hence

$$\Psi^{-1} = \Phi = \frac{g^2}{a^2+b^2+c^2}. \tag{21}$$

The last member of this equation, when real, evidently expresses the square of the velocity of light. If we set

$$n^2 = k^2\frac{a^2+b^2+c^2}{g^2}, \tag{22}$$

k denoting the velocity of light *in vacuo*, we have

$$n^2 = k^2\Psi = k^2\Phi^{-1}. \tag{23}$$

When n^2 is positive, which is the case of perfectly transparent bodies, the positive root of n^2 is called the index of refraction of the medium. In the most general case, it would be appropriate to call n—or perhaps that root of n^2 of which the real part is positive—the (complex) index of refraction, although the terminology is hardly settled in this respect. A negative value of n^2 would represent a body from which light would be totally reflected at all angles of incidence. No such cases have been observed. Values of n^2 in which the coefficient of ι is negative, indicate media in which light is absorbed. Values in which the coefficient of ι is positive would represent media in which the opposite phenomenon took place.*

It is no part of the object of this paper to go into the details by which we may derive, so far as observable phenomena are concerned, Fresnel's law of double refraction for transparent bodies, as well as the more general law of the same character which relates to aeolotropic bodies of more or less opacity, and which differs from Fresnel's only in that certain quantities become complex, or Fresnel's laws for the intensities of reflected and refracted light at the boundary of transparent isotropic media, with the more general laws for the case of bodies aeolotropic or opaque or both. The principal cases have already been discussed on the new elastic theory in the *Philosophical Magazine* † and a further discussion is promised. For the electrical theory, the case of double refraction in perfectly transparent media has been discussed quite in detail in this Journal, ‡ and the intensities of reflected and refracted light have been abundantly deduced from the above conditions by various authors. § So far as all these laws are concerned, the object of this paper will be attained if if it has been made clear that the two theories, in their extreme cases, give identical results. The greater or less degree of elegance, or completeness, or perspicuity, with which these laws may be developed by different authors, should weigh nothing in favor of either theory.

The non-magnetic rotation of the plane of polarization, with the allied phenomena in aeolotropic bodies, lie in a certain sense outside of the above laws, as depending on minute quantities which have been neglected in this discussion. The manner in which these minute quantities affect the equations of motion on the electrical theory has been shown in a former paper, ‖ where these phenomena in transparent bodies are treated quite at length. For the new theory, a discussion of this subject is promised by Mr. Glazebrook.

But the magnetic rotation of the plane of polarization, with the allied phenomena when an aeolotropic body is subjected to magnetic influence, fall entirely within the scope of the above equations and surface-conditions. The characteristic of this case is that Ψ and Φ are not self-conjugate. ¶ This is what we might expect on the electric

* But ι might have been introduced into the equations in such a way that a positive coefficient in the value of n^2 would indicate absorption, and a negative coefficient the impossible case.

† Sir William Thomson, *loc. citat.* R. T. Glazebrook, *loc. citat.*

‡ This vol. p. 182.

§ Lorentz, Schlömilch's *Zeitschrift*, vol. xxii, pp. 1-30 and 205-219; vol. xxiii, pp. 197-210; Fitzgerald, *Phil. Trans.*, vol. clxxi, p. 691; J. J. Thomson, *Phil. Mag.* (5), vol. ix, p. 284; Rayleigh, *Phil. Mag.* (5), vol. xii, p. 81. Glazebrook, *Proc. Cambr. Phil. Soc.*, vol. iv, p. 155.

‖ This vol. p. 195.

¶ See this vol. p. 217.

theory from the experiments of Dr. Hall, which show that the operators expressing the relation between electromotive force and current are not in general self-conjugate in this case.

In the preceding comparison, we have considered only the limiting cases of the two theories. With respect to the sense in which the limiting case is admissible, the two theories do not stand on quite the same footing. In the electric theory, or in any in which the velocity of the missing wave is very great, if we are satisfied that the compressibility is so small as to produce no appreciable results, we may set it equal to zero in our mathematical theory, even if we do not regard this as expressing the actual facts with absolute accuracy. But the case is not so simple with an elastic theory in which the forces resisting certain kinds of motion vanish, so far at least as they are proportional to the strains. The first requisite for any sort of optical theory is that the forces shall be proportional to the displacements. This is easily obtained in general by supposing the displacements very small. But if the resistance to one kind of distortion vanishes, there will be a tendency for this kind of distortion to appear at some places in an exaggerated form, and even to an infinite degree, however small the displacements may be in other parts of the field. In the case before us, if we suppose the velocity of the missing wave to be absolutely zero, there will be infinite condensations and rarefactions at a surface where ordinary waves are reflected. That is, a certain volume of ether will be condensed to a surface, and *vice versâ*. This prevents any treatment of the extreme case, which is at once simple and satisfactory. The difficulty has been noticed by Sir William Thomson, who observes that it may be avoided if we suppose the displacements infinitely small in comparison with the wave-length of the wave of compression. This implies a finite velocity for that wave. A similar difficulty would probably be found to exist (in the extreme case) with regard to the deformation of the ether by the molecules of ponderable matter, as the ether oscillates among them. If the statical resistance to irrotational motions is zero, it is not at all evident that the statical forces evoked by the disturbance caused by the molecules would be proportional to the motions. But this difficulty would be obviated by the same hypothesis as the first.

These circumstances render the elastic theory somewhat less convenient as a working hypothesis than the electric. They do not necessarily involve any complication of the equations of optics. For it may still be possible that this velocity of the missing wave is so small that the quantities on which it depends may be set equal to zero in the equations which represent the phenomena of optics.

But the mental processes by which we satisfy ourselves of the validity of our results (if we do not work out the whole problem in the general case of no assumption in regard to the velocity of the missing wave) certainly involve conceptions of a higher degree of difficulty on account of the circumstances mentioned. Perhaps this ought not to affect our judgment with respect to the question of the truth of the hypothesis.

Although the two theories give laws of exactly the same form for monochromatic light in the limiting case, their deviations from this limit are in opposite directions, so that if the phenomena of optics differed in any marked degree from what we would have in the limiting case, it would be easy to find an *experimentum crucis* to decide between the two theories. A little consideration will make it evident, that when the principal indices of refraction of a crystal are given, the intermediate values for oblique wave-planes will be less if the velocity of the missing wave is small but finite, than if it is infinitesimal, and will be greater if the velocity of the missing wave is very great than if it is infinite.* Hence, if the velocity of the missing wave is small but finite, the intermediate values of the indices of refraction will be less than are given by Fresnel's law, but if the velocity of the missing wave is very great but finite, the intermediate values of the indices of refraction will be greater than are given by Fresnel's law. But the recent experiments of Professor Hastings on the law of double refraction in Iceland spar do not encourage us to look in this direction for the decision of the question.†

In a simple train of waves in a transparent medium, the potential energy, on the elastic theory, may be divided into two parts, of which one is due to that general deformation of the ether which is represented by the equations of wave-motion, and the other to those deformations which are caused by the interference of the ponderable particles with the wave-motion, and to such displacements of the ponderable matter as may be caused, in some cases at least, by the motion of the ether. If we write h for the amplitude, l for the wave-length, and p for the period, these two parts of the statical energy (estimated per unit of volume for a space including many wave-lengths) may be represented respectively by

$$\frac{\pi^2 \mathrm{B} h^2}{l^2} \text{ and } \frac{b h^2}{4}.$$

* This may be more clear if we consider the stationary waves formed by two trains of waves moving in opposite directions. The case then comes under the following theorem: "If the system undergo such a change that the potential energy of a given configuration is diminished, while the kinetic energy of a given motion is unaltered, the periods of the free vibrations are all increased, and conversely." See Lord Rayleigh's *Theory of Sound*, vol. i, p. 85.

† *Am. Jour. Sci.*, ser 3, vol. xxxv, p. 60.

The sum of these may be equated to the kinetic energy, giving an equation of the form

$$\frac{\pi^2 \mathrm{B} h^2}{l^2} + \frac{b h^2}{4} = \frac{\pi^2 \mathrm{A}' h^2}{p^2}. \tag{24}$$

B is an absolute constant (the rigidity of the ether, previously represented by the same letter), A′ and b will be constant (for the same medium and the same direction of the wave-normal) except so far as the type of the motion changes, i.e., except so far as the manner in which the motion of the ether distributes itself between the ponderable molecules, and the degree in which these take part in the motion, may undergo a change. When the period of vibration varies, the type of motion will vary more or less, and A′ and b will vary more or less.

In a manner entirely analogous,* the *kinetic* energy, on the electrical theory, may be divided into two parts, of which one is due to those general fluxes which are represented by the equations of wave-motions, and the other to those irregularities in the fluxes which are caused by the presence of the ponderable molecules, as well as to such motions of the ponderable particles themselves as may sometimes occur. These parts of the kinetic energy may be represented respectively by

$$\frac{\pi \mathrm{F} l^2 h^2}{p^2} \quad \text{and} \quad \frac{\pi^2 f h^2}{p^2}.$$

Their sum equated to the potential energy gives

$$\frac{\pi \mathrm{F} l^2 h^2}{p^2} + \frac{\pi^2 f h^2}{p^2} = \frac{\mathrm{G} h^2}{4}. \tag{25}$$

Here F is the constant of electrodynamic induction, which is unity if we use the electromagnetic system of units, f and G (like A′ and b) vary only so far as the type of motion varies.

We have the means of forming a very exact numerical estimate of the ratio of the two parts into which the statical energy is thus divided on the elastic theory, or the kinetic energy on the electric theory. The means for this estimate is afforded by the principle that the period of a natural vibration is stationary when its type is infinitesimally altered by any constraint.† Let us consider a case of simple wave-motion, and suppose the period to be infinitesimally varied: the wave-length will also vary, and presumably to some extent the type of vibration. But, by the principle just stated, if the ether or the electricity could be constrained to vibrate in the original type, the variations of l and p would be the same as in the actual

* See page 182 of this volume.

† See Lord Rayleigh's *Theory of Sound*, vol. i, p. 84. The application of the principle is most simple in the case of stationary waves.

case. Therefore, in finding the differential equation between l and p, we may treat b and A′ in (24) and f and G in (25) as constant, as well as B and F. These equations may be written

$$4\pi^2 B \frac{p^2}{l^2} + bp^2 = 4\pi^2 A',$$

$$\pi F \frac{l^2}{p^2} + \frac{\pi^2 f}{p^2} = \tfrac{1}{4} G.$$

Differentiating, we get

$$4\pi^2 B\, d\frac{p^2}{l^2} = -b\, d(p^2),$$

$$\pi F\, d\frac{l^2}{p^2} = -\pi^2 f d(p^{-2});$$

or

$$4\pi^2 B \frac{p^2}{l^2}\, d \log \frac{p^2}{l^2} = -bp^2 d \log p^2,$$

$$\pi F \frac{l^2}{p^2}\, d \log \frac{l^2}{p^2} = -\frac{\pi^2 f}{p^2}\, d \log p^{-2}.$$

Hence, if we write V for the wave-velocity (l/p), n for the index of refraction, and λ for the wave-length *in vacuo*, we have for the ratio of the two parts into which we have divided the potential energy on the elastic theory,

$$\frac{bh^2}{4} \div \frac{\pi^2 B h^2}{l^2} = \frac{d \log V}{d \log p} = -\frac{d \log n}{d \log \lambda}, \qquad (26)$$

and for the ratio of the two parts into which we have divided the kinetic energy on the electrical theory,

$$\pi^2 \frac{fh^2}{p^2} \div \frac{\pi F l^2 h^2}{p^2} = \frac{d \log V}{d \log p} = -\frac{d \log n}{d \log \lambda}. \qquad (27)$$

It is interesting to see that these ratios have the same value. This value may be expressed in another form, which is suggestive of some important relations. If we write U for what Lord Rayleigh has called the velocity of a group of waves,*

$$\frac{U}{V} = 1 - \frac{d \log V}{d \log l},$$

$$\frac{d \log V}{d \log l} = \frac{V - U}{V},$$

$$\frac{d \log V}{d \log p} = \frac{V - U}{U}. \qquad (28)$$

It appears, therefore, that in the elastic theory that part of the potential energy which depends on the deformation expressed

* See his "Note on Progressive Waves," *Proc. Lond. Math. Soc.*, vol. ix, No. 125, reprinted in his *Theory of Sound*, vol. ii, p. 297.

by the equations of wave-motion, bears to the whole potential energy the same ratio which the velocity of a group of waves bears to the wave-velocity. In the electrical theory, that part of the kinetic energy which depends on the motions expressed by the equations of wave-motion bears to the whole kinetic energy the same ratio.

Returning to the consideration of equations (26) and (27), we observe that in transparent bodies the last member of these equations represents a quantity which is small compared with unity, at least in the visible spectrum, and diminishes rapidly as the wave-length increases. This is just what we should expect of the first member of equation (27). But when we pass to equation (26), which relates to the elastic theory, the case is entirely different. The fact that the kinetic energy is affected by the presence of the ponderable matter and affected differently in different directions, shows that the motion of the ether is considerably modified. This implies a distortion superposed upon the distortion represented by the equations of wave-motion, and very much greater, since the body is very fine-grained as measured by a wave-length. With any other law of elasticity, we should suppose that the energy of this superposed distortion would enormously exceed that of the regular distortion represented by the equations of wave-motion. But it is the peculiarity of this new law of elasticity that there is one kind of distortion, of which the energy is very small, and which is therefore peculiarly likely to occur. Now if we can suppose the distortion caused by the ponderable molecules to be almost entirely of this kind, we may be able to account for the smallness of its energy. We should still expect the first member of (26) to increase with the wave-length, on account of the factor l^2, instead of diminishing, as the last member of the equation shows that it does. We are obliged to suppose that b, and therefore the type of the vibrations, varies very rapidly with the wave-length, even in those cases which appear farthest removed from anything like selective absorption.

The electrical theory furnishes a relation between the refractive power of a body and its specific dielectric capacity, which is commonly expressed by saying that the latter is equal to the square of the index of refraction for waves of infinite length. No objection can be made to this statement, but the great uncertainty in determining the index for waves of infinite length by extrapolation prevents it from furnishing any very rigorous test of the theory. Yet, as the results of extrapolation in some cases agree strikingly with the specific dielectric capacity, although in other cases they are quite different, the correspondence is generally regarded as corroborative, in some degree, of the theory. But the relation between refractive power and dielectric capacity may be expressed in a form which will furnish a more rigorous test, as not involving extrapolation.

We have seen on page 242 how we may determine numerically the ratio of the two first terms of equation (25). We thus easily get the ratio of the first and last term, which gives

$$\frac{Gh^2}{4}=\frac{d\log l}{d\log\lambda}\frac{\pi F l^2 h^2}{p^2}. \tag{29}$$

In the corresponding equation for a train of waves of the same amplitude and period *in vacuo*, l becomes λ, F remains the same, and for G we may write G′. This gives

$$\frac{G'h^2}{4}=\frac{\pi F\lambda^2 h^2}{p^2}. \tag{30}$$

Dividing, we get

$$\frac{G}{G'}=\frac{d\log l}{d\log\lambda}\frac{l^2}{\lambda^2}=\frac{d(l^2)}{d(\lambda^2)}. \tag{31}$$

Now G′ is the dielectric elasticity of pure ether. If K is the specific dielectric capacity of the body which we are considering, G′/K is the dielectric elasticity of the body and G′/2K is the potential energy of the body (per unit of volume), due to a unit of ordinary electrostatic displacement. But $Gh^2/4$ is the potential energy in a train of waves of amplitude h. Since the average square of the displacement is $h^2/2$, the potential energy of a unit displacement such as occurs in a train of waves is G/2. Now in the electrostatic experiment the displacement distributes itself among the molecules so as to make the energy a minimum. But in the case of light the distribution of the displacement is not determined entirely by statical considerations. Hence

$$\frac{G}{2}\geqq\frac{G'}{2K}, \tag{32}$$

$$K\geqq\frac{G'}{G},$$

and

$$K\geqq\frac{d(\lambda^2)}{d(l^2)}. \tag{33}$$

It is to be observed that if we should assume for a dispersion-formula

$$n^{-2}=a-b\lambda^{-2}, \tag{34}$$

$1/a$, which is the square of the index of refraction for an infinite wave-length, would be identical with the second member of (33).

Another similarity between the electrical and optical properties of bodies consists in the relation between conductivity and opacity. Bodies in which electrical fluxes are attended with absorption of energy absorb likewise the energy of the motions which constitute light. This is strikingly true of the metals. But the analogy does not stop here. To fix our ideas, let us consider the case of an isotropic body and circularly polarized light, which is geometrically the simplest case although its analytical expression is not so simple as that of plane-polarized light. The displacement at any point may be symbolized by the rotation of a point in a circle. The external force necessary to maintain the displacement $\mathfrak{F}$ is represented by $n^{-2}\mathfrak{F}$. In transparent bodies, for which n^{-2} is a positive number, the force is radial and in the direction of the displacement, being principally employed in counterbalancing the dielectric elasticity, which tends to diminish the displacement. In a conductor n^{-2} becomes complex, which indicates a component of the force in the direction of $\dot{\mathfrak{F}}$, that is, tangential to the circle. This is only the analytical expression of the fact above mentioned. But there is another optical peculiarity of metals, which has caused much remark, viz., that the real part of n^2 (and therefore of n^{-2}) is negative, i.e., the radial component of the force is directed towards the center. This inwardly directed force, which evidently opposes the electrodynamic induction of the irregular part of the motion, is small compared with the outward force which is found in transparent bodies, but increases rapidly as the period diminishes. We may say, therefore, that metals exhibit a second optical peculiarity,—that the dielectric elasticity is not prominent as in transparent bodies. This is like the electrical behavior of the metals, in which we do not observe any elastic resistance to the motion of electricity. We see, therefore, that the complex indices of metals, both in the real and the imaginary part of their inverse squares, exhibit properties corresponding to the electrical behavior of the metals.

The case is quite different in the elastic theory. Here the force from outside necessary to maintain in any element of volume the displacement $\mathfrak{E}$ is represented by $n^2\ddot{\mathfrak{E}}$. In transparent bodies, therefore, it is directed toward the center. In metals, there is a component in the direction of the motion $\dot{\mathfrak{E}}$, while the radial part of the force changes its direction and is often many times greater than the opposite force in transparent bodies. This indicates that in metals the displacement of the ether is resisted by a strong elastic force, quite enormous compared to anything of the kind in transparent bodies, where it indeed exists, but is so small that it has been neglected by most writers except when treating of dispersion. We can make these suppositions, but they do not correspond to anything which we know independently of optical experiment.

It is evident that the electrical theory of light has a serious rival, in a sense in which, perhaps, one did not exist before the publication of Sir William Thomson's paper in November last.* Nevertheless, neither surprise at the results which have been achieved, nor admiration for that happy audacity of genius, which, seeking the solution of the problem precisely where no one else would have ventured to look for it, has turned half a century of defeat into victory, should blind us to the actual state of the question.

It may still be said for the electrical theory, that it is not obliged to invent hypotheses,† but only to apply the laws furnished by the science of electricity, and that it is difficult to account for the coincidences between the electrical and optical properties of media, unless we regard the motions of light as electrical. But if the electrical character of light is conceded, the optical problem is very different from anything which existed in the time of Fresnel, Cauchy, and Green. The third wave, for example, is no longer something to be gotten rid of *quocunque modo*, but something which we must dispose of in accordance with the laws of electricity. This would seem to rule out the possibility of a relatively small velocity for the third wave.

* "Since the first publication of Cauchy's work on the subject in 1830, and of Green's in 1837, many attempts have been made by many workers to find a dynamical foundation by Fresnel's laws of reflexion and refraction of light, but all hitherto ineffectually." Sir William Thomson, *loc. citat.*

"So far as I am aware, the electric theory of Maxwell is the only one satisfying these conditions (of explaining at once Fresnel's laws of double refraction in crystals and those governing the intensity of reflexion when light passes from one isotropic medium to another)." Lord Rayleigh, *Phil. Mag.*, September, 1888.

† Electrical motions in air, since the recent experiments of Professor Hertz, seem to be no longer a matter of hypothesis. We can hardly suppose that the case is essentially different with the so-called vacuum. The theorem that the electrical motions of light are solenoidal, although it is convenient to assume it as a hypothesis and show that the results agree with experiment, need not occupy any such fundamental position in the theory. It is in fact only another way of saying that two of the constants of electrical science have a certain ratio (infinity). It would be easy to commence without assuming this value, and to show in the course of the development of the subject that experiment requires it, not of course as an abstract proposition, but in the sense in which experiment can be said to require any values of any constants, that is, to a certain degree of approximation.

XVI.

REVIEWS OF NEWCOMB AND MICHELSON'S "VELOCITY OF LIGHT IN AIR AND REFRACTING MEDIA" AND OF KETTELER'S "THEORETISCHE OPTIK."

[*American Journal of Science*, ser. 3, vol. XXXI. pp. 62-67, Jan. 1886.]

Velocity of Light in Air and Refracting Media.

Astrononomical Papers prepared for the use of the American Ephemeris and Nautical Almanac, vol. II. parts 3 and 4,* Washington, 1885.

PROFESSOR NEWCOMB obtains as the final result of his experiments at Washington 299,860±30 kilometers per second for the velocity of light *in vacuo*. Professor MICHELSON'S entirely independent experiments at Cleveland give substantially the same result (299,853±60) His former experiments at the Naval Academy, after correction of two small errors which he now reports, give 299,910±50. All these experiments were made with the revolving mirror, but the arrangements of the two experimenters were in other respects radically different. The first of these values of the velocity of light with Nyrén's value of the constant of aberration (20″·492) gives 149·60 for the distance of the sun in millions of kilometers. On acount of the recent announcement by Messrs. Young and Forbes of a difference of about two per cent. in the velocities of red and blue light, especial attention was paid to this point by both experimenters, without finding the least indication of any difference. In Professor Newcomb's experiments, a difference of only one thousandth in these velocities would have produced a well-marked iridescence on the edges of the return image of the slit formed by reflection from the revolving mirror. No trace of such iridescence could ever be seen. Professor Michelson made an experiment, in which a red glass covered one-half the slit. The two halves of the image—the upper white, the lower red—were exactly in line.

Since Maxwell's electromagnetic theory of light makes the velocity of light in air equal to the ratio of the electromagnetic and

*[Part 3, "Measures of the Velocity of Light," S. Newcomb; part 4, "Supplementary Measures of the Velocities of white and colored Light in air, water, and carbon disulphide," A. A. Michelson.]

electrostatic units of electricity, it will be interesting to compare some recent determinations of this ratio. These we give in the following table. Since the determinations are affected by any error in the standard of resistance, we have corrected the results, first, on the supposition that the B.A. ohm = ·987 true ohms (Lord Rayleigh's result), and secondly, on the supposition that the B.A. ohm = ·989 true ohms, which is essentially assuming that the legal ohm represents the true value.

Ratio of Electromagnetic and Electrostatic units of Electricity in millions of meters and seconds.

	Date.	As published.	B.A. ohm = ·987.	B.A. ohm = ·989.
Ayrton & Perry,*	1878	298·0	296·1	296·4
Hockin, †	1879	298·8	296·9	297·2
Shida, ‡	1880	299·5	295·6	296·2
Exner, §	1882	301·1 (?)	291·7 (?)	292·3 (?)
J. J. Thomson, ‖	1883	296·3	296·3	296·9
Klemenčič, ¶	1884	301·88 (?)	301·88 (?)	302·48 (?)

These numbers are to be compared with the velocity of light in air, in millions of meters per second, for which Professor Newcomb gives 299·778. Of the electrical determinations, that of J. J. Thomson appears by far the most worthy of confidence. That of Klemenčič—the only one as great as the velocity of light—was obtained by the use of a condenser with glass,—a method which would presumably give too great a ratio. Exner's value is obtained from the mean of three determinations, one of which differed from the others by about three per cent. If we reject this discordant determination, the mean of the other two would give when corrected for resistance 294·4 and 295·0. If we set aside the determinations of Exner and Klemenčič, the remaining four, which represent three different methods, are very accordant, the mean being nearly identical with the result of J. J. Thomson, and about one per cent. less than the velocity of light.

Professor Michelson's experiments on the velocity of light in carbon disulphide afford an interesting illustration of the difference between the velocity of waves and the velocity of groups of waves—a subject which is treated at length in an appendix to the second volume of Lord Rayleigh's *Theory of Sound.* If we write V for the velocity of waves, U for that of a group of waves, L for the wave-length, and T for the period of vibration,

$$V=\frac{L}{T}, \qquad U=\frac{d(T^{-1})}{d(L^{-1})}.$$

For purposes of numerical calculation, it will be convenient to transform these formulæ by the use of λ for the wave-length *in*

* *Phil. Mag.*, (5), vol. vii, p. 277. † *Report Brit. Assoc.*, 1879, p. 285.
‡ *Phil. Mag.*, (5), vol. x, p. 431. § *Sitzungsberichte Wien. Akad.*, vol. lxxxvi, p. 106.
‖ *Phil. Trans.*, vol. clxxiv, p. 707. ¶ *Sitzungsberichte Wien. Akad.*, vol. lxxxix, p. 298.

vacuo, n for the index of refraction of the medium considered, and k for the velocity of light *in vacuo*, which we shall regard as constant, in accordance with general usage. By substitution of these letters we easily obtain

$$\frac{k}{V}=n, \qquad \frac{k}{U}=\frac{d(n\lambda^{-1})}{d(\lambda^{-1})}.$$

The data for the calculation of these quantities for carbon disulphide are given by Verdet (*Annales de Chimie et de Physique*, (3), vol. lxix, p. 470). They give

for the line D, $k/V=1{\cdot}624$, $k/U=1{\cdot}722$,
for the line E, $k/V=1{\cdot}637$, $k/U=1{\cdot}767$.

The quotient of the velocity *in vacuo* divided by the velocity in carbon disulphide, according to Professor Michelson's experiments with the light of an arc lamp, is $1{\cdot}76\pm{\cdot}02$, which agrees very well with k/U. Another theory, which would make the velocity observed in such experiments V^2/U (*Nature*, vol. xxv, p. 52), receives no countenance from these experiments. The value of kU/V^2 would be about 1·53. Some may think that the experiments on water point in a different direction. Taking our data from Beer's *Einleitung in die höhere Optik*, 1853, p. 411, we get

for D, $k/V=1{\cdot}334$, $k/U=1{\cdot}352$, $kU/V^2=1{\cdot}316$,
for E, $k/V=1{\cdot}336$, $k/U=1{\cdot}359$, $kU/V^2=1{\cdot}313$.

The number obtained by experiment was 1,330, which agrees better with k/V, or even with kU/V^2, than with k/U, but the differences are here too small to have much significance.

Theoretische Optik, gegründet auf das Bessel-Sellmeier'sche Princip, zugleich mit den experimentellen Belegen.

Von Dr. E. KETTELER, Professor an der Universität in Bonn. Viewig und Sohn. Braunschweig, 1885.

The principle of Sellmeier, here referred to, relates to vibrations of ponderable particles excited by the etherial vibrations of light, and to the reaction of the former upon the latter. The name of Bessel is added on account of his previous solution of a somewhat analogous problem relating to the pendulum. The object of this work is "to treat theoretical optics in a complete and uniform manner on the new foundation of the simultaneous vibration of etherial and ponderable particles, and to substitute a consistent and systematic new structure for the present conglomerate of more or less disconnected principles." Such a work demands a critical examination, which should not be undertaken from any narrow point of view. Any faults of detail will be readily forgiven, if the author shall give the theory of optics the πoῦ στῶ which it has sought so long in vain. We may add that if this effort shall not be judged successful by the scientific world, the author will at least have the satisfaction of being associated in his failure with many of the most distinguished names in mathematical physics.

We have sought to test the proposed theory with respect to that law of optics which seems most conspicuous in its definite mathematical form, and in the rigor of the experimental verifications to which it has been subjected, as well as in the magnificent developments to which it has given rise: the law of double refraction due to Huyghens and Fresnel, and geometrically illustrated by the wave-surface of the latter. We cannot find that the law of Fresnel is proved at all in this treatise. We find on the contrary, that a law is deduced which is different from Fresnel's, and inconsistent with it. We do not refer to anything relating to the direction of vibration of the rays in a crystal, which is a point not touched by the experimental verifications to which we have alluded. We shall confine our comparison to those equations from which the direction of vibration has been eliminated, and which therefore represent relations subject to experimental control. For this purpose equation (13) on page 299 is suitable. It reads

$$\frac{u^2}{n_x^2-n^2}+\frac{v^2}{n_y^2-n^2}+\frac{w^2}{n_z^2-n^2}=0,$$

n_x, n_y, n_z being the principal indices of refraction. This the author calls the equation of the wave-surface or surface of ray-velocities. It has the form of the equation of Fresnel's wave-surface, expressed in terms of the direction-cosines and reciprocal of the radius vector, and if u, v, w are the direction-cosines of the *ray*, and n the velocity of light *in vacuo* divided by the so-called *ray-velocity* in the crystal the equation will express Fresnel's law. But it is impossible to give these meanings to u, v, w and n. They are introduced into the discussion in the expression for the vibrations (p. 295), viz.,

$$\rho=\mathfrak{A}\cos 2\pi\left(\frac{t}{\mathrm{T}}-\frac{n(ux+vy+wz)}{\lambda}\right).$$

The form of this equation shows that u, v, w are proportional to the direction-cosines of the *wave-normal*, and as the relation $u^2+v^2+w^2=1$ is afterwards used, they must be the direction-cosines of the wave-normal. *They cannot possibly denote the direction-cosines of the ray*, except in the particular case in which the ray and wave-normal coincide. Again, from the form of this equation, λ/n must be the wave-length in the crystal, and if λ here as elsewhere in the book (see p. 25) denotes the wave-length *in vacuo* of light of the period considered, which we doubt not is the intention of the author, n must be the wave-length *in vacuo* divided by the wave-length in the crystal, i.e., the velocity of light *in vacuo* divided by the *wave-velocity* in the crystal. With these definitions of u, v, w, and n, equation (13) expresses a law which is different from Fresnel's. Applied to the simple case of a uniaxial crystal, it makes the relation between the wave-velocity of the extraordinary ray and the angle of the wave-normal with the principal axis the same as that of the radius vector and the angle in an ellipse. The law of Huyghens and Fresnel makes the *reciprocal* of the wave-velocity stand in this relation.

The law which our author has deduced has come up again and again in the history of theoretical optics. Professor Stokes (*Report of the British Assoc.*, 1862, part i, p. 269) and Lord Rayleigh (*Phil. Mag.*, (4), vol. xli, p. 525) have both raised the question whether Huyghens and Fresnel might not have been wrong, and it might not be the wave-velocity and not its reciprocal which is represented by the radius vector in an ellipse. The difference is not very great, for if we lay off on the radii vectores of an ellipse distances inversely proportional to their lengths, the resultant figure will have an oval form approaching that of an ellipse when the eccentricity of the original ellipse is small. Rankine appears to have thought that the difference might be neglected (see *Phil. Mag.*, (4), vol. i, pp. 444, 445) at least he claims that his theory leads to Fresnel's law, while really it would give the same law which our author has found. (Concerning Rankine's "splendid failure," and the whole history of the subject, see Sir Wm. Thomson's *Lectures on Molecular Dynamics at the Johns Hopkins University*, chap. xx.) Professor Stokes undertook experiments to decide the question. His result, corroborated by Glazebrook (*Pro. Roy. Soc.*, vol. xx, p. 443; *Phil. Trans.*, vol. clxxi, p. 421), was that Huyghens and Fresnel were right and that the other law was wrong.

To return to our author, we have no doubt from the context that he regards u, v, w, and n as relating to the ray and not to the wave-normal. We suppose that that is the meaning of his remark that the expression for the vibrations (quoted above) is to be referred to the direction of the ray. It seems rather hard not to allow a writer the privilege of defining his own terms. Yet the reader will admit that when the vibrations have been expressed in the above form an inexorable necessity fixes the significance of the direction determined by u, v, w, and leaves nothing in that respect to the choice of the author.

The historical sketches of the development of ideas in the theory of optics, enriched by very numerous references, will be useful to the student. An exception, however, must be made with respect to the statements concerning the electromagnetic theory of light. We are told (p. 450) that the English theory, founded by Maxwell and represented by Glazebrook and Fitzgerald, makes the plane of polarization coincide with the plane of vibration, while Lorentz, on the basis of Helmholtz's equations comes to the conclusion that these planes are at right angles. Since all these writers make the electrical displacement perpendicular to the plane of polarization, we can only attribute this statement to some confusion between the electrical displacement and the magnetic force or "displacement" at right angles to it. We are also told that Glazebrook's "surface-conditions" which determine the intensity of reflected and refracted light are different from those of Lorentz,—a singular error in view of the fact that Mr. Glazebrook (*Proc. Camb. Phil. Soc.*, vol. iv, p. 166) expressly states that his results are the same as those of Lorentz, Fitzgerald, and J. J. Thomson. We have spent much fruitless labor in trying to discover where and how the expressions were obtained which are attributed to Glazebrook, but in which the notation has been altered. They ought to come from Glazebrook's equations (24)–(27) (*loc. cit.*), but these appear identical with Lorentz's equations (58)–(61) (*Zeitschrift f. Math. u. Phys.*, vol. xxii, p. 27). They might be obtained by interchanging the expressions for vibrations in the plane of incidence and at right angles to it, with two changes of sign.

The reader must be especially cautioned concerning the statements and implications of what has not been done in the electromagnetic theory. These are such as to suggest the question whether the author has taken the trouble to read the titles of the papers which have been published. We refer especially to what is said on pages 248, 249 concerning absorption, dispersion, and the magnetic rotation of the plane of polarization.

In the Experimental Part, with which the treatise closes, we have a comparison of formulæ with the results of experiments by the author and others. The author has been particularly successful in the formula for dispersion. In the case of quartz (p. 545), the formula (with four constants) represents the results of experiment in a manner entirely satisfactory through the entire range of wave-length from 2·14 to 0·214. Those who may not agree with the author's theoretical views will nevertheless be glad to see the results of experiment brought together, and, so far as may be, represented by formulæ.

XVII.

ON THE VELOCITY OF LIGHT AS DETERMINED BY FOUCAULT'S REVOLVING MIRROR.

[*Nature*, vol. XXXIII. p. 582, April 22, 1886.]

It has been shown by Lord Rayleigh and others that the velocity (U) with which a group of waves is propagated in any medium may be calculated by the formula

$$U = V\left(1 - \frac{d\log V}{d\log\lambda}\right),$$

where V is the wave-velocity, and λ the wave-length. It has also been observed by Lord Rayleigh that the fronts of the waves reflected by the revolving mirror in Foucault's experiment are inclined one to another, and in consequence must rotate with an angular velocity

$$\frac{dV}{d\lambda}a,$$

where a is the angle between two successive wave-planes of similar phase. When $dV/d\lambda$ is positive (the usual case), the direction of rotation is such that the following wave-plane rotates towards the position of the preceding (see *Nature*, vol. XXV. p. 52).

But I am not aware that attention has been called to the important fact, that while the individual wave rotates the wave-normal of the group remains unchanged, or, in other words, that if we fix our attention on a point moving with the group, therefore with the velocity U, the successive wave-planes, as they pass through that point, have all the same orientation. This follows immediately from the two formulæ quoted above. For the interval of time between the arrival of two successive wave-planes of similar phase at the moving point is evidently $\lambda/(V-U)$, which reduces by the first formula to $d\lambda/dV$. In this time the second of the wave-planes, having the angular velocity $a\,dV/d\lambda$, will rotate through an angle a towards the position of the first wave-plane. But a is the angle between the two planes. The second plane, therefore, in passing the moving point, will have exactly the same orientation which the first had. To get a picture of the phenomenon, we may imagine that we are able to see a few inches of the top of a moving carriage-wheel. The individual spokes rotate, while the group maintains a vertical direction.

This consideration greatly simplifies the theory of Foucault's experiment, and makes it evident, I think, that the results of all such experiments depend upon the value of U, and not upon that of V.

The discussion of the experiment by following a single wave, and taking account of its rotation, is a complicated process, and one in which it is very easy to leave out of account some of the elements of the problem. The principal objection to it, however, is its unreality. If the dispersion is considerable, no wave which leaves the revolving mirror will return to it. The individual disappears, only the group has permanence. Prof. Schuster, in his communication of March 11 (p. 439), has nevertheless obtained by this method, as the quantity determined by "the experiments hitherto performed," $V^2/(2V-U)$, which, as he observes, is nearly equal to U. He would, I think, have obtained U precisely, if for the angle between two successive wave-planes of similar phase, instead of $2w\lambda/V$, he had used the more exact value $2w\lambda/U$.

By the kindness of Prof. Michelson, I am informed with respect to his recent experiments on the velocity of light in bisulphide of carbon that he would be inclined to place the maximum brilliancy of the light between the spectral lines D and E, but nearer to D. If we take the mean between D and E, we have

$$\frac{K}{U}=1{\cdot}745, \qquad \frac{K(2V-U)}{V^2}=1{\cdot}737,$$

K denoting the velocity *in vacuo* (see p. 249 of this volume). The number observed was 1·76, "with an uncertainty of two units in the second place of decimals." This agrees best with the first formula. The same would be true if we used values nearer to the line D.

J. WILLARD GIBBS.

New Haven, Connecticut, April 1. [1886.]

XVIII.

VELOCITY OF PROPAGATION OF ELECTROSTATIC FORCE.

[*Nature*, vol. LIII. p. 509, April 2, 1896.]

As we may have to wait some time for the experimental solution of Lord Kelvin's very instructive and suggestive problem concerning two pairs of spheres charged with electricity (see *Nature* of February 6, p. 316), it may be interesting to see what the solution would be from the standpoint of existing electrical theories.

In applying Maxwell's theory to the problem it will be convenient to suppose the dimensions of both pairs of spheres very small in comparison with the unit of length, and the distance between the two pairs very great in comparison with the same unit. These conditions, which greatly simplify the equations which represent the phenomena, will hardly be regarded as affecting the essential nature of the question proposed.

Let us first consider what would happen on the discharge of (A, B), if the system (c, d) were absent.

Let m_0 be the initial value of the *moment* of the charge of the system (A, B), (this term being used in a sense analogous to that in which we speak of the *moment* of a magnet), and m the value of the moment at any instant. If we set

$$m = \mathrm{F}(t), \tag{1}$$

and suppose the discharge to commence when $t=0$, and to be completed when $t=h$, we shall have

$$\mathrm{F}(t) = m_0 \quad \text{when} \quad t<0, \tag{2}$$

and

$$\mathrm{F}(t) = 0 \quad \text{when} \quad t>h, \tag{3}$$

Let us set the origin of coordinates at the centre of the system (A, B), and the axis of x in the direction of the centre of the positively charged sphere. A unit vector in this direction we shall call i, and the vector from the origin to the point considered ρ. At any point outside of a sphere of unit radius about the origin, the electrical displacement ($\mathfrak{D}$) is given by the vector equation

$$\begin{aligned} 4\pi\mathfrak{D} = &[3r^{-5}\mathrm{F}(t-cr)+3cr^{-4}\mathrm{F}'(t-cr)+c^2r^{-3}\mathrm{F}''(t-cr)]x\rho \\ &-[r^{-3}\mathrm{F}(t-cr)+cr^{-2}\mathrm{F}'(t-cr)+c^2r^{-1}\mathrm{F}''(t-cr)]i, \end{aligned} \tag{4}$$

where F denotes the function determined by equation (1), F′ and F″ its derivatives, and c the ratio of electrostatic and electromagnetic units of electricity, or the reciprocal of the velocity of light. For this satisfies the general equation

$$-\nabla^2\mathfrak{D}=c^2d^2\mathfrak{D}/dt^2, \tag{5}$$

as well as the so-called "equation of continuity," and also satisfies the special conditions that when $t<0$

$$4\pi\mathfrak{D}=m_0(3r^{-5}x\rho - r^{-3}i)$$

outside of the unit sphere, and that at any time at the surface of this sphere

$$4\pi\mathfrak{D}=m(3x\rho-i),$$

if we consider the terms containing the factor c as negligible, when not compensated by large values of r. That equation (4) satisfies the general conditions is easily verified, if we set

$$u=r^{-1}\mathrm{F}(t-cr), \tag{6}$$

and observe that

$$-\nabla^2u=c^2d^2u/dt^2, \tag{7}$$

and that the three components of $\mathfrak{D}$ are given by the equations

$$\left.\begin{aligned}4\pi f&=-d^2u/dy^2-d^2u/dz^2\\4\pi g&=d^2u/dxdy\\4\pi h&=d^2u/dxdz\end{aligned}\right\} \tag{8}$$

Equation (4) shows that the changes of the electrical displacement are represented by three systems of spherical waves, of forms determined by the rapidity of the discharge of the system (A, B), which expand with the velocity of light with amplitudes diminishing as r^{-3}, r^{-2}, and r^{-1}, respectively. Outside of these waves, the electrical displacement is unchanged, inside of them it is zero.

If we write (with Maxwell) $-d\mathfrak{A}/dt$ for the force of electrodynamic induction at any point, and suppose its rectangular components calculated from those of $-d^2\mathfrak{D}/dt^2$ by the formula used in calculating the potential of a mass from its density, we shall have by Poisson's theorem

$$\nabla^2(d\mathfrak{A}/dt)=4\pi d^2\mathfrak{D}/dt^2,$$

or by (5),

$$\nabla^2(d\mathfrak{A}/dt)=-4\pi c^{-2}\nabla^2\mathfrak{D},$$

whence

$$d\mathfrak{A}/dt=-4\pi c^{-2}\mathfrak{D}. \tag{9}$$

From this, with (4), and the general equation

$$d\mathfrak{A}/dt+4\pi c^{-2}\mathfrak{D}+\nabla\mathrm{V}=0,$$

we see that during the discharge of the system (A, B) the electrostatic force $-\nabla\mathrm{V}$ vanishes throughout all space, while its place is taken by a precisely equal electrodynamic force $-d\mathfrak{A}/dt$.

This electrodynamic force remains unchanged at every point until the passage of the waves, after which the electrostatic force, the electrodynamic force, and the displacement, have the permanent value zero.

If we write *Curl* for the differentiating vector operator which Maxwell calls by that name, equations (8) may be put in the form

$$4\pi\mathfrak{D} = \text{Curl Curl}\,(iu),$$

whence $$d\mathfrak{D}/dt = (4\pi)^{-1}\,\text{Curl Curl}\,(i\,du/dt).$$

From $d\mathfrak{D}/dt$ we may calculate the magnetic induction $\mathfrak{B}$ by an operation which is the inverse of $(4\pi)^{-1}$ Curl. We have therefore

$$\mathfrak{B} = \text{Curl}\,(i\,du/dt),$$

or $$\mathfrak{B} = [r^{-3}F'(t-cr) + cr^{-2}F''(t-cr)](yk - zj).$$

The magnetic induction is therefore zero except in the waves.

Equations (4) and (9) give the value of $d\mathfrak{A}/dt$ as function of t and r. By integration, we may find the value of $\mathfrak{A}$, Maxwell's "vector potential." This will be of the form of the second member of (4) multiplied by $-c^{-2}$, if we should give each F one accent less, and for an unaccented F should write F_1, to denote the primitive of F which vanishes for the argument ∞.

That which seems most worthy of notice is that although simultaneously with the discharge of the system (A, B) the values of what we call the electric potential, the electrodynamic force of induction, and the "vector potential," are changed throughout all space, this does not appear connected with any physical change outside of the waves, which advance with the velocity of light.

If we now suppose that there is a second pair of charged spheres (c, d), as in the original problem, the discharge of this pair will evidently occur when the relaxation of electrical displacement reaches it. The time between the discharges is, therefore, by Maxwell's theory, the time required for light to pass from one pair to the other.

It may also be interesting to observe that in the axis of x, on both sides of the origin, $x\rho = r^2 i$, and equation (4) reduces to

$$4\pi\mathfrak{D} = [2r^{-3}F(t-cr) + 2cr^{-2}F'(t-cr)]i.$$

Here, therefore, the oscillations are normal to the wave-surfaces. This might seem to imply that plane waves of normal oscillations may be propagated, since we are accustomed to regard a part of an infinite sphere as equivalent to a part of an infinite plane. Of course, such a result would be contrary to Maxwell's theory. The paradox is explained if we consider that the parts of the wave-motion, expressed by F and F′, diminish more rapidly than those expressed by F″, so that it is unsafe to take the displacements in the axis of x as approximately representing those at a moderate distance from it. In fact, if we consider the displacements not merely in the axis of x, but within a cylinder about that axis, and follow the waves to an infinite distance from the origin, we find no approximation to what is usually meant by plane waves with normal oscillations.

J. WILLARD GIBBS.

New Haven, Conn., March 12 [1896].

XIX.

FOURIER'S SERIES.

[*Nature*, vol. LIX, p. 200, Dec. 29, 1898.]

I SHOULD like to add a few words concerning the subject of Prof. Michelson's letter in *Nature* of October 6. In the only reply which I have seen (*Nature*, October 13), the point of view of Prof. Michelson is hardly considered.

Let us write $f_n(x)$ for the sum of the first n terms of the series

$$\sin x - \tfrac{1}{2}\sin 2x + \tfrac{1}{3}\sin 3x - \tfrac{1}{4}\sin 4x + \text{etc.}$$

I suppose that there is no question concerning the form of the curve defined by any equation of the form

$$y = 2f_n(x).$$

Let us call such a curve C_n. As n increases without limit, the curve approaches a limiting form, which may be thus described. Let a point move from the origin in a straight line at an angle of 45° with the axis of X to the point (π, π), thence vertically in a straight line to the point $(\pi, -\pi)$, thence obliquely in a straight line to the point $(3\pi, \pi)$, etc. The broken line thus described (continued indefinitely forwards and backwards) is the limiting form of the curve as the number of terms increases indefinitely. That is, if any small distance d be first specified, a number n' may be then specified, such that for every value of n greater than n', the distance of any point in C_n from the broken line, and of any point in the broken line from C_n, will be less than the specified distance d.

But this limiting line is not the same as that expressed by the equation

$$y = \operatorname*{limit}_{n=\infty} 2f_n(x).$$

The vertical portions of the broken line described above are wanting in the locus expressed by this equation, except the points in which they intersect the axis of X. The process indicated in the last equation is virtually to consider the intersections of C_n with fixed vertical transversals, and seek the limiting positions when n is increased without limit. It is not surprising that this process does not give the vertical portions of the limiting curve. If we should consider the intersections of C_n with horizontal transversals, and seek the limits which they approach when n is increased indefinitely we should obtain the vertical portions of the limiting curve as well as the oblique portions.

It should be observed that if we take the equation

$$y = 2f_n(x),$$

and proceed to the limit for $n = \infty$, we do not necessarily get $y = 0$ for $x = \pi$. We may get that ratio by first setting $x = \pi$, and then passing to the limit. We may also get $y = 1$, $x = \pi$, by first setting $y = 1$, and then passing to the limit. Now the limit represented by the equation of the broken line described above is not a special or partial limit relating solely to some special method of passing to the limit, but it is the complete limit embracing all sets of values of x and y which can be obtained by any process of passing to the limit.

J. WILLARD GIBBS.

New Haven, Conn., November 29 [1898].

[*Nature*, vol. LIX, p. 606, April 27, 1899.]

I should like to correct a careless error which I made (*Nature*, December 29, 1898) in describing the limiting form of the family of curves represented by the equation

$$y = 2\left(\sin x - \frac{1}{2}\sin 2x \ldots \pm \frac{1}{n}\sin nx\right) \tag{1}$$

as a zigzag line consisting of alternate inclined and vertical portions. The inclined portions were correctly given, but the vertical portions, which are bisected by the axis of X, extend beyond the points where they meet the inclined portions, their total lengths being expressed by four times the definite integral

$$\int_0^\pi \frac{\sin u}{u}\, du.$$

If we call this combination of inclined and vertical lines C, and the graph of equation (1) C_n, and if any finite distance d be specified, and we take for n any number greater than $100/d^2$, the distance of every point in C_n from C is less than d, and the distance of every point in C from C_n is also less than d. We may therefore call C the limit (or limiting form) of the sequence of curves of which C_n is the general designation.

But this limiting form of the graphs of the functions expressed by the sum (1) is different from the graph of the function expressed by the limit of that sum. In the latter the vertical portions are wanting, except their middle points.

I think this distinction important, for (with exception of what relates to my unfortunate blunder described above) whatever differences of opinion have been expressed on this subject seem due, for the most part, to the fact that some writers have had in mind the *limit of the graphs*, and others the *graph of the limit* of the sum. A misunderstanding on this point is a natural consequence of the usage which allows us to omit the word *limit* in certain connections, as when we speak of the sum of an infinite series. In terms thus abbreviated, either of the things which I have sought to distinguish may be called the graph of the sum of the infinite series.

J. WILLARD GIBBS.

New Haven, April 12 [1899].

XX.

RUDOLF JULIUS EMANUEL CLAUSIUS.

[*Proceedings of the American Academy*, new series, vol. XVI, pp. 458–465, 1889.]

RUDOLF JULIUS EMANUEL CLAUSIUS was born at Cöslin in Pomerania, January 2, 1822. His studies, after 1840, were pursued at Berlin, where he became Privat-docent in the University, and Instructor in Physics in the School of Artillery. He was Professor of Physics at Zürich in the Polytechnicum (1855–67) and in the University (1857–67), at Würzburg (1867–69), and finally at Bonn (1869–88), where he died on the 24th of August, 1888.

His literary activity commenced in 1847, with the publication of a memoir in *Crelle's Journal*, "Ueber die Lichtzerstreuung in der Atmosphäre, und über die Intensität des durch die Atmosphäre reflectirten Sonnenlichts."* This was immediately followed by other writings relating to the same subject, two of which were subsequently translated from *Poggendorff's Annalen* † for Taylor's *Scientific Memoirs*. A treatise entitled "Die Lichterscheinungen der Atmosphäre" formed part of Grunert's "Beiträge zur meteorologischen Optik."

An entirely different subject, the elasticity of solids, was discussed in his paper (1849), "Ueber die Veränderungen, welche in den bisher gebräuchlichen Formeln für das Gleichgewicht und die Bewegung fester Körper durch neuere Beobachtungen nothwendig geworden sind." ‡

But it was with questions of quite another order of magnitude that his name was destined to be associated. The fundamental questions concerning the relation of heat to mechanical effect, which had been raised by Rumford, Carnot, and others, to meet with little response, were now everywhere pressing to the front.

"For more than twelve years," said Regnault in 1853, "I have been engaged in collecting the materials for the solution of this question:—Given a certain quantity of heat, what is, theoretically, the amount of mechanical effect which can be obtained by applying the heat to evaporation, or the expansion of elastic fluids, in the various circumstances which can be realised in practice?" § The twenty-first

* Vol. xxxiv, p. 122, and vol. xxxvi, p. 185.

† Vol. lxxvi, pp. 161 and 188.

‡ *Pogg. Ann.*, vol. lxxvi, p. 46 (1849).

§ *Comptes Rendus*, vol. xxxvi, p. 676.

volume of the Memoirs of the Academy of Paris, describing the first part of the magnificent series of researches which the liberality of the French government enabled him to carry out for the solution of this question, was published in 1847. In the same year appeared Helmholtz's celebrated memoir, "Ueber die Erhaltung der Kraft." For some years Joule had been making those experiments which were to associate his name with one of the fundamental laws of thermodynamics and one of the principal constants of nature. In 1849 he made that determination of the mechanical equivalent of heat by the stirring of water which for nearly thirty years remained the unquestioned standard. In 1848 and 1849 Sir William Thomson was engaged in developing the consequences of Carnot's theory of the motive power of heat, while Professor James Thomson in demonstrating the effect of pressure on the freezing point of water by a Carnot's cycle, showed the flexibility and the fruitfulness of a mode of demonstration which was to become canonical in thermodynamics. Meantime Rankine was attacking the problem in his own way, with one of those marvellous creations of the imagination of which it is so difficult to estimate the precise value.

Such was the state of the question when Clausius published his first memoir on thermodynamics: "Ueber die bewegende Kraft der Wärme, und die Gesetze, welche sich daraus für die Wärmelehre selbst ableiten lassen." *

This memoir marks an epoch in the history of physics. If we say, in the words used by Maxwell some years ago, that thermodynamics is "a science with secure foundations, clear definitions, and distinct boundaries," † and ask when those foundations were laid, those definitions fixed, and those boundaries traced, there can be but one answer. Certainly not before the publication of that memoir. The materials indeed existed for such a science, as Clausius showed by constructing it from such materials, substantially, as had for years been the common property of physicists. But truth and error were in a confusing state of mixture. Neither in France, nor in Germany, nor in Great Britain, can we find the answer to the question quoted from Regnault. The case was worse than this, for wrong answers were confidently urged by the highest authorities. That question was completely answered, on its theoretical side, in the memoir of Clausius, and the science of thermodynamics came into existence. And as Maxwell said in 1878, so it might have been said at any time since the publication of that memoir, that the foundations of the science were secure, its definitions clear, and its boundaries distinct.

---

* Read in the Berlin Academy, February 18, 1850, and published in the March and April numbers of *Poggendorff's Annalen.*

† *Nature*, vol. xvii, p. 257.

The constructive power thus exhibited, this ability to bring order out of confusion, this breadth of view which could apprehend one truth without losing sight of another, this nice discrimination to separate truth from error,—these are qualities which place the possessor in the first rank of scientific men.

In the development of the various consequences of the fundamental propositions of thermodynamics, as applied to all kinds of physical phenomena, Clausius was rivalled, perhaps surpassed, in activity and versatility by Sir William Thomson. His attention, indeed, seems to have been less directed toward the development of the subject in extension, than toward the nature of the molecular phenomena of which the laws of thermodynamics are the sensible expression. He seems to have very early felt the conviction, that behind the second law of thermodynamics, which relates to the heat absorbed or given out by a body, and therefore capable of direct measurement, there was another law of similar form but relating to the quantities of heat (i.e., molecular *vis viva*) absorbed in the performance of work, external or internal.

This may be made more definite, if we express the second law in a mathematical form, as may be done by saying that in any reversible cyclic process which a body may undergo

$$\int \frac{dQ}{t} = 0,$$

where dQ is an elementary portion of the heat imparted to the body, and t the absolute temperature of the body, or the portion of it which receives the heat. Or, without limitation to cyclic processes, we may say that for any reversible infinitesimal change,

$$dQ = t\,dS,$$

where S denotes a certain function of the state of the body, called by Clausius the *entropy*. The element of heat may evidently be divided into two parts, of which one represents the increase of molecular *vis viva* in the body, and the other the work done against forces, either external or internal. If we call these parts dH and dQ_w, we have

$$dQ = dH + dQ_w.$$

Now the proposition of which Clausius felt so strong a conviction was that for reversible cyclic processes

$$\int \frac{dQ_w}{dt} = 0,$$

and that for any reversible infinitesimal change

$$dQ_w = t\,dZ,$$

where Z is another function of the state of the body, which he called the *disgregation*, and regarded as determined by the positions of the elementary parts of the body without reference to their velocities. In this respect it differed from the entropy. An immediate consequence of these relations is that for any reversible cyclic process

$$\int \frac{dH}{t} = 0,$$

and therefore that H, the molecular *vis viva* of the body, must be a function of the temperature alone. This important result was expressed by Clausius in the following words: "Die Menge der in einem Körper wirklich vorhandenen Wärme ist nur von seiner Temperatur und nicht von der Anordnung seiner Bestandtheile abhängig."

To return to the equation

$$dQ_w = t\,dZ.$$

This expresses that heat tends to increase the disgregation, and that the intensity of this tendency is proportional to the absolute temperature. In the words of Clausius: "Die mechanische Arbeit, welche die Wärme bei irgend einer Anordnungsänderung eines Körpers thun kann, ist proportional der absoluten Temperatur, bei welcher die Aenderung geschieht."

Such in brief and in part were the views advanced by Clausius in 1862, in his memoir, "Ueber die Anwendung des Satzes von der Aequivalenz der Verwandlungen auf die innere Arbeit."* Although they were advanced rather as a hypothesis than as anything for which he could give a formal proof, he seems to have little doubt of their correctness, and his confidence seems to have increased with the course of time.

The substantial correctness of these views cannot now be called in question. The researches especially of Maxwell and Boltzmann have shown that the molecular *vis viva* is proportional to the absolute temperature, and Boltzmann has even been able to determine the precise nature of the functions which Clausius called entropy and disgregation.† But the anticipation, to a certain extent, at so early a period in the history of the subject, of the ultimate form which the theory was to take, shows a remarkable insight, which is by no means to be lightly esteemed on account of the acknowledged want of a rigorous demonstration. The propositions, indeed, as relating to quantities which escape direct measurement, belong to molecular science, and seem to require for their complete and satisfactory demonstration a considerable development of that science. This

* *Pogg. Ann.*, vol. cxvi, p. 73. See also vol. cxxvii, p. 477 (1866).

† *Sitzungsberichte Wien. Akad.*, vol. lxiii, p. 728 (1871).

development naturally commenced with the simplest case involving the characteristic problems of the subject,—the case, namely, of gases.

The origin of the kinetic theory of gases is lost in remote antiquity, and its completion the most sanguine cannot hope to see. But a single generation has seen it advance from the stage of vague surmises to an extensive and well established body of doctrine. This is mainly the work of three men, Clausius, Maxwell, and Boltzmann, of whom Clausius was the earliest in the field, and has been called by Maxwell the principal founder of the science.* We may regard his paper (1857), "Ueber die Art der Bewegung, welche wir Wärme nennen,"† as marking his definite entrance into this field, although many points were incidentally discussed in earlier papers.

This was soon followed by his papers, "Ueber die mittlere Länge der Wege, welche bei der Molecularbewegung gasförmiger Körper von den einzelnen Molecülen zurückgelegt werden,"‡ and "Ueber die Wärmeleitung gasförmiger Körper."§

A very valuable contribution to molecular science is the conception of the *virial*, defined in his paper (1870), "Ueber einen auf die Wärme anwendbaren Satz,"‖ where he shows that in any case of stationary motion the mean *vis viva* of the system is equal to its virial.

In the mean time, Maxwell and Boltzmann had entered the field. Maxwell's first paper, "On the Motions and Collisions of perfectly elastic Spheres,"¶ was characterized by a new manner of proposing the problems of molecular science. Clausius was concerned with the mean values of various quantities which vary enormously in the smallest time or space which we can appreciate. Maxwell occupied himself with the relative frequency of the various values which these quantities have. In this he was followed by Boltzmann. In reading Clausius, we seem to be reading mechanics; in reading Maxwell, and in much of Boltzmann's most valuable work, we seem rather to be reading in the theory of probabilities. There is no doubt that the larger manner in which Maxwell and Boltzmann proposed the problems of molecular science enabled them in some cases to get a more satisfactory and complete answer, even for those questions which do not at first sight seem to require so broad a treatment.

Boltzmann's first work, however (1866), "Ueber die mechanische Bedeutung des zweiten Hauptsatzes der Wärmetheorie,"** was in a line in which no one had preceded him, although he was followed by

* *Nature*, vol. xvii, p. 278.

† *Pogg. Ann.*, vol. c, p. 353 (1857).

‡ *Ibid.*, vol. cv, p. 239 (1858). See also *Wied. Ann.*, vol. x, p. 92.

§ *Ibid.*, vol. cxv, p. 1 (1862).

‖ *Ibid.*, vol. cxli, p. 124. See also *Jubelband*, p. 411.

¶ *Phil. Mag.*, vol. xix, p. 19 (1860).

** *Sitzungsberichte Wien. Akad.* vol. liii, p. 195.

some of the most distinguished names among his contemporaries. Somewhat later (1870) Clausius, whose attention had not been called to Boltzmann's work, wrote his paper, "Ueber die Zurückführung des zweiten Hauptsatzes der mechanischen Wärmetheorie auf allgemeine mechanische Principien."*

The point of departure of these investigations, and others to which they gave rise, is the consideration of the mean values of the force-function and of the *vis viva* of a system in which the motions are periodic, and of the variations of these mean values when the external influences are changed. The theorems developed belong to the same general category as the principle of least action, and the principle or principles known as Hamilton's, which have to do, explicitly or implicitly, with the variations of these mean values.

Among other papers of Clausius on this subject, we may mention the two following: "Ueber einen neuen mechanischen Satz in Bezug auf stationäre Bewegung"† (1873), and "Ueber den Satz vom mittleren Ergal und seine Anwendung auf die Molecularbewegungen der Gase" ‡ (1874).

The first problem of molecular science is to derive from the observed properties of bodies as accurate a notion as possible of their molecular constitution. The knowledge we may gain of their molecular constitution may then be utilized in the search for formulas to represent their observable properties. A most notable achievement in this direction is that of van der Waals, in his celebrated memoir, "On the Continuity of the Gaseous and Liquid States." To this part of the subject belong the following papers of Clausius: "Ueber das Verhalten der Kohlensäure in Bezug auf Druck, Volumen und Temperatur,"§ and "Ueber die theoretische Bestimmung des Dampfdruckes und der Volumina des Dampfes und der Flüssigkeit" (two papers).||

Another matter in which Clausius showed his originality and power was the vexed subject of electrodynamics, as treated in his memoir, "Ueber die Ableitung eines neuen electrodynamischen Grundgesetzes."¶ Various points in the theory of electricity in which the principles of thermodynamics or of molecular science were involved, had previously been treated in different papers, of which the earliest appeared in 1852,** while the doctrine of the

* *Pogg. Ann.*, vol. cxlii, p. 433.

† *Ibid.*, vol. cl, p. 106.

‡ *Ibid.*, *Ergänzungsband* vii, p. 215.

§ *Wied. Ann.*, vol. ix, p. 337 (1880).

|| *Ibid.*, vol. xiv, p. 279 and p. 692 (1881).

¶ *Crelle's Journal*, vol. lxxxii, p. 85 (1877).

** "Ueber das mechanische Aequivalent einer electrischen Entladung und die dabei stattfindende Erwärmung des Leitungsdrahtes." *Pogg. Ann.*, vol. lxxxvi, p. 337. "Ueber die bei einem stationären electrischen Strome in dem Leiter gethane Arbeit

potential (electrical and gravitational) was treated in a separate book, which appeared in 1859, with the title, "Die Potentialfunction und das Potential, ein Beitrag zur mathematischen Physik." This subsequently went through several editions, in which it was revised and enlarged. All these subjects, with others, were brought together in a single volume, "Die mechanische Behandlung der Electricität," which appeared in 1879, forming the second volume of his "Mechanische Wärmetheorie." * Later papers on electricity related to the principles of electrodynamics,† electrical and magnetic units,‡ and dynamo-electric machines.§

The Royal Society's catalogue of scientific papers, and the excellent indices to the *Annalen der Physik und Chemie*, in which Clausius's work usually appeared, render it unnecessary to enumerate in detail his scientific papers. The list, indeed, would be a long one. The Royal Society's catalogue gives seventy-seven titles for the years 1847–1873. Subsequently twenty-five papers have appeared in the *Annalen* alone, and about half as many others elsewhere.

But such work as that of Clausius is not measured by counting titles or pages. His true monument lies not on the shelves of libraries, but in the thoughts of men, and in the history of more than one science.

---

und erzeugte Wärme." *Pogg. Ann.*, vol. lxxxvii, p. 415 (1852). "Ueber die Anwendung der mechanischen Wärmetheorie auf die thermoelectrischen Erscheinungen." *Pogg. Ann.*, vol. xc, p. 513 (1853). "Ueber die Electricitätsleitung in Electrolyten." *Pogg. Ann.*, vol. ci, p. 338 (1857).

* The first volume of this work appeared in 1876, and contained the general theory with the more immediate consequences of the two fundamental laws. The third volume has not yet appeared, but it is expected very soon, edited by Professor Planck and Dr. Pulfrich. In a certain sense this work may be regarded as a second edition of an earlier one (1864 and 1867), which consisted of a reprint of papers and had the title "Abhandlungen über die mechanische Wärmetheorie."

† *Wied. Ann.*, vol. x, p. 608; vol. xi, p. 604.

‡ *Ibid.*, vol. xvi, p. 529; vol. xvii, p. 713.

§ *Ibid.*, vol. xx, p. 353; vol. xxi, p. 385.

XXI.

HUBERT ANSON NEWTON.

[*American Journal of Science*, ser. 4, vol. III, pp. 359–376, May 1897.]

(Read before the National Academy of Sciences, in April, 1897.)

HUBERT ANSON NEWTON was born on March 19th, 1830, at Sherburne, N.Y., and died at New Haven, Conn., on the 12th day of August, 1896. He was the fifth son of a family of seven sons and four daughters, children of William and Lois (Butler) Newton. The parents traced their ancestory back to the first settlers of Massachusetts and Connecticut,* and had migrated from the latter to Sherburne, when many parts of central New York were still a wilderness. They both belonged to families remarkable for longevity, and lived themselves to the ages of ninety-three and ninety-four years. Of the children, all the sons and two daughters were living as recently as the year 1889, the youngest being then fifty-three years of age. William Newton was a man of considerable enterprise, and undertook the construction of the Buffalo section of the Erie canal, as well as other work in canal and railroad construction in New York and Pennsylvania. In these constructions he is said to have relied on his native abilities to think out for himself the solution of problems which are generally a matter of technical training. His wife was remarkable for great strength of character united with a quiet temperament and well-balanced mind, and was noted among her neighbors for her mathematical powers.

Young Newton, whose mental endowments were thus evidently inherited, and whose controlling tastes were manifested at a very early age, fitted for college at the schools of Sherburne, and at the age of sixteen entered Yale College in the class graduating in 1850. After graduation he pursued his mathematical studies at New Haven and at home, and became tutor at Yale in January, 1853, when on account of the sickness and death of Professor Stanley the whole charge of the mathematical department devolved on him from the first.

* Richard Butler, the great-grandfather of Lois Butler, came over from England before 1633, and was one of those who removed from Cambridge to Hartford. An ancestor of William Newton came directly from England to the New Haven colony about the middle of the same century.

In 1855, he was appointed professor of mathematics at the early age of twenty-five. This appointment testifies to the confidence which was felt in his abilities, and is almost the only instance in which the Yale Corporation has conferred the dignity of a full professorship on so young a man.

This appointment being accompanied with a leave of absence for a year, in order to give him the opportunity to study in Europe, it was but natural that he should be attracted to Paris, where Chasles was expounding at the Sorbonne that modern higher geometry of which he was to so large an extent the creator, and which appeals so strongly to the sense of the beautiful. And it was inevitable that the student should be profoundly impressed by the genius of his teacher and by the fruitfulness and elegance of the methods which he was introducing. The effect of this year's study under the inspiring influence of such a master is seen in several contributions to the *Mathematical Monthly* during its brief existence in the years 1858-61. One of these was a problem which attracted at once the attention of Cayley, who sent a solution. Another was a discussion of the problem "to draw a circle tangent to three given circles," remarkable for his use of the principle of inversion. A third was a very elaborate memoir on the construction of curves by the straight edge and compasses, and by the straight edge alone. These early essays in geometry show a mind thoroughly imbued with the spirit of modern geometry, skilful in the use of its methods, and eager to extend the bounds of our knowledge.

Nevertheless, although for many years the higher geometry was with him a favorite subject of instruction for his more advanced students, either his own preferences, or perhaps rather the influence of his environment, was destined to lead him into a very different field of research. In the attention which has been paid to astronomy in this country we may recognize the history of the world repeating itself in a new country in respect to the order of the development of the sciences, or it may be enough to say that the questions which nature forces on us are likely to get more attention in a new country and a bustling age, than those which a reflective mind puts to itself, and that the love of abstract truth which prompts to the construction of a system of doctrine, and the refined taste which is a critic of methods of demonstration, are matters of slow growth. At all events, when Professor Newton was entering upon his professorship, the study of the higher geometry was less consonant with the spirit of the age in this country than the pursuit of astronomical knowledge, and the latter sphere of activity soon engrossed his best efforts.

Yet it was not in any of the beaten paths of astronomers that Professor Newton was to move. It was rather in the wilds of a *terra incognita*, which astronomers had hardly troubled themselves to claim as belonging to their domain, that he first labored to establish law and order. It was doubtless not by chance that he turned his attention to the subject of shooting stars. The interest awakened in this country by the stupendous spectacle of 1833, which was not seen in Europe, had not died out. This was especially true at New Haven, where Mr. Edward C. Herrick was distinguished for his indefatigable industry both in personal observation and in the search for records of former showers. A rich accumulation of material was thus awaiting development. In 1861, the Connecticut Academy of Arts and Sciences appointed a committee "to communicate with observers in various localities for combined and systematic observations upon the August and November meteors." In this committee Professor Newton was preeminently active. He entered zealously upon the work of collecting material by personal observation and correspondence and by organizing corps of observers of students and others, and at the same time set himself to utilize the material thus obtained by the most careful study. The value of the observations collected was greatly increased by a map of the heavens for plotting meteor-paths, which was prepared by Professor Newton and printed at the expense of the Connecticut Academy for distribution among observers.

By these organized efforts, in a great number of cases observations were obtained on the same meteor as seen from different places, and the actual path in the atmosphere was computed by Professor Newton. In a paper published in 1865 * the vertical height of the beginning and the end of the visible part of the path is given for more than one hundred meteors observed on the nights of August 10th and November 13th, 1863. It was shown that the average height of the November meteors is fifteen or twenty miles higher than that of the August meteors, the former beginning in the mean at a height of ninety-six miles and ending at sixty-one, the latter beginning at seventy and ending at fifty-six.

We mention this paper first, because it seems to represent the culmination of a line of activity into which Professor Newton had entered much earlier. We must go back to consider other papers which he had published in the meantime.

His first papers on this subject, 1860–62,† were principally devoted to the determination of the paths and velocities of certain brilliant meteors or fireballs, which had attracted the attention of observers in different localities. Three of these appeared to have velocities much greater than is possible for permanent members of the solar system. To another a particular interest attached as belonging to the August

* *Amer. Jour. Sci.*, ser. 2, vol. xl, p. 250.

† *Amer. Jour. Sci.*, ser. 2, vol. xxx, p. 186; xxxii, p. 448; and xxxiii, p. 338.

shower, although exceptional in size. For this he calculated the elements of the orbit which would give the observed path and velocity. But the determination of the velocity in such cases, which depends upon the estimation by the observers of the time of flight, is necessarily very uncertain, and at best affords only a lower limit for the value of the original velocity of the body before it encountered the resistance of the earth's atmosphere. This would seem to constitute an insuperable difficulty in the determination of the orbits of meteoroids, to use the term which Professor Newton applied to these bodies, before they enter the earth's atmosphere to appear for a moment as luminous meteors. Yet it has been completely overcome in the case of the November meteors, or Leonids as they are called from the constellation from which they appear to radiate. This achievement constitutes one of the most interesting chapters in the history of meteoric science, and gives the subject an honorable place among the exact sciences.

In the first place, by a careful study of the records, Professor Newton showed that the connection of early showers with those of 1799 and 1833 had been masked by a progressive change in the time of the year in which the shower occurs. This change had amounted to a full month between A.D. 902, when the shower occurred on October 13, and 1833, when it occurred on November 13. It is in part due to the precession of the equinoxes, and in part to the motion of the node where the earth's orbit meets that of the meteoroids. This motion must be attributed to the perturbations of the orbits of the meteoroids which are produced by the attractions of the planets, and being in the direction opposite to that of the equinoxes, Professor Newton inferred that the motion of the meteoroids must be retrograde.

The showers do not, however, occur whenever the earth passes the node, but only when the passage occurs within a year or two before or after the termination of a cycle of 32·25 years. This number is obtained by dividing the interval between the showers of 902 and 1833 by 28, the number of cycles between these dates, and must therefore be a very close approximation. For if these showers did not mark the precise end of cycles the resultant error would be divided by 28. Professor Newton showed that this value of the cycle requires that the number of revolutions performed by the meteoroids in one year should be either $2 \pm \frac{1}{33 \cdot 25}$ or $1 \pm \frac{1}{33 \cdot 25}$ or $\frac{1}{33 \cdot 25}$. In other words, the periodic time of the meteoroids must be either 180·0 or 185·4 or 354·6 or 376·6 days, or 33·25 years. Now the velocity of any body in the solar system has a simple relation to its periodic time and its distance from the sun. Assuming, therefore, any one of these five values of the periodic time, we have the velocities of the Leonids at the node very sharply determined. From this velocity, with the position of the apparent radiant, which gives the direction of the relative motion, and with the knowledge that the heliocentric motion is retrograde, we may easily determine the orbit.

We have, therefore, five orbits from which to choose. The calculation of the secular motion of the node due to the disturbing action of the planets, would enable us to decide between these orbits.

Such are the most important conclusions which Professor Newton derived from the study of these remarkable showers, interesting not only from the magnificence of the spectacle occasionally exhibited, but in a much higher degree from the peculiarity in the periodic character of their occurrence, which affords the means of the determination of the orbit of the meteoroids with a precision which would at first sight appear impossible.

Professor Newton anticipated a notable return of the shower in 1866, with some precursors in the years immediately preceding, a prediction which was amply verified. In the meantime he turned his attention to the properties which belong to shooting stars in general, and especially to those average values which relate to large numbers of these bodies not belonging to any particular swarm.

This kind of investigation Maxwell has called *statistical*, and has in more than one passage signalized its difficulties. The writer recollects a passage of Maxwell which was pointed out to him by Professor Newton, in which the author says that serious errors have been made in such inquiries by men whose competency in other branches of mathematics was unquestioned. Doubtless Professor Newton was very conscious of the necessity of caution in these inquiries, as is indeed abundantly evident from the manner in which he expressed his conclusions; but the writer is not aware of any passage in which he has afforded an illustration of Maxwell's remark.

The results of these investigations appeared in an elaborate memoir "On Shooting Stars," which was read to the National Academy in 1864, and appeared two years later in the *Memoirs of the Academy*.* An abstract was given in the *American Journal of Science* in 1865.† The following are some of the subjects treated, with some of the more interesting results:

The distribution of the apparent paths of shooting stars in azimuth and altitude.

The vertical distribution of the luminous part of the real paths. The value found for the mean height of the middle point of the luminous path was a trifle less than sixty miles.

The mean length of apparent paths.

The mean distance of paths from the observer.

---

* Vol. i, 3d memoir.

† Series 2, vol. xxxix, p. 193.

The mean foreshortening of paths.

The mean length of the visible part of the real paths.

The mean time of flight as estimated by observers.

The distribution of the orbits of meteoroids in the solar system.

The daily number of shooting stars, and the density of the meteoroides in the space which the earth traverses.

The average number of shooting stars which enter the atmosphere daily, and which are large enough to be visible to the naked eye, if the sun, moon and clouds would permit it, is more than seven and a half millions. Certain observations with instruments seem to indicate that this number should be increased to more than four hundred millions, to include telescopic shooting stars, and there is no reason to doubt that an increase of optical power beyond that employed in these observations would reveal still larger numbers of these small bodies. In each volume of the size of the earth, of the space which the earth is traversing in its orbit about the sun, there are as many as thirteen thousand small bodies, each of which is such as would furnish a shooting star visible under favorable circumstances to the naked eye.

These conclusions are certainly of a startling character, but not of greater interest than those relating to the velocity of meteoroids. There are two velocities to be considered, which are evidently connected, the velocity relative to the earth, and the velocity of the meteoroids in the solar system. To the latter, great interest attaches from the fact that it determines the nature of the orbit of the meteoroid. A velocity equal to that of the earth, indicates an orbit like that of the earth; a velocity $\sqrt{2}$ times as great, a parabolic orbit like that of most comets, while a velocity greater than this indicates a hyperbolic orbit.

Professor Newton sought to form an estimate of this critical quantity in more than one way. That on which he placed most reliance was based on a comparison of the numbers of shooting stars seen in the different hours of the night. It is evident that in the morning, when we are in front of the earth in its motion about the sun, we should see more shooting stars than in the evening, when we are behind the earth; but the greater the velocity of the meteoroids compared with that of the earth, the less the difference would be in the numbers of evening and morning stars.*

---

* It may not be out of place to notice here an erratum which occurs both in the *Memoirs of the National Academy* and in the abstract in the *American Journal of Science*, and which the writer finds marked in a private copy of Professor Newton's. In the table on p. 20 of the memoir and 206 of the abstract, the column of numbers under the head "hour of the night" should be inverted. There is another displacement in the table in the memoir, which is, however, corrected in the abstract.

After a careful discussion of the evidence Professor Newton reached the conclusion that "we must regard as almost certain (on the hypothesis of an equable distribution of the directions of absolute motions), that the mean velocity of the meteoroids exceeds considerably that of the earth; that the orbits are not approximately circular, but resemble more the orbits of comets."

This last sentence, which is taken from the abstract published in the *American Journal of Science* in 1865, and is a little more definitely and positively expressed than the corresponding passage in the original memoir, indicating apparently that the author's conviction had been growing more positive in the interval, or at least that the importance of the conclusion had been growing upon him, embodies what is perhaps the most important result of the memoir, and derives a curious significance from the discoveries which were to astonish astronomers in the immediate future.

The return of the November or Leonid shower in 1865, and especially in 1866, when the display was very brilliant in Europe, gave an immense stimulus to meteoric study, and an especial prominence to this group of meteoroids. "Not since the year 1759," says Schiaparelli, "when the predicted return of a comet first took place, had the verified prediction of a periodic phenomenon made a greater impression than the magnificent spectacle of November, 1866. The study of cosmic meteors thereby gained the dignity of a science, and took finally an honorable place among the other branches of astronomy." * Professor J. C. Adams, of Cambridge, England, then took up the calculation of the perturbations determining the motion of the node. We have seen that Professor Newton had shown that the periodic time was limited to five sharply determined values, each of which with the other data would give an orbit, and that the true orbit could be distinguished from the other four by the calculation of the secular motion of the node.

Professor Adams first calculated the motion of the node due to the attractions of Jupiter, Venus, and the Earth for the orbit having a period of 354·6 days. This amounted to a little less than 12′ in 33·25 years. As Professor Newton had shown that the dates of the showers require a motion of 29′ in 33·25 years, the period of 354·6 days must be rejected. The case would be nearly the same with a period of 376·6 days, while a period of 180 or 185·4 days would give a still smaller motion of the node. Hence, of the five possible periods indicated by Professor Newton, four were shown to be entirely incompatible with the motion of the node, and it only remained to

* Schiaparelli, *Entwurf einer astronomischen Theorie der Sternschnuppen*, p. 55

examine whether the fifth period, viz. that of 33·25 years, would give a motion of the node in accordance with the observed value. As this period gives a very long ellipse for the orbit, extending a little beyond the orbit of Uranus, it was necessary to take account of the perturbations due to that planet and to Saturn. Professor Adams found 28′ for the motion of the node. As this value must be regarded as sensibly identical with Professor Newton's 29′ of observed motion, no doubt was left in regard to the period of revolution or the orbit of the meteoroids.*

About this time, M. Schiaparelli was led by a course of reasoning similar to Professor Newton's to the same conclusion,—that the mean velocity of the meteoroids is not very different from that due to parabolic orbits. In the course of his speculations in regard to the manner in which such bodies might enter the solar system, the questions suggested themselves: whether meteoroids and comets may not have a similar origin; whether, in case a swarm of meteoroids should include a body of sufficient size, this would not appear as a comet; and whether some of the known comets may not belong to streams of meteoroids. Calculating the orbit of the Perseids, or August meteoroids, from the radiant point, with the assumption of a nearly parabolic velocity, he found an orbit very similar to that of the great comet of 1862, which may therefore be considered as one of the Perseids,—probably the largest of them all.†

At that time no known cometic orbit agreed with that of the Leonids, but a few months later, as soon as the definitive elements of the orbit of the first comet of 1866 were published, their resemblance to those of the Leonids, as calculated for the period of 33·25 years, which had been proved to be the correct value, was strikingly manifested, attracting at once the notice of several astronomers.

Other relations of the same kind have been discovered later, of which that of Biela's comet and the Andromeds is the most interesting, as we have seen the comet breaking up under the influence of the sun; but in no case is the coincidence so striking as in that of the Leonids, since in no other case is the orbit of the meteoroids completely known, independently of that of the comet, and without any arbitrary assumption in regard to their periodic time.

The first comet of 1866 is probably not the only one belonging to the Leonid stream of meteoroids. Professor Newton has remarked that the Chinese annals mention two comets which passed rapidly in succession across the sky in 1366, a few days after the passage of the earth through the node of the Leonid stream, which was marked in Europe by one of the most remarkable star-showers on record. The

* *Monthly Notices Roy. Ast. Soc.*, vol. xxvii, p. 247. † *Entwurf*, etc., pp. 49–54.

course of these comets, as described by the annalists, was in the line of the Leonid stream.*

This identification of comets with meteors or shooting-stars marks an epoch in the study of the latter. Henceforth, they must be studied in connection with comets. It was presumably this discovery which led Professor Newton to those statistical investigations respecting comets, which we shall presently consider. At this point, however, at the close as it were of the first chapter in the history of meteoric science, it seems not unfitting to quote the words of an eminent foreign astronomer, written about this time, in regard to Professor Newton's contributions to this subject. In an elaborate memoir in the *Comptes Rendus,* M. Faye says, with reference to our knowledge of shooting-stars and their orbits, "we may find in the works of M. Newton, of the United States, the most advanced expression of the state of science on this subject, and even the germ, I think, of the very remarkable ideas brought forward in these last days by M. Schiaparelli and M. Le Verrier." †

The first fruit of Professor Newton's statistical studies on comets appeared in 1878 in a paper "On the Origin of Comets." In this paper he considers the distribution in the solar system of the known cometic orbits, and compares it with what we might expect on either of two hypotheses: that of Kant, that the comets were formed in the evolution of the solar system from the more distant portion of the solar nebula; and that of Laplace, that the comets have come from the stellar spaces and in their origin had no relation to the solar system.

In regard to the distribution of the aphelia, he shows that, except so far as modified by the perturbations due to the planets, the theory of internal origin would require all the aphelia to be in the vicinity of the ecliptic; the theory of external origin would make all directions of the aphelia equally probable, i.e., the distribution in latitude of the aphelia should be that in which the frequency is as the cosine of the latitude. The actual distribution comes very near to this, but as the effect of perturbations would tend to equalize the distribution of aphelia in all directions, Professor Newton does not regard this argument as entirely decisive. He remarks, however, that if Kant's hypothesis be true, the comets must have been revolving in their orbits a very long time, and the process of the disintegration of comets must be very slow.

In regard to the distribution of the orbits in inclination, the author shows that the theory of internal origin would make all inclinations equally probable; the theory of external origin would make all

* *Amer. Jour. Sci.*, ser. 2, vol. xliii, p. 298, and vol. xlv, p. 91, or *Encycl. Britann.*, article Meteor.

† *Comptes Rendus*, t. lxiv, p. 551.

directions of the normal to the plane of the orbit equally probable. On the first hypothesis, therefore, we should expect a uniform distribution in inclination; on the second, a frequency proportioned to the sine of the inclination. It was shown by a diagram in which the actual and the two theoretical distributions are represented graphically, that the actual distribution agrees pretty well with the theory of external origin and not at all with that of internal origin. It was also shown that the curve of actual distribution cannot be made to agree with Kant's hypothesis by any simple and reasonable allowances for perturbations. On the other hand, if we assume the external origin of comets, and ask how the curve of sines must be modified in order to take account of perturbations, it is shown that the principal effect will be to increase somewhat the number of inclinations between 90° and 135° at the expense of those between 45° and 90°. It is apparent at once from the diagram that such a change would make a very good agreement between the actual and theoretical curves, the only important difference remaining being due to comets of short periods, which mostly have small inclinations with direct motion. These should not weigh very much, the author observes, in the general question of the distribution of inclinations, because they return so frequently and are so easily detected that their number in a list of observed comets is out of all proportion to their number among existing comets. But this group of comets of short periods can easily be explained on the theory of an external origin. For such comets must have lost a large part of their velocity by the influence of a planet. This is only likely to happen when a comet overtakes the planet and passes in front of it. This implies that its original motion was direct and in an orbit of small inclination to that of the planets, and although it may lose a large part of its velocity, its motion will generally remain direct and in a plane of small inclination. This very interesting case of the comets of short periods and small inclinations, which was treated rather briefly in this paper, was discussed more fully by Professor Newton at the meeting of the British Association in the following year.*

Many years later, Professor Newton returned to the same general subject in a very interesting memoir "On the Capture of Comets by Planets; especially their Capture by Jupiter," which was read before the National Academy in 1891, and appeared in the *Memoirs of the Academy* two years later.† It also appeared in the *American Journal of Science* in the year in which it was read.‡ This contains

* *Rep't Brit. Assoc. Adv. Sci.* for 1879, p. 272.

† *Mem. Nat. Acad.*, vol. vi, 1st memoir.

‡ *Amer. Jour. Sci.*, ser. 3, vol. xlii, pp. 183 and 482.

the results of careful statistical calculations on the effect of perturbations on orbits of comets originally parabolic. It corroborates the more general statements of the paper "On the Origin of Comets," giving them a precise quantitative form. One or two quotations will give some idea of the nature of this very elaborate and curious memoir, in which, however, the results are largely presented in the form of diagrams.

On a certain hypothesis regarding an original equable distribution of comets in parabolic orbits about the sun, it is shown that "if in a given period of time a thousand million comets come in parabolic orbits nearer to the sun than Jupiter, 126 of them will have their orbits changed" by the action of that planet "into ellipses with periodic times less than one-half that of Jupiter; 839 of them will have their orbits changed into ellipses with periodic times less than that of Jupiter; 1701 of them will have their orbits changed into ellipses with periodic times less than once and a half that of Jupiter, and 2670 of them will have their orbits changed into ellipses with periodic times less than twice that of Jupiter." A little later, Professor Newton considers the question, which he characterizes as perhaps more important, of the direct or retrograde motion of the comets after such perturbations. It is shown that of the 839 comets which have periodic times less than Jupiter, 203 will have retrograde motions, and 636 will have direct motions. Of the 203 with retrograde motion, and of the 636 with direct motion, 51 and 257, respectively, will have orbits inclined less than 30° to that of Jupiter.

We have seen that the earliest of Professor Newton's more important studies on meteors related to the Leonids, which at that time far surpassed all other meteoric streams in interest. One of his later studies related to another stream which in the mean time had acquired great importance. The identification of the orbit of the Andromed meteors with that of Biela's comet, which we have already mentioned, gave these bodies a unique interest, as the comet had been seen to break up under the influence of the sun. Here the evolution of meteoroids was taking place before our eyes; and this interest was heightened by the showers of 1872 and 1885, which in Europe seem to have been unsurpassed in brilliancy by any which have occurred in this century.

The phenomena of each of these showers were carefully discussed by Professor Newton. Among the principal results of his paper on the latter shower are the following:*

The time of the maximum frequency of meteors was Nov. 27, 1885 6 h. 15 m. Gr. m. t. The estimated number per hour visible at one

* *Amer. Jour. Sci.*, ser. 3, vol. xxxi, p. 409.

place was then 75,000. This gives a density of the meteoroids in space represented by one to a cube of twenty miles edge. Three hours later the frequency had fallen to one-tenth of the maximum value. The really dense portion of the stream through which we passed was less than 100,000 miles in thickness, and nearly all would be included in a thickness of 200,000 miles.

A formula is given to express the effect of the earth's attraction on the approaching meteoroids in altering the position of the radiant. This is technically known as the zenithal attraction, and is quite important in the case of these meteors on account of their small relative velocity. The significance of the formula may be roughly expressed by saying that the earth's attraction changes the radiant of the Biela meteors, toward the vertical of the observer, one-tenth of the observed zenith distance of the radiant, or more briefly, that the zenithal attraction for these meteors is one-tenth of the observed zenith distance. The radiant even after the correction for zenithal attraction, and another for the rotation of the earth on its axis, is not a point but an area of several degrees diameter. The same has been observed in regard to other showers, but the result comes out more distinctly in the present case because the meteors were so numerous and the shower so carefully observed.

This implies a want of parallelism in the paths of the meteors, and it is a very important question whether it exists before the meteoroids enter our atmosphere, or whether it is due to the action of the atmosphere.

Professor Newton shows that it is difficult to account for so large a difference in the original motions of the meteoroids, and thinks it reasonable to attribute a large part of the want of parallelism to the action of the atmosphere on bodies of an irregular form, such as we have every reason to believe that the meteoroids have, when they enter our atmosphere. The effect of the heat generated will be to round off the edges and prominent parts, and to reduce the meteor to a form more and more spherical. It is, therefore, quite natural that the greater portion of the curvature of the paths should be in the invisible portion and thus escape our notice. It is only in exceptional cases that the visible path is notably curved.

But the great interest of the paper centers in his discussion of the relation of this shower to preceding showers, and to the orbit of Biela's comet. The changes in the date of the shower (from Dec. 6 to Nov. 27) and in the position of the radiant are shown to be related to the great perturbations of Biela's comet in 1794, 1831, and 1841–2. The showers observed by Brandes, Dec. 6th, 1798, by Herrick, Dec. 7th, 1838, and by Heis, Dec. 8th and 10th, 1847, are related to the orbit of Biela's comet as it was in 1772; while the great showers of 1872 and 1885, as well as a trifling display in 1867, are related to the orbit of 1852.*

Assuming, then, that the meteoroids which we met on the 27th of November, 1872, did not leave the immediate neighborhood of the Biela comet before 1841–2, we seem to have the data for a very precise determination of their orbit between those dates. The same is true of those which we met in 1885. The computation of these orbits, the author remarks, may possibly give evidence for or against the existence of a resisting medium in the solar system.

In his last public utterance on the subject of meteors, which was on the occasion of the recent sesquicentennial celebration of the American Philosophical Society, Professor Newton returns to the Biela meteoroids, and finds in the scattering which they show in the plane of their orbit the proof of a disturbing force in that plane, and therefore not due to the planets. The force exerted by the sun appears to be modified somewhat as we see it in the comet's tails, where indeed the attraction is changed into a repulsion. Something of the same sort on a smaller scale relatively to the mass of the bodies appears to modify the sun's action on the meteoroids.

In 1888 Professor Newton read a paper before the National Academy "Upon the relation which the former Orbits of those Meteorites that are in our collections, and that were seen to fall, had to the Earth's Orbit." This was based upon a very careful study of more than 116 cases for which we have statements indicating more or less definitely the direction of the path through the air, as well as 94 cases in which we only know the time of the fall. The results are expressed in the following three propositions:

1. The meteorites which we have in our cabinets and which were seen to fall were originally (as a class, and with a very small number of exceptions) moving about the sun in orbits that had inclinations less than 90°; that is, their motions were direct, not retrograde.

2. The reason why we have only this class of stones in our collections is not one wholly or even mainly dependent on the habits of men; nor on the times when men are out of doors; nor on the places where men live; nor on any other principle of selection acting at or after the arrival of the stones at the ground. Either the stones which are moving in the solar system across the earth's orbit move in general in direct orbits; or else for some reason the stones which

---

* It is a curious coincidence that the original discoverer of the December shower as a periodic phenomenon, Mr. Edward C. Herrick, should have been (with a companion, Mr. Francis Bradley,) the first to observe that breaking up of the parent body which was destined to reinforce the meteoric stream in so remarkable a manner. See *Amer. Jour. Sci.*, ser. 3, vol. xxxi, pp. 85 and 88.

move in retrograde orbits do not in general come through the air to the ground in solid form.

3. The perihelion distances of nearly all the orbits in which these stones moved were not less than 0·5 nor more than 1·0, the earth's radius vector being unity.

Professor Newton adds, that it seems a natural and proper corollary to these propositions (unless it shall appear that stones meeting the earth are destroyed in the air) that the larger meteorites moving in our solar system are allied much more closely with the group of comets of short period than with comets whose orbits are nearly parabolic. All the known comets of shorter periods than 33 years move about the sun in direct orbits that have moderate inclinations to the ecliptic. On the contrary, of the nearly parabolic orbits that are known only a small proportion of the whole number have small inclinations with direct motion.

We have briefly mentioned those papers which seem to constitute the most important contributions to the science of meteors and comets. To fully appreciate Professor Newton's activity in this field, it would be necessary to take account of his minor contributions.*

Most interesting and instructive to the general reader are his utterances on occasions when he has given a résumé of our knowledge on these subjects or some branch of them, as in the address "On the Meteorites, the Meteors, and the Shooting Stars," which he delivered in 1886 as retiring president of the American Association for the Advancement of Science, or in certain lectures in the public courses of the Sheffield Scientific School of Yale University, entitled "The story of Biela's Comet" (1874), "The relation of Meteorites to Comets" (1876), "The Worship of Meteorites" (1889), or in the articles on Meteors in the *Encyclopædia Britannica* and *Johnson's Cyclopædia*.

If we ask what traits of mind and character are indicated by these papers, the answer is not difficult. Professor Klein has divided mathematical minds into three leading classes: the logicians, whose pleasure and power lies in subtility of definition and dialectic skill; the geometers, whose power lies in the use of the space-intuitions; and the formalists, who seek to find an algorithm for every operation.† Professor Newton evidently belonged to the second of these classes, and his natural tastes seem to have found an equal gratification in the development of a system of abstract geometric truths, or

* These were detailed in a bibliography annexed to this paper in *Amer. Jour. Sci.*, ser. 4, vol. iii.

† *Lectures on Mathematics* (Evanston), p. 2.

in the investigation of the concrete phenomena of nature as they exist in space and time.

But these papers show more than the type of mind of the author; they give no uncertain testimony concerning the character of the man. In all these papers we see a love of honest work, an aversion to shams, a distrust of rash generalizations and speculations based on uncertain premises. He was never anxious to add one more guess on doubtful matters in the hope of hitting the truth, or what might pass as such for a time, but was always willing to take infinite pains in the most careful test of every theory. To these qualities was joined a modesty which forbade the pushing of his own claims, and desired no reputation except the unsought tribute of competent judges. At the close of his article on meteors in the *Encyclopædia Britannica,* which has not the least reference to himself as a contributor to the science, he remarks that "meteoric science is a structure built stone by stone by many builders." We may add that no one has done more than himself to establish the foundations of the science, and that the stones which he has laid are not likely to need relaying.

The value of Professor Newton's work has been recognized by learned societies and institutions both at home and abroad. He received the honorary degree of Doctor of Laws from the University of Michigan in 1868. He was president of the section of Mathematics and Astronomy in the American Association for the Advancement in Science in 1875, and president of the Association in 1885. On the first occasion he delivered an address entitled "A plea for the study of pure Mathematics"; on the second the address on Meteorites, etc., which we have already mentioned. Of the American Mathematical Society he was vice-president at the time of his death. In 1888 the J. Lawrence Smith gold medal was awarded to him by the National Academy for his investigations on the orbits of meteoroids. We may quote a sentence or two from his reply to the address of presentation, so characteristic are they of the man that uttered them: "To discover some new truth in nature," he said, "even though it concerns the small things in the world, gives one of the purest pleasures in human experience. It gives joy to tell others of the treasure found."

Besides the various learned societies in our own country of which he was a member, including the American Academy of Arts and Sciences from 1862, the National Academy of Sciences from its foundation in 1863, the American Philosophical Society from 1867, he was elected in 1872 Associate of the Royal Astronomical Society of London, in 1886 Foreign Fellow of the Royal Society of Edinburgh, and in 1892 Foreign Member of the Royal Society of London.

But the studies which have won for their author an honorable reputation among men of science of all countries, form only one side of the life of the man whom we are considering. Another side, probably the most important, is that in which he was identified with the organic life of the College and University with which he had been connected from a very early age. In fact, we might almost call the studies which we have been considering, the recreations of a busy life of one whose serious occupation has been that of an instructor. If from all those who have come under his instruction we should seek to learn their personal recollections of Professor Newton, we should probably find that the most universal impression made on his students was his enthusiastic love of the subject which he was teaching.

A department of the University in which he took an especial interest was the Observatory. This was placed under his direction at its organization, and although he subsequently resigned the nominal directorship, the institution remained virtually under his charge, and may be said to owe its existence in large measure to his untiring efforts and personal sacrifice in its behalf.

One sphere of activity in the Observatory was suggested by a happy accident which Professor Newton has described in the *American Journal of Science,* September, 1893. An amateur astronomer in a neighboring town, Mr. John Lewis, accidentally obtained on a stellar photograph the track of a large meteor. He announced in the newspapers that he had secured such a photograph, and requested observations from those who had seen its flight. The photographic plate and the letters received from various observers were placed in Professor Newton's hands, and were discussed in the paper mentioned. The advantages of photographic observations were so conspicuous that Professor Newton was anxious that the Observatory should employ this method of securing the tracks of meteors. With the aid of an appropriation granted by the National Academy from the income of the J. Lawrence Smith fund, a battery of cameras was mounted on an equatorial axis. By this means, a number of meteor-tracks have been obtained of the August meteors, and in one case, through a simultaneous observation by Mr. Lewis in Ansonia, Professor Newton was able to calculate the course of the meteor in the atmosphere with a probable error which he estimated at less than a mile. The results which may be expected at the now near return of the Leonids, will be of especial interest, but it will be for others to utilize them.

Professor Newton was much interested in the collection of meteorites, and the fine collection of stones and irons in the Peabody Museum of Yale University owes much to his efforts in this direction.

Professor Newton was a member of the American Metrological Society from the first, and was conspicuously active in the agitation which resulted in the enactment of the law of 1866, legalizing the use of the metric system. He prepared the table of the metric equivalents of the customary units of weights and measures which was incorporated in the act, and by which the relations of the fundamental units were defined. But he did not stop here. Appreciating the weakness of legislative enactment compared with popular sentiment, and feeling that the real battle was to be won in familiarizing the people with the metric system, he took pains to interest the makers of scales and rulers and other devices for measurement in adopting the units and graduations of the metric system, and to have the proper tables introduced into school arithmetics.

He was also an active member of the Connecticut Academy of Arts and Sciences, serving several years both as secretary and president,—also as member of the council. He was associate editor of the *American Journal of Science* from 1864, having especial charge of the department of astronomy. His notes on observations of meteors and on the progress of meteoric science, often very brief, sometimes more extended, but always well considered, were especially valuable.

In spite of his studious tastes and love of a quiet life, he did not shirk the duties of citizenship, serving a term as alderman in the city council, being elected, we may observe, in a ward of politics strongly opposed to his own.

Professor Newton married, April 14th, 1859, Anna C., daughter of the Rev. Joseph C. Stiles, D.D., of Georgia, at one time pastor of the Mercer Street Presbyterian Church in New York City, and subsequently of the South Church in New Haven. She survived her husband but three months, leaving two daughters.

In all these relations of life, the subject of this sketch exhibited the same traits of character which are seen in his published papers, the same modesty, the same conscientiousness, the same devotion to high ideals. His life was the quiet life of the scholar, ennobled by the unselfish aims of the Christian gentleman; his memory will be cherished by many friends; and so long as astronomers, while they watch the return of the Leonids marking off the passage of the centuries, shall care to turn the earlier pages of this branch of astronomy, his name will have an honorable place in the history of the science.